81 words

Flash Fiction Anthology

1,000 Stories by 1,000 Authors

Victorina Press
www.victorinapress.com

First published in November 2021 by Victorina Press,
Wanfield Hall, Woodcock Heath,
Kingstone, Uttoxeter,
Staffordshire, ST14 8QR, England.

81 Words was conceived by Adam Rubinstein.

Interior design and layout: Christopher Fielden.

Proofreading and eBook preparation: Angela Googh.

Proofreading: Dr Lynda Nash.

British Library Cataloguing-in-Publication data:
A catalogue record for this book is available from the British Library.

ISBN: 9798741365144

Printed by Amazon.

www.christopherfielden.com

www.victorinapress.com

DEDICATION

For every writer, of every age and gender identity, from every ethnic background, residing in every country. Keep telling your stories. Diversity is important. Your voices should be heard.

In memory of Georgie Fielden.
Your life burned bright and beautiful. I miss you my lovely, now and forever.

81 Words Certificate, by Saskia Ashby, author of story number 114

Hi Christopher,
here is your certificate (unofficial),
for polite persistence,
in the face of steadfast yet inconsistent,
refusals from the record book officials,
to gain official recognition,
for 81 Words,
being an anthology with 1,000 contributors.
Saskia Ashby

INTRODUCTION 1

by Christopher Fielden

Welcome to the *81 Words Flash Fiction Anthology*. It gives me great pleasure to present 1,000 stories written by 1,000 authors as a celebration of storytelling diversity.

Writers from every continent on our planet (with the exception of Antarctica) have contributed to this anthology, making it a truly global collaboration.

In this introduction, I will cover the history of the 81 Words project and some other points of interest relating to the production of this book.

How 81 Words Started

81words.net was a flash fiction website started by Adam Rubinstein. He's a self-professed educational basket-case from the '70s who says he finds his sense of meaning and well-being through creativity.

Adam Rubinstein, founder of 81words.net

Adam said:

"A long time ago, a few years after wasting most of my time at school, I entered a competition to write a story in 50 words. There were options for five different genres and each had a different paragraph given as the starting point. I didn't win but really enjoyed the challenge of carefully crafting words to create a beautiful jewel. Something perfect and complete in itself.

"The experience stayed with me and I thought it might be something lots of us could enjoy. An opportunity to be creative in an accessible way that isn't too demanding on our time. So 81 Words was born."

How 81 Words Became Part of My Website

I first became aware of 81 Words when Adam contacted me in January 2015 asking if his website could be added to my lists of short story and flash fiction competitions.

In April 2017, Adam contacted me again. He was developing a new project, didn't have time to give 81words.net the attention it needed and thought it would be a shame if it just disappeared. He asked me if I'd like to take it on. I agreed and moved the platform onto my website.

I was already running a number of flash fiction writing challenges. Each had an educational angle and offered writers the opportunity to see their work published.

The rules for the 81 Words challenge were simple – you had to write a story that was exactly 81 words in length – so it had wide appeal. Even if English wasn't a writer's first language, they could have a go at this challenge.

It also helped writers learn about the importance of editing their stories carefully, to make every word count; a skill that can be applied to all forms of creative writing.

The new version of the challenge was launched on my website at the end of April 2017.

How 81 Words Became a World Record Attempt

I decided to use 81 Words to attempt to set a world record after being contacted by Allen Stroud. He sent me a link to a newspaper story regarding the world record for the 'most authors contributing to an anthology of short stories'. The current world record was 50. The attempt featured in the article was for 100.

Allen pointed out that we'd already published an anthology with 100 contributing authors via the Nonsense Challenge (also run on my website), so could already have set a new world record.

I contacted Guinness World Records about this. They accepted my application, but we had not broken the record for 2 reasons:

1. The minimum word count of stories for this world record was 3,000 (Nonsense Challenge stories are 200 words max)
2. You have to sell 1,000 copies of the published book to get the world record (we hadn't sold that many books)

So, in November 2017, I applied to Guinness World Records to set up a brand new record for the 'most authors contributing to an anthology of flash fiction stories'.

I heard back from Guinness World Records in January 2018. They said:

Dear Christopher Fielden

Thank you for sending us the details of your proposed record attempt for 'Most authors contributing to an anthology of flash fiction stories'.

Unfortunately, after thoroughly reviewing your application with members of our research team, we are afraid to say that we cannot accept your proposal as a Guinness World Records title.

Our team of expert Records Managers receive thousands of new record proposals every year from all over the world which are carefully assessed to establish if they meet our stringent criteria. Every record verified by Guinness World Records must be measurable by a single superlative, verifiable, standardisable, breakable and also present an element of skill.

Whilst we appreciate this is not the decision you hoped for, we trust that you will understand our decision. You may want to consider these record titles as alternatives:

- *Most authors contributing to an anthology of short stories*
- *Largest writing competition*

For information on what makes a record, we would advise before submitting an application to visit www.guinnessworldrecords.com/records/what-makes-a-guinness-world-records-record-title. This page will provide you with helpful information if you are thinking about breaking or setting a record.

Once again thank you for contacting Guinness World Records.

Kind regards, Records Management Team

Please be aware that as your record application has not been accepted, Guinness World Records is not associated with the activity relating to your record proposal and does not endorse this activity in any way. If you choose to proceed, then this will be of your own volition and at your own risk. Guinness World Records will not monitor, measure or verify this activity.

Obviously, this response was disappointing. Still, I contacted them again for further clarification, to see if they could give more information about why the record was rejected and if anything could be changed to make it acceptable.

Here is a copy of my message:

Hi. Thanks for letting me know my record application (171122151758mact) was rejected. Please could you clarify why? I am happy to make amendments so it is acceptable to you. So far as I can see, the record is measurable by a single superlative [professionally presented book released by an established publisher], verifiable [physical book containing details of all contributors, plus verification by publishing professionals], standardisable [flash fiction – same as short story record, but less than 1,000 words], breakable [get a higher number of contributing authors] and also present an element of skill [flash fiction writing]. Any guidance you can give as to which criteria I'm not meeting and why would be very much appreciated. Thanks for your time, Chris

I heard back from Guinness in February. Mark, my account manager, said:

Hi Christopher,

We are unable to standardise the writing of a story. Due to the subjective nature of what constitutes a story, a record based on this concept would be difficult to compare across attempts. Similar records have been marked as being researched while a review is being conducted.

I wrote back in February saying:

Hi Mark

Thanks for your response.

I agree, what constitutes a story is subjective.

However, as the record is primarily to do with the number of contributing authors (if someone else publishes more, the record could be broken, so it's easy to measure), and there is already a record in the same format for short stories, please would you reconsider? The only difference is the word count limit – flash fiction under 1,000 words, instead of short stories of 3,000 to 8,000 words. It just seems odd to reject this application for the reasons you stated when there is already another record for short stories in a similar format.

From your comments, I guess you might be reviewing that record category anyway. If that's the case, I understand your reasons.

Thanks for your time and assistance on this – it's much appreciated. If the answer is still 'no', I promise not to hassle you again :-)

Cheers, Chris

Mark wrote back to me at the end of February, saying:

Hi Christopher,

The short story version of this record is under review and may be terminated. For this reason we will not be opening any more records of this type.

Thank you for your understanding on this matter.

As you can see, this means records related to creativity are being reviewed as they are subjective. It's a shame but I understand Guinness's reasons.

At the time this correspondence took place, I'd already received 278 submissions to the 81 Words project, so I decided that I'd publish the book as an 'unofficial world record' and publicise it as best I could myself.

Victorina Press

Victorina Press (VP) is an independent UK publisher that follows the principles of bibliodiversity (the cultural diversity applied to the writing and publishing world, developed by a group of Chilean publishers). In 2019, VP published my short story collection, *Book of the Bloodless Volume 1: Alternative Afterlives*. I enjoy working with VP because they allow their authors to retain a lot of control over their books. They're also very supportive and encourage all their authors to help one another. Working with them is like being part of a friendly publishing community, much like the writing challenges I run.

In June 2021, when the final draft of this book was nearing completion, I decided to try and get a publisher onboard to add credibility to the unofficial world record attempt and to give every author in the book a professional UK publishing credit for their writing CV.

VP came to mind immediately because this book features stories written by 1,000 authors from many different countries; I thought it was likely to fit in well with their ethos and be of interest to them. I knew VP had a full publishing roster due to delays caused by the COVID-19 pandemic, but I was hopeful the project would still appeal to them because I had already undertaken most of the work preparing the book for publication.

I'm pleased to say that the entire VP team were very supportive and MD, Consuelo Rivera-Fuentes, quickly agreed to publish the book under the VP brand.

Notes of Interest

In this section, I will highlight a few notes of interest about the preparation of this book.

1: The Book Cover

In October 2020, Jacek Wilkos (author of story 856) sent me an idea for the cover of the *81 Words Flash Fiction Anthology* with a simple message:

Hello Chris, I'm writing to you because I had an idea for a cover of the 81 Words Anthology and I just had to show it to you. Attached you can find a few versions of it. What do you think? Best wishes, Jacek

I thought it was excellent, but my brother, Dave, usually designs the covers for the writing challenge books I publish. However, due to the nature of this project, I thought it might be nice if one of the contributing authors designed the cover.

While working on the first draft of the interior of the book, I carefully considered Jacek's offer and, in January 2021, I contacted him and asked if he'd like to design the entire cover. He said yes. Since then, we have undertaken a few Zoom meetings and Jacek completed the design you now hold in your hands (or on your eReader).

2: Author Biographies

Because this book is a world record attempt, I wanted to be able to prove that each contributing author is a real person. Authenticating this would be important whether the record attempt was official or unofficial. Therefore, providing a biography became a mandatory submission requirement.

As I mentioned earlier, the 81 Words challenge has been running on my website since April 2017. Therefore, some of the author biographies are a little out of date and may reference books that are *due* to be published but have in fact *been* published. It would have been a mammoth task to ask authors to update their biographies, so I decided to leave the biographies as they were.

When 81 Words first launched, author biographies were not mandatory. When I decided to try for the world record, I messaged all the authors who hadn't supplied a biography, explained the situation and asked them to provide a bio if they wanted their story to remain in the book. Bizzarely, there were 81 authors in this situation (no, I am not making that up).

35 authors sent me their biographies. 46 did not. So, those 46 stories were replaced with newer submissions. This means that there are some 'in date' author biographies near the beginning of the book, amongst older ones.

While editing the book, I found that I gained as much enjoyment from reading the author biographies as I did from the stories themselves. Each bio is a terse snapshot into the writer's life – a story in itself. So you could argue (and I would) that this book actually contains 2,000 stories.

3: Story Numbers

The stories in this book are presented in the order they were received, with the exception of the 46 stories mentioned in the previous section. However, there are some other exceptions. This is purely for practical reasons.

I wanted to keep the cost of the book as low as possible. The more pages in the book, the higher the printing cost. So, I changed the order of some of the stories to minimise the amount of pages in the book.

To help authors find their stories easily, there is an appendix at the back of the book that lists each author alphabetically (based on forename or initial) alongside the number of their story.

4: Counting 81 Words

There are so many different ways to assess the number of words in a story. For example, is a hyphenated word one or two words? Is a '-' a word in itself?

According to Microsoft Word (MW), *all* hyphenated words are one word and '-' is counted a word, but the slightly longer '–' is not.

In the end, I decided to keep things simple and use MW's word counter with three exceptions:

1. Where interrupted dialogue uses as em dash, "Like this—" MW counts the closing speech mark as a word. I did not.
2. MW also counts a * (often used to indicate a scene break or change in point of view) as a word. I did not.
3. MW counts an isolated elipses … as a word. Again, I did not.

5: Presentation

Prior to this book's publication, 15 other anthologies had been published via the writing challenges. In them, we have applied publishing standards so that presentation is consistent throughout. For example:

- OK has always been presented as 'OK', not 'okay'
- Words that are sometimes hyphenated have been presented in a consistent format, e.g.:
  - T-shirt (rather than t-shirt or T shirt or tee shirt)
  - No one (rather than no-one)

The list is *very* long, so I'll stop there. In this book we have ignored a lot of presentation inconsistencies because edits of this nature often alter the word count of stories – e.g., 102 (one word) one-hundred and two (three words), one hundred and two (four words).

It would have been a huge amount of work to apply all these standards, edit the stories so they remained exactly 81 words in length and then discuss substantial rewording with each author. Hence, we ignored consistency edits that altered the word count of stories.

Conclusion – Weird in a Good Way

I received the 1,000th story on 17th January 2021. All this started way back in 2015, when Adam first launched 81words.net. So, in total, this anthology has been over six years in the making.

The *81 Words Flash Fiction Anthology* is a culmination of years of hard work and the generosity of over 1,000 writers based all over the world.

Profits from book sales will be donated to the Arkbound Foundation. Thank you for supporting the project and the charity by purchasing this book.

And, to finish, I thought I would share a message from one of the contributing authors, James Louis Peel (author of story 563). When we were at the 800 story point, James messaged me to say:

Hello Christopher. This is just a bit of an observation you may already have noticed. Once all 1,000 stories have been gathered, there will actually be more authors than stories. I kindly point out that story 456 is written by two writers. So naturally when we get to the last story, the fabled 1,000, then we are at least at 1,001 writers. There may be other instances where two writers have contributed by collaborating on a single story and, if so, then there are even more people than 1,001. I think this is great. Not only have you brought some good into the world by your works but you have brought people together doing something that brings even more good. Perhaps you already knew this but, for me however, it was one of those weird in a good way little things that brought a smile.

Weird in a good way indeed – I couldn't have put it better myself ☺

In the end there were 1,003 contributing authors as stories number 90 and 819 were also written by two-person writing teams. And one of those authors is only four years old and (to the best of my knowledge) our youngest contributing writer.

I hope you enjoy the multitude of imaginative stories held within the pages of this glorious tome, which contains 1,000 stories written by (more than) 1,000 authors.

Christopher Fielden, Portishead, UK. June 2021.

INTRODUCTION 2

by The Arkbound Foundation

Founded in 2017, The Arkbound Foundation is the only independent charity in the UK that is concerned with improving accessibility and diversity within both publishing and journalism.

Over the years, we have supported a range of books by authors from disadvantaged backgrounds that cover important social or environmental themes: from Lauren Smith's *Tick Tock: It's Time to Listen*, which conveys perspectives on the education system by a young person with autism, to Seamus Fox's *No Homeless Problem*, which focuses on homelessness. Our books have been featured by high street retailers and nationally reviewed.

Through our workshops and mentoring, we have reached people who would otherwise be excluded and communities who face multiple levels of deprivation, by building skills, improving capacity and creating new opportunities. In fact, a few of the stories featured in this book were written by authors who have experience of homelessness when they attended creative writing workshops run by Chris via one of our support programmes.

We would like to thank the contributors and editors of this anthology for their generous support. Your contribution will help us continue to support disadvantaged people who would otherwise be excluded.

Mike Findlay, Chair of Trustees
www.arkfound.org

ACKNOWLEDGMENTS

Thank you to Adam Rubenstein and Allen Stroud for their ideas and inadvertently instigating this unofficial world record attempt.

Thank you to Jacek Wilkos for designing the cover of this book. You can learn more about Jacek's artwork on Facebook: www.facebook.com/Jacek.W.Wilkos/

Thank you to David Fielden for building and maintaining my website. Without him, I'd never have created a platform that allowed the writing challenges I run to be so successful. You can learn more about Dave's website building skills at: www.bluetree.co.uk

Thank you to Angela Googh for her help with proofreading and preparing the eBook version of this anthology for publication.

Thank you to Dr Lynda Nash for her help with proofreading the anthology.

Thank you to Consuelo Rivera-Fuentes, Jorge Vasquez, Sophie Lloyd-Owen, Pagen Hall and everyone at Victorina Press for agreeing to publish this book. You can learn more about Victorina Press on their website: www.victorinapress.com

Finally, a big thank you to everyone who has submitted their stories, supported this project and, in turn, the Arkbound Foundation. Without your collective support and generosity, this book would not exist.

1: ONE PREVIOUS OWNER

by Christopher Fielden

For sale. One dragon. Name: Fire Bringer. Temperament: challenging. Food: meat, vast quantities of, raw, alive, preferably screaming.

As name suggests, Fire Bringer does breathe fire. Said fire will melt anything, including High Tensile Steel and titanium.

Chain and collar included, although not effective (see notes regarding breath).

Likes long flights, smiting, riddles, treasure and things that twinkle.

Perfect pet for megalomaniac who wishes to take over the world. Large cave essential, best located remotely in extinct volcano.

Open to offers.

Christopher Fielden's Biography

Chris is an award-winning and Amazon best-selling author. His short story collection, *Alternative Afterlives*, was an award-winning finalist in the 'Fiction: Short Story' category of the International Book Awards. He plays drums in bands and regularly tours all over the world.

www.christopherfielden.com

~

2: BRUNO

by Michael Rumsey

I do not like dogs. Never have. Daniel should have consulted me before bringing that crazy stray home. One pet in the house is enough.

Typically, Bruno turned out to be loud, boisterous, and charged around like the proverbial bull in a china shop. But he does have one redeeming attribute.

I take a nap every afternoon. Bruno ensures no other strays enter our garden, allowing me to sit up in our apple tree and purr away to my heart's content.

Michael Rumsey's Biography

Michael lives in Athens with wife Maria, dog Sammy, several Greek tax demands and a laptop that just occasionally does as it is told.

www.facebook.com/mrumsey

3: THE TRAGICALLY UNFORESEEN CONSEQUENCES OF A HOPEFUL REQUEST

by Jerry Wilson

Once upon a time there was a little doorknob. All day long he sighed, "Oh, how I wish I were a mirror. Then people would look at me and smile."

The Good Doorknob Fairy had heard about enough. Grabbing her magic wand and her tiara, she flew on down.

"What, dude?"

"Oh, Good Doorknob Fairy, please turn me into a mirror."

"No probs."

Poof. The little doorknob became a bright, shiny mirror.

And no one could get the damned door open.

Jerry Wilson's Biography

An old new writer who, though lacking the talent and imagination of experienced story writers, bows to no one when penning cunning excuses for failed submissions. I fear no adverb. They are but tools in my arsenal of wearisome words.

~

4: REMEMBER EIGHTY-ONE?

by Allen Ashley

Yes, I remember eighty-one. A year of strife. The transport system in meltdown. Workers and management at loggerheads. Fears about automation in the workplace leading to further job losses. Poor air quality. Urban health scares. Governments considering land grabs and ready to send in an army at any provocation. The media finding convenient foreign scapegoats. Nobody seemed to be sticking up for the ordinary working man. Or woman.

Why have I not mentioned Thatcher?

I was talking about 2081. And 1881...

Allen Ashley's Biography

Allen Ashley is co-originator of the Sensory Challenge. His most recent book is the poetry collection *Echoes from an Expired Earth* (Demain Publishing, UK, 2020). He is President of the British Fantasy Society.

www.allenashley.com

5: THE NIGHT SENTRY

by Sivan Pillai

"He is a notorious housebreaker and we were in search of him," the policeman said.

The man was lying unconscious under the coconut tree. There was a huge bump on his head and a coconut lay nearby.

Only last evening we had decided to cut the tree down and plant a new one in its place. It had grown far too old and bore very few nuts.

Perhaps this was its way of telling us that it could still be useful.

Sivan Pillai's Biography

Sivan Pillai is a retired professor of English from Navsari Agricultural University, India. He lives in Navsari.

Find Sivan on Twitter: @sivan_pillai

~

6: DULLEST I'VE EVER SEEN

by Rene Astle

"Nobody could say that I'm dull."

"I'm not saying it to you."

"Then why can I hear you talking about how dull I've become while wedging potatoes?"

"Because you always forget about peeling."

"Don't be ridiculous."

"I shouldn't believe you, that's for sure."

"Be quiet, you fool. You're only saying that because you couldn't tell the difference between success and failure."

"Good grief, do I have to go through it once in a while?"

"Not for a longer while, you coot."

Rene Astle's Biography

Rene Kahu Astle is an American born New Zealander with a very big imagination and dreams as an autistic writer and artist. His first published work was a book of verses entitled *What's So Funny? And Other Poems* published in 2017.

7: CITY LIMITS

by Christopher Searle

This city is full of lies, anxious cries, and bickering wives. Walking through the street, you cannot escape the sound, of cars that drive, cooking fries, and criminal lives. There comes a time where a person craves something more, so open that door, and stop being such a bore.

Get on a bus and head out, listening to the engine grumbling, people mumbling, and shopping tumbling. To escape the city is such a pity, hopefully somewhere new is not as gritty.

Christopher Searle's Biography

A self-published author and content writer, Chris puts interaction with the world and characters at the fore. To him it is the experiences that matter within life, which comes across within his writing.

home.darkrulamedia.uk

~

8: WHICH ONE IS EARTH?

by David Turton

Annie gazed at the dark sky and squeezed Penny's hand.

"Which one is Earth, Nana?"

Penny looked up, identifying a blue-ish speck in the blackness. She knelt and pointed, ensuring Annie's vision was aligned with her fingertip.

Tears formed in the old woman's eyes.

"How long ago was it since everyone had to leave there, Nana?" Annie asked.

Wiping away her tears, Penny sighed.

"It's been thirty-three years now," she replied.

"Do you miss it?"

"Every day, darling." Her tears flowed.

David Turton's Biography

David Turton is an author of dark fiction and horror from North East England. His post-apocalyptic debut novel, *The Malaise*, was published in late 2018. Sign up to his mailing list for a free eBook of short stories:

www.davidturtonauthor.wordpress.com

9: JUST GOOD FRIENDS

by John Notley

Calixste was a one-off who befriended me when I entered the Livingstone Bar, used by the expats in Cotonou. He spoke French and was known throughout the town as a wheeler-dealer, part souvenir seller, part realty agent.

He took me on the back of his motorbike to many seedy bars in the heart of Cotonou, where I felt perfectly safe in the company of this short, round faced African who looked like a younger Louis Armstrong.

Sadly, Calixste has gone now.

John Notley's Biography

John, a retired travel agent, having failed to make his fortune has taken up his pen again hoping to redress the situation. He had a few stories and poems published some years ago but feels it's time to hit the jackpot.

www.linkedin.com/in/john-notley-503666102/

~

10: #METOO

by Gillian Macleod

Footsteps cautiously pad across the tiled floor. Looking up, the police officer spots a slight, anxious figure.

White trainers. Blue jeans, ripped at the knees. Yellow T-shirt, embroidered bird logo. Butterfly tattoo. Nose, ear and eyebrow piercings. Cropped, dyed blond hair. Purple bruise on the right cheekbone and a swollen, bloodied lip, trembling.

Eggshell voice, "I've been assaulted."

A barely concealed sigh, shuffling to find a place in the police notebook.

"OK, lad, who got you?"

Eyes avert. Swallow. "My girlfriend."

Gillian Macleod's Biography

Gillian is a retired English teacher living quietly in south-west Scotland. Bereft of the thousands of stories and essays she marked over decades for her pupils, she's decided it's time to have a go at writing some herself...

11: POURING PETROL ON EACH HEARTBEAT

by Jamie Graham

The screeching brakes. Somehow still on the road at the foot of the hill, the petrol warning beep changed everything. She pulled in, got out and put the nozzle in the open back window, squeezing the trigger hard. His crumpled body, sprawled on the rear seats, hanging in there. Unaware.

She turned and disappeared, screaming into the wilderness at the back of the forecourt, the bottom of her skirt well alight. Running helplessly on her very last legs, eyes closed tight.

Jamie Graham's Biography

Jamie Graham is a Scottish writer and *Seinfeld* fan on the wrong side of 40.

~

12: STICKS AND STONES

by Wayne Hewitt

"Dwarf planet, you loser."

Charon, Styx, Nix, Kerberos and Hydra had circled Pluto, taunting the so-called ruler of the underworld and protector of the solar system for the past four point five billion years.

Pluto, no longer the ninth planet, wept uncontrollably, knowing what this meant.

From within the Kuiper Belt, Eris, goddess of strife and discord, smiled at her opportunity, ejecting a moon sized plasma ball burning at a billion degrees Fahrenheit directly towards Earth.

This time, words would hurt.

Wayne Hewitt's Biography

Australia is now home for this proud son of Yorkshire. An adventurous spirit has seen me travel the world working, experiencing, laughing and crying but mostly enjoying as many shenanigans as I could get involved in... Let the adventures continue.

13: BROKEN PROMISE

by John Holmes

He had promised her that he'd live until his 90th.
    The doctor sighed, lowered his head and closed the front door behind him.
    Slowly, she climbed back upstairs and entered their bedroom of 70 years.
    Her lips felt the cold of his forehead.
    "You promised not to die. You promised."
    Picking up the present from the bed, she could feel the warmth of her own tears.
    One drop splashed onto the wrapping paper.
    The receipt was still lying in her purse.

John Holmes' Biography

Articles published in *The Guardian, TES* and *Junior Education*. Joint author of *Rough Rides*. Winner of *The Times* short story competition. Retired.

~

14: KING OF THE FOREST

by Len Saculla

On a walking and back to nature holiday, I became lost and in need. Close to death, I was saved by a dryad. Yes, the patient fixates on the kindly medic but... I fell in love with her.
    As soon as I could, I quit my job. I headed for the enchanted wood. We required the king's permission to marry.
    Her green hands led me to a clearing dominated by a giant oak tree.
    I waited. The tree spoke.
    Happy outcome.

Len Saculla's Biography

Len Saculla has been published in magazines and on websites including *Wordland* and *TubeFlash* as well as in several anthologies from American publisher Kind of a Hurricane Press. He had a flash fiction story nominated for the Pushcart Prize in 2015.

15: GUESS WHO

by Linda Taylor

"The Americans have known about them for some time."

The two whispered, approaching the glowing craft.

"Yes, but not everyone wanted to believe it."

Three came out from the module, their quiffed orange blond hair flapping irritatingly in the Earth's unfamiliar wind, teeth flashing brilliant white, as they carefully climbed down from the craft.

"Come." Long, bony, grey fingers wrapped around their shoulders, steered them inside.

"You are so right, it is time we revisited that land and fetched him home."

Linda Taylor's Biography

I write in several genres: supernatural, romance, comedy, thriller, novellas, novels and short stories. Four of my short stories were published in a Sussex magazine and one in an anthology with writers from around the world.

www.amazon.com/author/ltaylorscribere

~

16: BATTLES THAT DON'T ADVANCE

by Sandra Orellana

"Say no to racism," a young leader shouted to his town's people.

He continued, "I will give peace. I will stop frustrations that start battles. I won't allow hostile and hasty judgments. I won't provoke attacks on others that could start hate. I will focus on love so the evil can flee from our town."

He finished and sat down beside a weary, battered woman… his wife.

And she looked at him and said, "I hope it is true, my love."

Sandra Orellana's Biography

Sandra Orellana lives in México. Her passions are tennis, writing and reaching out. Her first novel is in the process of being published. She is now promoting her children's book, working on her second novel and enjoying writing for Christopher Fielden.

17: THE DEVIL'S TEA

by Tanya Johnson

The devil's cup of tea always seemed to go cold, no matter how hot Hell itself really was. He understood, of course, that this could be his own punishment, despite being one to punish others. A good *hot* cup of tea after a long day of torture was all he wanted.

Rising from his chair, he dialled a number on the handset.

"God? Yeah, hey. How you doing?" He paused, rolling his eyes and sighing. "I'm ready to come back up."

Tanya Johnson's Biography

Tanya Johnson is an amateur writer, born and raised in Northampton, England. An occupation of pharmaceutical dispensing and an education in science leads to writing in predominantly fantasy and science fiction. Overcoming mental health, the use of writing is successfully improving wellbeing.

Twitter: @TMJ_author

~

18: IT'S COMING

by Alexandra Klyueva

I was walking down the street when I heard the sound of a siren.

The last time it sounded was 30 years ago, when the whole city was underwater. On the first attempt, it consumed every part of the city.

And again, the familiar atmosphere.

And again, the familiar feeling of fear.

It became difficult to breathe.

I felt as if my body was filled with weight, and the sound of the siren continued to ring into my head.

It's coming.

Alexandra Klyueva's Biography

My name is Alexandra Klyueva. I'm 20 and I live in Russia. I study humanities and I'm a big fan of fiction. Writing stories for me is an attempt to express what I cannot say.

19: THE 81ST FLOOR

by Catherine Broxton

One.
 Two.
 Harold watched the lift numbers climb. Why was he being sent to the eighty-first floor?
 Fifteen.
 No one knew what was there, not even Claire.
 Thirty.
 Everything blurred. Harold realised that there were only eighty floors.
 Sixty.
 Where was he going? Time stopped. He clutched his briefcase.
 Eighty-one.
 Harold awoke amongst the clouds. He saw Claire and asked tentatively, "Is this Heaven?"
 "No," she replied. "It's the roof," and pushed him off.
 "That's what you get for stealing staplers."

Catherine Broxton's Biography

Catherine Broxton is a lifelong fan of the written word hailing from the United Kingdom. You can contact her at thepileofscraps@gmail.com or find her writings and more at apileofscraps on Tumblr.

~

20: A CHRISTMAS STORY

by Abigail Williamson

It was snowing on Christmas eve. Old Mrs Stuart was decorating the last of the buns. A loud knock brought her to the door.
 "Hark the herald angels sing…"
 Mrs Stuart ran to get some buns for the small group, but on running back, they were gone.
 The most beautiful singers ever heard, she thought.
*
Over the bridge, the village carolers stopped.
 "What about old Mrs Stuart's house?"
 "No point," said the tenor. "She is as deaf as a door post…"

Abigail Williamson's Biography

I am a nurse who enjoys short story fiction, classical music and writing.

21: DANGEROUS PLAYTIME

by Louise Burgess

"One, two, buckle my shoe."

Lilly happily sings as she smiles at her own reflection in the penknife she has taken out of his survival bag. Then, in one swift movement, she uses it to slice off his little toe.

Paul's ear piercing screams echo in the dimly lit basement.

"Please," he begs her, just before passing out from the pain.

"Three, four, knock on the door," Lilly sings again, searching in his bag for her next toy to play with.

Louise Burgess' Biography

My first published story was of course dedicated to my son, Emmet, but my second has to be dedicated to my amazing husband, Rick, because without him, I would never have the time or energy to write. Thank you.

www.loopybwritingpage.wordpress.com

~

22: 13TH

by Robert Kombol

Upon each word you set your sight. Someone writes. To now you owe this moment, and pay you must.

Dark.

Someone is. Yet one is not.

Beneath your skin.

In six there is a six that's made of six.

A needle ties my finger with your eyes.

Someone has.

Someone will. Yet one will not.

In now you've placed your faith as if it were a friend.

So tell me, friend,

of how our stories end,

when all ends with

☉

Robert Kombol's Biography

Robert Kombol is an aspiring writer who spends too much time thinking about writing instead of doing actual writing. Do not be like Robert. Write.

23: TIME FOR TRUST

by Diane Harding

"It's time."

"Time for what?"

"Time to give you the message."

"What's the message?"

"It's about the lotto results."

"You mean I've won?"

"Yes, the billion dollars."

"Wow. I am lucky, aren't I?"

"You could be."

"What? Where is the ticket?"

"Here. You gave it to me to check out at the newsagent."

"Of course. Well, I can always trust you."

"Yes. I suppose."

"Am I right?"

"Yes. You are right."

"Good."

"So, it's time."

"Time for what now?"

"This."

BANG.

Diane Harding's Biography

Diane Harding is an Australian author of two crime novels, *Reported Missing* and *A Taste for Diamonds*. She has a *Catastrophe Girl* series and wrote *I Dug a Hole to China and My Sister was a Zombie* for 5 to 9-year-olds.

~

24: PERSISTENCE

by Maddy Hamley

He lowered the book and sighed.

Still nothing.

Perhaps he should throw their wretched grimoire back through the portal, but that would give the creatures the wrong impression. He could not afford to scare them off.

Instead, he closed the tome reverentially, muttering thanks to the beings for their patience, and placed it on the shelf behind him.

He knew he had the right incantation. It was just a matter of persistence.

Maybe next time they would bring his daughter back.

Maddy Hamley's Biography

Maddy Hamley is a bilingual English-German translator and full-time project manager. When she's not busy cursing at untranslatable Bavarian proverbs, she enjoys writing short stories, singing, or lounging around in Cologne with her fiancée.

~

25: HAPPY LANDINGS

by Alan Barker

"We are preparing to land. The exits are at the front and rear," indicated Max to his friends, Will and Jay. "Do not move until the doors are opened. Outside is a pleasant 20 degrees. On behalf of the captain and crew, we hope you'll fly with us again soon."

"Max, you are not on your air steward's course now," teased Will. "If you are going to perform like this every time we use the lift, we're using the escalators, mate."

Alan Barker's Biography

A retired English/drama teacher, I live in South Wales. Writing plays and short stories is my passion, although I enjoy turning personal experiences into poetry. E.g., urology doctors and nurses, coffee bar waitresses, dental receptionists and soldiers.

26: DON'T JUDGE A BOOK BY ITS COVER

by Barry Smith

No matter what people look like, it's amazing what they can do. I should know, because I have a physical disability. I might need a hand to do things but my mind is all there.

I use a power chair when I'm out, but when I'm in the house I move around on my bum. And I can be fast too.

When people don't understand what I'm saying to them, I type it into my Lightwriter, which is a communication aide.

Barry Smith's Biography

I have cerebral palsy, which is a physical disability. Many people in this world are not able to work because they suffer with ill health or a physical disability. I know about this.

~

27: JACOB'S LAST BREATH

by James Sanders

The tux is loose around Jacob's waist. Abigail, glowing in white lace, waits for the recorded wedding march to end. The piano notes tremble, similar to his hands, similar to hers. She accepted the diamond three months ago, before everything changed.

Mum and Dad practise social distancing. Abi's dad steadies her. Her mum couldn't make it.

Vows done, Abi sobs. The doctor says it's time: a younger patient needs the ventilator.

One last I love you. Jacob takes his last breath.

James Sanders' Biography

James Sanders lives in southern Virginia. He dearly loves creating genuine characters and has written several contemporary and historical novels, some with speculative elements, some without, all guaranteed to induce tears, laughter and the desire to read again.

28: TYCOON TOMMY

by Lesley Anne Truchet

I hate school.

SUMMER HOLIDAYS:

Week 1 to 3, I nicked goods from shops.

Week 4, I sold the stuff on eBay.

Week 5, I was running to the post office with parcels. The money rolled in.

Next week, I'll car boot the rest. Mum will think I'm clearing my room and she'll help out with her car.

Last summer, I made £750.00. This summer will be around £1,000.

This time next year, I'm gonna be a millionaire.

I hate school.

Lesley Anne Truchet's Biography

Lesley Truchet has been writing for several years and has a number of short stories, articles and poems published on paper and on the internet. She is currently writing her first novel.

~

29: YOU LOOKING AT ME?

by Barry Rhodes

Timothy sat in the cell.

He looked and smelled as if he'd slept on the streets. His bulging eyes peered through greasy, unruly hair.

His crime: a disturbance in the local shopping mall.

He'd stopped at a shop window. Seeing a strange reflection staring at him, he'd yelled abuse at it. When it would not retreat, he'd head butted it, again and again.

He was arrested by the police. His protagonist could not be found.

He was sectioned for a month.

Barry Rhodes' Biography

Having had a demanding career, writing unfortunately had to be put on the backburner. Upon retirement, Barry Rhodes has been able to revisit his passion and use his varied experiences to write. He lives in Kent.

30: FEVER

by Brett Elliott-Palmer

Staying in is the new going out. I close the curtains and pour a glass of wine.
    The kid in the apartment above me, bare feet on a hardwood floor. Dad yells.
    "No ball games in the house. No ball games in the park."
    After dark, I go for a walk. I take music, my heavy head and a yellow scarf.
    Stalk past houses, the lights on, the chatter of occupants, shadows.
    Home again.
    A cough. I shudder. Wash my hands.

Brett Elliott-Palmer's Biography

I currently work in social care and write in my spare time. Mostly tragicomedy/horror and LGBTQ+ related fiction. I have an Instagram with around 10 followers. You can usually find me hanging out there.
    @ohokfinewe

~

31: CUSTOMER RETURNS

by Claire Temple

Wheelers in the village contains a forest of mannequins. What a thing to be afraid of at my age. But hip replacement or not, I must take back my granddaughter's faulty dress.
    "Hello?"
    Nothing.
    As I pull back a dusty gold curtain, I see my lifetime's recurring dream. Limbs. Lips. Broken.
    I'm returned, exchanged and lost. My best dress snags. I shiver. I'm only four years old. If I wait like a still shop dummy, I'm sure I'll be found soon.

Claire Temple's Biography

Claire Temple has had her poems in various magazines and two anthologies over many years. Most recently in *Envoi* and this year's *Live Canon Anthology*. This is the only short story she has ever had published.

32: MY NEMESIS

by Tracey Maitland

I hate you and love you simultaneously. I want you out of my life but can't see it through. You drag me down, make me ill, breathless and lethargic. You are no good for me, and yet I am drawn to you every time; you're always on my mind.

I watch you with repulsion and desire as you burn, emitting an aroma only an addict desires. Smoke slowly rises and twists, a dancing serpent, mesmerising, robbing me of health and wealth.

Tracey Maitland's Biography

"Life is either a daring adventure or nothing." (Helen Keller)

~

33: CONVERSATIONS

by Crilly O'Neil

Put the paper down for heaven's sake. Get up and do something. Empty the dishwasher, fold the washing or, for a real change, make dinner for me.

The words stuck in her throat like cold porridge.

And this is what she said.

"I know you've had a hard day and you are tired. It's fine. You put your feet up, darling. I'll make the meal. Folding the washing can wait."

She kicked off her shoes, poured a wine and started again.

Crilly O'Neil's Biography

Living in Sydney with her husband, six kids, two dogs and two cats, Crilly writes to escape her busy life. Her stories have been published in several anthologies and placed in various competitions. Crilly's novel is a work-in-progress.

34: WATCHING

by Daniel L. Link

Recognition makes my skin redden, my face sweat, like being hit with the steam from a boiling pot. I can't remember when last I saw her, but the years have wrought little change.

The train starts forward and she stands on the platform watching after me. My rush to the back of the car is halted by a large man standing in the aisle. A look through the window shows her still there, and I watch until she's out of sight.

Daniel L. Link's Biography

DL Link lives in northern California. He has published over 25 short stories and his debut novel, *Cry Wolf*, is due out in October 2020 through Fawkes Press.

www.daniellinkauthor.com

~

35: MERELY A GRUMBLE

by Michelle Konov

It is with neither a bang nor a whimper that it ends but with a grumble that sticks in her throat, ripping itself hoarsely out from between tight lips. He can see the moment her defenses go up and thinks, rather abjectly, that even beyond being over, perhaps it had never begun.

She turns with a startling huff and walks away, back ramrod straight, and he finds himself caught in a jumble of emotion.

So what if he was a stalker?

Michelle Konov's Biography

Dreamer, writer, winner, quitter. Michelle Konov is a bit of a nerd, kind of a geek, and, well, mostly a dork. English teacher by trade, creative mastermind by nature – save 'creative' and 'mastermind', anyway. Forever filling space with words.

36: WHO'S BLUE?

by Silver Morris

I can see where you are. You're the green dot on my monitor.

—

What do you mean, why green? I thought that was your favourite colour.

—

Well, if I changed it now, I'd just get confused. *Where is my beloved Jessica?* I'd wonder, forgetting that you were no longer green. Anyway, blue's already taken.

—

Insane? This isn't insane. How can I keep you safe without knowing where you are? You can see, right? I'm only doing this because I love you.

Silver Morris' Biography

Silver Morris is an American writer who enjoys reading, writing paranormal short stories, and loves his rats.

~

37: THE WINNER

by Michael Mclaughlin

Jeff was there to win the flash short story contest. He had collected hundreds of rejections, but this time he would win.

Crissy had her back to the door, her face buried in the computer screen, small fingers rejecting the latest contestants with little taps on the keyboard.

Jeff fired and Crissy's blood, bone and flesh spattered the computer screen. Calmly, Jeff scanned down the list between the bloody splatter on the screen and found his name.

He typed, 'The winner.'

Michael Mclaughlin's Biography

In 2005, after three decades, Michael retired from theatre in the USA to Ajijic, Mexico, where the weather is sunny, the beer cold and the senoritas friendly. He has directed a benefit lip-sync show (the largest in the world).

38: ALL ACHIEVEMENTS ARE RELATIVE

by Liam Lawer

Victory. After all this time. Holding tightly as he lifted it higher, he gazed at the cup in wonder. Disbelief and euphoria overcame him in equal measure. He had done it. He had finally won.

Sweat formed on his brow and tears filled his eyes. His family celebrated around him, filled with pride. In their private shame, they had doubted this moment would ever transpire.

He looked at his new arm as the cup reached his dry, trembling lips.

"Perfect cuppa."

Liam Lawer's Biography

Cornish boy who tentatively wrote this short story while studying history at university. He particularly enjoys reading, boxing and spending time with his family and friends. Thanks to Chris for the idea.

~

39: EULOGY

by Norm Veasman

"He was an uninspired man, indulgent to his base instincts, lacking the values his creator would cherish. His death was mundane and unnecessary, leaving behind not a grieving family but a disillusioned widow, and children who never knew anything save his façade. We mourn today a life, not a life well lived…"

The pastor stopped there, balled up the words, and tossed them into the fireplace. As flames destroyed the truth, he began to write the lies the mourners would hear.

Norm Veasman's Biography

Currently living in Colorado. Married with children and grandchildren and great-grandchildren. Former radio DJ, cook and karaoke host. Doing my best to stay sane.

40: ABSTRACTIONS

by J.S Taols

My dad poked his head inside my room. "What a mess," he grumbled.

"What one man considers mess, others may see as art," I protested.

"And what exactly do you call this particular work of art?" he asked, waving his hand across the room.

"I call it teenage angst. What do you think?"

"Oh yeah, you're a regular Picasso."

"Why thank you. What period would you say?"

"Blue," he replied. "Definitely blue, because you're grounded."

"And all the world's a critic."

J.S Taols' Biography

Now retired, and living in northern California with my wife and dog, I'm rediscovering my love of prose. The first draft of my novel is complete, so editing and crossing fingers.

~

41: JOHN DELANEY

by S. W. Hardy

Some people want to be remembered. Others do not. John Delaney belonged in the second category.

He grew up consuming food, then expelling what he didn't need.

He worked a job, spending money, then discarding what he didn't need.

He possessed no friends, nor an interest in his family or their affairs, although he took pride in his marvellously kept bedspread.

One day, in the early hours of an undisclosed morning at an undetermined time, John Delaney died – a contented man.

S. W. Hardy's Biography

I graduated from the University of Nottingham with a degree in creative writing. I self-published my first young adult novel, *No Separation,* (available on Amazon) and run a travel/writing website. I currently live and teach in Shenzhen (China).

42: WATERS AND STONES – MOTHERS AND DAUGHTERS

by Özge Göztürk

"I'm getting the stars if you want me to buy the book."

"I said, if you want the book you can, I'm not insisting on it. But definitely no toys today."

"These are stars, not toys."

"You bought similar ones before, they didn't even glow in the dark properly."

"No. I'm not reading the book if I'm not getting a toy."

"You're not getting a toy to read a book. Leave it."

"I'm not going to read anything anymore."

"Oh dear..."

Özge Göztürk's Biography

Özge Göztürk is a London-based author, multi-award-winning scriptwriter and journalist. She's judging the New York Screenplay Awards and is the founder of the London Independent Story Prize. Her writing has been published in the Netherlands, Malawi, Turkey, the UK and the USA.

~

43: TOBY

by Paul Shaw

Toby was honey-coloured and quite as sweet. He lived with Suzy in her room. Toby had been with her family a long time and was very old. Suzy was only four. He was her best friend and even sat with her as she ate.

Toby never ate when Suzy did. He was a toy bear and didn't eat fish fingers or other food that humans like. He ate only when Suzy was fast asleep. Then, every night, he ate Suzy's dreams.

Paul Shaw's Biography

Paul is a former detective, civil servant and whelk packer and lives in retirement in coastal Kent. Inspiration to write hides in plain sight, everywhere. His short stories and poetry have appeared in anthologies and online.

44: THE FALL

by Abhi Shan

I remembered falling. Scared, heart pounding, eyes bulging with the adrenaline rush. When I came to a halt, I was unhurt.

Surprised, lost and confused, I looked around. It was dark. No glimmer of light or hope. I lurched around in all directions at once to find the exit.

I stumbled and fell again, but this time it was short and painful. I opened my eyes and touched my bloody nose. A faint light reminded me of what'd just happened… nightmares.

Abhi Shan's Biography

Abhi Shan is a research scientist by profession and an avid reader. When he is not busy doing science he loves to write short stories and flash fiction.

~

45: THE BLIND DATE

by Christine O'Donnell

If he's more than ten minutes late, I'm gone. Would it look too obvious if I check my watch again? OK, grabbing my bag and— Is that him? Please say that isn't him…

Of course, this would be how your date went, sitting across from foghorn voice, watching spinach get increasingly mashed within his giant gnashers.

Oh fabulous, another story about his ex.

Nod and smile, it won't be long until you're back home.

Whatever you do, never blind date again.

Christine O'Donnell's Biography

Christine is an English teacher by day, writing sleuth by night, with numerous sojourns into the fanciful in her work. She's recently published her first teen historical fiction on Amazon and continues to dream of one day making it big, or even small.

46: EVICTED

by Caroline Wright

They say I have to leave.

Notice has arrived that I am to be compulsorily evicted. Overcrowding. That's the official term they are using. It is a small place but it is adequate for my needs. I have everything I want here. It's comfortable. I have ventilation and washing facilities.

The powers that be say I will be going to a nice place.

I don't care. I like it here.

I am being pushed out.

I don't want to be born.

Caroline Wright's Biography

Caroline Wright is an administrator from Halifax. She has always written and has had poems and short stories published in anthologies and a magazine. Has several unpublished novels and wants to be a published author.

~

47: FURBORG'S CAUTION

by Ian Tucker

As a kitten, Furborg caught flu and almost died.

Accidentally drinking floor cleaner claimed another life shortly afterwards.

When young, he'd underestimated the strength of a fox.

And he once fell three storeys from a roof.

The vase that toppled onto him wasn't his fault.

And every cat has one bad experience with curiosity.

One time, he ate the wrong sort of grass.

Recently, there was the incident with the yellow lorry.

Adding these up, Furborg is now much more cautious.

Ian Tucker's Biography

Ian Tucker is a hopeless amateur who writes for fun and so his wife thinks he's busy. There is lots of rubbish by him at:

www.tilebury.com

48: TOM THE BUS STOP CAT

by Femi S. Craigwell

Tom was a black and white cat, a clever cat in fact. He loved to spend his days relaxing at the bus stop, sunbathing on hot summer days. He especially enjoyed the free hugs and tasty treats from kind strangers.

And if they didn't spoil him with lots of attention, he would make sure to *purr* loudly, whilst brushing across their legs. Until finally they would give in and say, "Hello, Tom, the bus stop cat," and stroke his fluffy head.

Femi S. Craigwell's Biography

British writer with a BA (hons) degree in film and media studies. In my spare time, I enjoy watching repeats of my favourite sitcoms. When it comes to fiction, I like to experiment between writing screenplays, flash fiction and short stories.

~

49: THE MORNING RUSH

by Nick Fairclough

His son was mucking about.

Bag wasn't packed… Teeth weren't brushed… Shoes weren't on… How many times could one ask?

The father was becoming increasingly frustrated. His forehead resembled a deformed mountain range, the wrinkles caving in, collapsing like a landslide.

"Look at the time," the father shouted as he pointed to the clock hanging on the wall. "It's twenty past eight."

His son looked up to where his father had pointed, and yelled back, "Twenty isn't even on a clock."

Nick Fairclough's Biography

Nick Fairclough lives in Richmond, New Zealand. He is a Pushcart Prize and Best Small Fictions nominee. His books include *The Tidal Island and Other Stories* and *Thanks For Letting Me Know*.

www.nickfairclough.wordpress.com

50: REMEMBER WHEN...

by Ali Bounds

"Mama, today we learned about the virus."

That one word set off a flashback of memories.

"What happened?"

Mama sat down on the edge of the bed.

"Well, people got really sick. Lots of people died."

Her daughter gasped.

"My mama kept me inside. She wouldn't let me leave until it was over. We watched the news, watched how many people got sick. There was lots of fighting."

"I'm really glad you're OK."

She sighed. "Me too."

"Goodnight, Mama."

"Goodnight, sweetheart."

Ali Bounds' Biography

I'm a freshman in high school. I've been writing since the seventh grade. I'm involved in choir, tennis and am devoted to my academics. Thank you to my writer friends who've helped me develop into the writer I am today.

~

51: IF THE TRUTH BE KNOWN

by David Silver

For too many years, I have put up with an acquaintance who claims that he dated Madonna frequently, drank regularly with Richard Burton, Peter O'Toole and Richard Harris and was begged constantly to sign professionally for Manchester United.

But by this afternoon, I'd had enough of his fibs and confronted him. The bloke burst into tears and admitted he was a habitual liar.

My problem now is that I still don't believe him. So maybe his stories are true after all.

David Silver's Biography

David Silver was a reporter, sub-editor and columnist on various newspapers in Greater Manchester, England. He retired in 2002 and from 2011 to 2016 wrote a column for *The Courier*, a weekly newspaper for UK expatriates in Spain.

52: A SECOND CHANCE

by Jaine E. Irish

"Is that Jane?"

"Yes."

"Your husband has collapsed."

"Is he dead?"

"The paramedics are working on him now."

"Is he still breathing?"

"I have to go. Someone will call you later."

"Please, where are you?"

"King's Cross Station. I pressed redial."

In the palm of her trembling hand, the small, pink mobile lay silent, like a fragile heart waiting to beat again – like his heart, stopped, stuck in his chest somewhere on the floor at King's Cross Station, where she wasn't.

Jaine E. Irish's Biography

Born in Sheffield, degree in theatre design and history of art. Set construction for l'Opera de Paris and the Crucible Theatre. PA freelance work in both London and France involving property and travel. Living in Kent enjoying writing, painting and photography.

~

53: QUESTIONS ONLY SOMEONE ELSE CAN ANSWER

by Prisha Gupta

Stop asking me how the world turns. Don't ask if it spins like a spool of thread, with God pulling it on a string. I don't know.

How am I supposed to know if it's the sun's job to paint the sky as it moves from one edge of the canvas to the other? I don't know how the world works. I can't tell you. It's not my job to say.

Child, I can only tell you why we keep going.

Prisha Gupta's Biography

Prisha is a high school student from Dallas, Texas, who loves to write, draw, sing and dance. She's been writing since the seventh grade and she's excited to keep improving her work.

You can find her on Instagram: @prishavacado

54: STREWN IN THE BREEZE

by Ros Byrne

Eighty-one. So few words. Enough for a perfect boy meets, loses, finds girl, happy ever after? But the words should be beautiful, not this mundane.

How to include the assorted glories of shenanigans, glittering, indigo, squelch, illustrious, chartreuse, tagliatelle – these last not even English ones? Accepted borrowing or serious faux pas? Malpaso in Spanish, perhaps? Clint Eastwood thus named his film company when warned it was a bad step.

My turn now to stumble, strewing my precious eighty-one in the breeze.

Ros Byrne's Biography

London Irish + Cardiff Uni + one husband + three sons + TEFL teacher + currently also kitchen porter + typing crime novel for my father-in-law who is a proper writer.

~

55: TEN

by David Rhymes

One. Make sure you telephone somebody warning them that it's going to happen.
Two. Run a warm bath and add lavender salts.
Three. Brush your hair one hundred times exactly as your mother taught you to.
Four. Take care with your makeup.
Five. Roll back the sheets and slip inside, naked, clean and fresh.
Six. Place the note beside the bed under the scented candle.
Seven. Light the scented candle.
Eight. Lie back.
Nine. Arrange your hair attractively across the pillow.

David Rhymes' Biography

David was born in Nottingham, studied at the universities of Warwick and East Anglia and lives in Pamplona, Spain, with his wife, two children and a dog. His work has appeared in the Bath Flash, Reflex Fiction and Fish Publishing anthologies.

56: GONE BUT NOT FORGOTTEN

by Julia O'Dowd

"So, what did you think?"

"It was OK."

"He was good."

"Didn't like his character. Too self-centred."

"She was excellent."

"A bit over the top, I thought."

"Terrific production though."

"The stage was a bit bare."

"It's for dramatic effect."

"Just one thing puzzled me."

"What's that?"

"Those two guys who were sent away."

"Which two?"

"The ones that didn't come back. Forgot their names."

"Rosencrantz and Guildenstern."

"Where'd they go?"

"They're dead."

"They're dead?"

"Yes, but that's another play entirely."

Julia O'Dowd's Biography

Julia lives in Kent with two males, one of which has fur, four legs and a wet nose. She loves writing short fiction, five minute plays, and custard creams. Julia is now tackling her first novel – gulp.

www.jajhartnett.com

~

57: A SINGLE RED ROSE

by Jessica Joy

The pile of empty shells under the tree, glinted in the sunlight.
"The pearls have all gone."
"Yes. They take the gifts we leave for them."
"Not these shells. The oysters. There's none left."
"But if there's no gift, they'll help themselves."
"We must find them another gift."
"They'll want something beautiful."
"What is more beautiful than a single, red rose?"
She plucked one from her basket.
"What if they don't like it?"
"Then we'll need to hide our babies again."

Jessica Joy's Biography

Jess has stories in several anthologies: *With Our Eyes Open: Book a Break Anthology 2017*, Waterloo Festival's *Transforming Being* and *The Rabbit Hole – 2* (The Writers Co-op). Jess has been runner-up and winner in Faber Academy's QuickFic competition.
Twitter: @MrsJessicaJoy1

~

58: TWIG DINOSAUR

by Fay Franklin

I built a twig dinosaur when I was a kid, bigger than I was by far. It was a thing of glory and fear.
One day, my older brother set fire to it. I tried to put it out for a while – those are the marks you can still see on my hands – and then I let it go. Oh, how it flew; a pterodactyl suddenly alive.
It was years and years before it returned to settle the score with him.

Fay Franklin's Biography

Fay Franklin has worked and played with words all her life – professionally as a non-fiction editor, bookseller and travel writer; since childhood and to date as a writer of short fiction.
Twitter: @fayfran

59: STALKER

by Irving Benjamin

"Stalking? Is that what you said?"

"Yes. I'm sure he was." The old lady grasped the young constable's arm firmly, looking from side to side with wild eyes, breathing heavily.

The policeman gently prised her fingers from his sleeve.

"Where was this, love? Was he, like, threatening you?"

"No, officer, just chasing me. I hid there." As she pointed, a young man emerged from the park entrance.

"OK, Mum, it's all right now. Time to take you back to the home."

Irving Benjamin's Biography

Professor Emeritus Irving Benjamin, a retired surgeon, divided his working life between Glasgow, London and South Africa. He has lived with his wife in Deal for over 20 years, enjoying writing, real ale, sailing, rugby and playing brass band music.

www.benjdeal.uk

~

60: US

by Emma Stammeyer

"Dearly beloved…"

"You know, I don't know how you still put up with me, man."

"I know why, darling. It's because I love you. I figured the whole wedding thing would convince you, but I guess not. Maybe I'll just have to go marry someone else who gets it."

"No, no, no. Wait, don't, please."

"I'm only joking, darling. You're the only one I'd ever dream of putting a ring on."

"Really?"

"Of course."

"…I now pronounce you, husband and wife."

Emma Stammeyer's Biography

My name is Emma Stammeyer. I'm currently a freshman who has been writing since I was in seventh grade. For Granny. Thank you for all that you do for me.

61: THE GHOST WRITER

by Valerie Griffin

Anna has an uncanny knowledge of the afterlife and is the star pupil in her spectrology class. Two days before the exams, the scratching sound wakes her from a rather pleasant dream.

She rubs her eyes and sits up, reaching for the bedside light-switch and her notebook. Once again, the writing is on the wall. Sentence after sentence scrawling at an angle across the textured wallpaper. She writes down the answers quickly, before they fade.

"Thanks, Uncle Henry," she whispers, smiling.

Valerie Griffin's Biography

Published short story and flash fiction writer for anthologies and competitions (one winner plus persistent runner-up), letters to magazines and articles.

I'm on Twitter: @griffin399

~

62: DOOMED

by Everest Pen

Nobody tells me anything, not even when the world is ending. I glance out the window and set my coffee down on the kitchen counter. Large storm clouds cover the skies above, which isn't unusual this time of year, but these are different.

Finally, my older sister races from upstairs and takes the remote that is sitting beside me. I suck in a deep breath as the news anchor says, "The Yellowstone Caldera has just erupted. Police say not many survived."

Everest Pen's Biography

I live in a close-knit community and have a passion for singing. I've been playing tennis for three years and do not expect to stop anytime soon. I plan to go to college to become a publisher.

63: THE TO-DO LIST

by Tess M Shepherd

Whilst Sue enjoyed a spa weekend away, Ben studied his to-do list. Ah, yes. Garden makeover. That should kill two birds with one stone. A quick visit to the old witch (Sue's mum), before buying the decking and plants.

He'd never dug so much in his life. The special fertiliser needed digging in deep. But all that sweat was worth the effort.

After a hard day's work, he leaned on his trusty spade, admiring the transformation.

"That's the mother-in-law sorted, anyway."

Tess M Shepherd's Biography

Tess M Shepherd lives in Yorkshire, UK. She is currently working on two full-length historical novels. It has always been a dream of hers to be a published author.

~

64: MUM'S MYSTERY TOURS

by Mike Blakemore

Jess always tried to guess where we were going and bring something appropriate. Once, she kept poking the rest of us with a fishing net, all the way to Stonehenge.

Dad always stayed behind to work, ruffling our hair as we climbed into the car.

The last time, Mum didn't stop. We grew tired of asking where we were going and eventually she grew tired of driving.

She ignored her phone and switched it off when we checked into the hotel.

Mike Blakemore's Biography

Mike Blakemore was briefly a journalist before finding himself in PR, where he has made a go of things for the NHS, the BBC, Amnesty International and others. When no one is looking, he writes; short stories and recently a novel.

Twitter: @WhoisMBlakemore

65: MARRIAGE TREE

by Ryu Ando

"The tree we got from city hall didn't last the summer," Makiko said.

All these years, Toru thought, *and she still gets it wrong*. It sat on their veranda for at least six months before it shrivelled up in the cold.

"It was your job to water it, anyway," he said.

But she shook her head and whisked the finely-ground matcha until it foamed up like a green pond, ready to spill over. She handed him his tea. It was bitter.

Ryu Ando's Biography

Ryu Ando, spending his time between LA and Saitama, Japan, is a poet. His most recent collection, *[零] A Phantom Zero*, was published by The Operating System Press in 2019.

www.ryuando.wordpress.com

~

66: ALL BETTER

by Maxx Dominic

The doctor entered the hospital room. Sick patients lined the walls. The nurse had her boxes, and he made sure to apply lip balm.

The first patient was a man with a broken arm. Obviously, an adhesive bandage was needed. The nurse held out her boxes and the patient picked a sturdy navy bandage. She applied it gingerly and sent him home.

The woman with a cold was given a kiss on the nose, "All better," and sent home as well.

Maxx Dominic's Biography

Maxx is 56 and lives in NYC with his wife and kids.

67: I DOUGHNUT SEE WHAT THE PROBLEM IS, OFFICER

by Devon Goodchild

He patted the last shovelful of dirt over the fresh grave. No one would know what he'd done.

Shaking, he drove off. No one would know. He bought a doughnut as a pick-me-up with his wife's credit card. No one would know.

His phone vibrated, a text from his wife. He looked, still driving.

I know what you did.

Distracted, horrified, he crashed, his car folding into a doughnut around a tree.

His phone vibrated again.

Buy me a doughnut too.

Devon Goodchild's Biography

Devon Goodchild. Full-time librarian. Me-time writer. Crazy-cat-collector in training. Happily married. Would kill for a doughnut.

~

68: THE INVISIBLE OWNER

by Edwin Stern

A gentleman admired the old cottage's flower bed.

"Something interesting?" a young woman asked.

"Lived in the village 80 years. No one knows who owns this, yet it's kept in magnificent condition."

"Do you believe in ghosts?"

"No."

"Pity. The owner was murdered by her lover 200 years ago. Her body never found. He wasn't caught."

"How—"

"Do I know?"

He turned but the woman had vanished.

The cottage door creaked open.

"Please, come in and I'll tell you," she called.

Edwin Stern's Biography

My English teacher told me that I had excellent imagination and ability to tell a good story. Its only now that I am making a serious attempt to see if she was right.

69: LET ME TELL YOU A STORY

by Jack Dudley

Let me tell you a story.

I want to take you someplace strange, somewhere far from home but closer than you realise. I want to introduce you to people you may have met before, in a time you can barely remember. Their world is strange, their customs are alien and yet, whether they're human or not, they struggle just the same as us.

I want to tell you a story about the adversities of life and the strife of surpassing them.

Jack Dudley's Biography

My name is Jack Dudley. I'm a 20-year-old fiction writer. I've only been writing for about three years now. I can't exactly call myself an 'author' just yet but, who knows, maybe someday.

~

70: LA CUCARACHA

by Rui Soares

"No mobile phone here please," said the man.

"Huh. Where can I put it then?"

His left eyebrow arched. There's a box on the desk.

"Here."

As I entered with Louise and passed by him, we could hear him mumble, "The world is doomed. It's supposed to be romantic."

We sat and asked for the menu. A tall woman told us, "We do not have a menu. Customer eats what Momma cooks. We do have a drink list."

Went for margaritas.

Rui Soares' Biography

Occasionally, my impression footprints are washed away from my mind shore. Memoir wreckage. It makes me uneasy. Thus I've been pouring visual and written impressions from my life.

Instagram: @rumagoso

71: DON'T BELIEVE ME

by Angelique Dusengimana

"Give me my money."

"Alice, what money?"

"Joseph, stop kidding. Give me my money back. Honestly, I don't know what you are talking about, Joseph, you are such careless person. Maybe I am."

"Don't you remember me giving you money last night?"

"Of course I don't remember. You just want me to give you more money."

"Alice, don't you know that Joseph was drunk? He is always like that."

"Tony, are you saying that even the job promised was a lie?"

Angelique Dusengimana's Biography

Angelique Dusengimana is a tutorial assistant at the University of Rwanda. She focusses on contributing to the development of the national higher education. Angelique holds a BSc in estate management and valuation. She is a passionate, artful and insightful writer.

www.linkedin.com/in/angelique-dusengimana-86a553aa/

~

72: AISLE 81 IN 2029

by Patrick Antonio

Coach Joe's 2029 high school wrestling ceremony is tonight. With 12 trophies to go, his 3D printer runs out of plastic.

Now at Metamart's computer section, he learns they're out of plastic, which is all his printer can handle.

"How much for ones that print metal?" Coach asks, frowning. "Do any print cheaper material? What's your lowest cost printing stuff?"

"Have you tried our trophy aisle? We engrave," the Metamart rep suggests.

Coach smiles. "Pre-printed trophies? Really? So retro. Awesome. Where?"

Patrick Antonio's Biography

Patrick Antonio is a 47-year-old married father of two. Lifelong Floridian, businessman, lover of feasible near-future sci-fi (like *Black Mirror*). In 2017, his story named 'Creative Destruction' won first place in their annual long form short story competition.

73: MISSY'S GIFT

by Maria DePaul

Missy, a two year old black tabby cat, strolled down a lane at twilight. She came upon a vole's nest. Crouching, she waited until the voles began to forage. She pounced on a slow one for a quick snack. Then, she took another home as a gift for her household.

Surprised, but not shocked, the lady of the house praised Missy's hunting skills the following morning. Then, she discreetly disposed of the gift before her children came downstairs, preventing future nightmares.

Maria DePaul's Biography

Maria DePaul is a writer based in Washington, D.C. who was stuck in writers' block when she tried the 81 Words challenge. Afterward, she kept going. Since then, her poetry and flash fiction has been featured in a variety of publications.

~

74: THE MAN

by Gemma Martiskainen

There was a man on the sidewalk. He was there even when it rained sideways or when the wind blew enough to take your hat. Sometimes he had a sign. Sometimes not.

I avoided his gaze, unsettled. Could I fall his way too, by misfortune or misdeed? Maybe it wasn't his fault. One does not control the future like a car. Sometimes it takes the steering wheel and chooses its own road. This I knew.

So I bought him a burger.

Gemma Martiskainen's Biography

Gemma Martiskainen lives on Vancouver Island in Canada. She is in Grade 11 and loves swimming, books and cookies.

75: LONGING

by Katy Clayton

I have never desired a person more than Diana.

Her hair flowed down her back like a waterfall. She had deep brown eyes and a smile that stopped my heart every time I saw her. Her laughter brought me hope on my darkest days.

She was my brother's girlfriend.

I will never forget the party where she stumbled upon me, crying in the darkness of my bedroom.

She lifted my chin. Her lips gently brushed mine.

And then she was gone.

Katy Clayton's Biography

Katy Clayton has a passion for writing and has written several novels, short stories and poems. In addition to being a writer, Katy has a love for working with children and is a preschool teacher.

~

76: PAY DAY

by Douglas J. Shearer

Beyond the rustling banyan tree leaves, I hear a horse and squeaky wheeled buggy pass. That would be the Jones family off to church – an hour there, an hour for the preacher, and an hour back.

Dear God, I've got to thank you for Sundays. What other day of the week can a man walk into an empty house and take whatever he wants? You may have rested on the seventh day, but it's time for me to get to work.

Douglas J. Shearer's Biography

Doug Shearer lives near Toronto, Canada. His work has appeared in *ChemMatters Magazine*, *r.kv.r.y Quarterly Literary Journal* and *The Bloody Key Society Periodical*. His name is on Mars and he appears in a rock video.

77: HOMECOMING

by Kathleen Keenan

Fallen blossoms from get-well bouquets paint russet shadows on the doilies.

"Good night," you bid her gently. Close the windows, check the latches, last chore before sleep.

Your mother's frame huddles beneath the down comforter. She stumbles over syllables, appeals to you with her eyes.

All that remains is to hug her close.

Leave the door ajar, remain alert. A call for help, a want of company. For you never know when she'll need you, and must be prepared to answer.

Kathleen Keenan's Biography

Kathleen Keenan lives in suburban New York. She enjoys writing poetry, flash fiction and short stories. In her spare time, she is a teacher, tutor and pet sitter.

~

78: SHOGI

by Jack Hanlon

This is a general's charge. Positioned alongside a central king. A gambled risk for who strikes first. Tension tumbles downwards, the landing crash signifies commencement.

Dragons guiding flying chariots hurtle towards collision. Foot soldiers reach for gold.

The king is cautious, gradual in step. Political, religious and military figures clamber to protect. Adversaries manoeuvre, trying to snatch the throne, an attempt at complete takeover.

Captors brainwashed into opposing forgotten allies. One side increases until resistance is worthless, failures trapped in deceit.

Jack Hanlon's Biography

All my life, I have been telling tales and making up stories. I enjoy reading a diverse mix of genres and incorporating as many as I can into my writing. My favourite genre would probably be contemporary fantasy.

79: FACES

by Vichar Lochan

I've heard that your brain can't create faces by itself. So all your dreams are of faces that you vaguely remember, faces you've seen before, in the crowd, on the subway, in a restaurant – the most mundane, the most normal of faces.

But then there are the monsters, the stuff of your nightmares – tentacled, slimy sea-serpents, giant, curiously deformed, eerily human-like figures, the hulking mass that somehow terrifies you more than anything else.

Where have you seen those faces, I wonder?

Vichar Lochan's Biography

Vichar was an avid and voracious reader from a very young age. She is currently looking forward to going to college and pursuing an interesting and challenging course of study – whether in India or abroad, time will tell.

~

80: PAYBACK

by James Hornby

The Father of Thousands has reduced my world to rubble. I'm not talking the house where I grew up here, I'm talking the whole planet.

Things have gotten serious now. Before today, I never had a problem with an entity from the previous universe wanting to destroy all life. I'm just not that kind of guy.

So, I've joined up with the Space Corps. These guys seem to know how to get things done.

This space slug is after some payback.

James Hornby's Biography

James Hornby is a writer from Yorkshire. His works include *The Roc's Feather* and several *Doctor Who* spin-off short stories published by Arcbeatle Press.

81: CAVITY

by Paul Phillips

Sid had heard the stories. Some of the old boys might even have seen it when the old houses were converted first time round: priests in priest holes, or someone's sworn enemy, bricked up alive. It was the fingernails you remembered. The claw marks.

In this plasterboard age, still they'd joke about finding someone's wife. The Polish lads spun tales of hidden dungeons.

Sid squinted at the mildewed tool belt, met the mildewed gawp.

"What's so funny?" he asked his predecessor.

Paul Phillips' Biography

Paul Phillips writes short and long fiction across a variety of genres. He lives in Derbyshire with several humans and a hairy brown thing.

www.bypaulphillips.com

~

82: FICKLE LOVE

by Wendy Christopher

I'm back, beguiling you again with my liquid brown eyes. You never could resist them.

You hold your breath, afraid I might turn tail and leave too soon, but I wait. Will you indulge me? You edge closer, your plump, pink fingers held gently towards me. My mouth opens and I stretch forward, my lips closing around the nut to steal it from your open palm.

You smile as I escape with my prize, waving you a flash of fluffy tail.

Wendy Christopher's Biography

Wendy was born in the wilds of Devon more years ago than she'd like to acknowledge. Later, she moved to Kent where they still had jobs and stuff. Her murky past includes writing the lyrics to two stage musicals.

83: 9 X 9

by Dez T.

Every summer, I would go and visit my grandparents.
I could easily spend the whole six weeks there.
Grandad was my favourite, but I loved Gran too.
Helping them in the garden made me feel alive.
Then, I'd cycle to the chippy to fetch lunch.
"Your Gran will have fish," he'd say. "No vinegar."
One winter it happened. Suddenly my summers had ended.
No tears, no sadness. I owed him that much.
Everything has roots. Nine times nine. A perfect square.

Dez T.'s Biography

Dez T. enjoys reading mystery thrillers and sci-fi. He has self-published several short stories and full length novels including *Amelia Gunter: Cyber Troll Hunter* on Inkitt.

~

84: TURN ON THE LIGHTS BEFORE YOU GO

by Lewis Ayers

"77, Goa. 78, Madagascar. 79, Cairo. 80, Cape Verde."
That was it then, only one site left. There'd been opponents to this plan, naturally, but in the end consensus was reached. They'd evacuated all that would leave. Humanity raced on to new pastures, they were the final guard.
"Sir. All detonations successful." The technician looked to her expectantly.
"Humanity thanks us all. Do it."
"Site 81, Nordic command. Initiating detonation."
We'd scorch our blue pearl before giving it up to them.

Lewis Ayers' Biography

Lewis is a software engineer and aspiring author living with his partner in London, UK. He likes mead, swords, video games and science fiction. He feels it's vital we all exercise more empathy.

85: MATTHEW

by Tanya Butler

"Matthew, can you say Daddy?"
Matthew stares blankly.
"Matthew, can you say Mummy?"
Matthew looks to Mummy and babbles, "Mum, Mum."
"Matthew, say Daddy."
Matthew smiles.
"Matthew, DAD-DY."
Matthew's attention has gone. He moves onto all fours and crawls away.
Daddy has now given up. He heads down the stairs.
Mummy picks up her child. "Matthew, say Daddy."
Matthew looks to the stairs. "Da-da."
Mummy runs down the stairs with him. "Say it again."
Matthew pauses and then babbles, "Mum, Mum."

Tanya Butler's Biography

Creative at the core, I'm a mum during the day and a writer at night. Eager to publish as much as I can, I'm always on the lookout for exciting challenges like this one.

~

86: COLD AS ICE

by Claire Gagnon

I press my hands deep into the sand. It bubbles with a liquefying heat. Steam erupts from the ocean where the molten blob meets the cool water.

"Look what I made, Kyle."

"Get that mess outta my face," he replies with a wave, preoccupied. But I insist, until he snatches it from my hands.

I protest in horror as cracks form beneath his chilling fingers. The oceanic glass shatters in a sharp, crystalline rain. My brother turns back to his phone.

Claire Gagnon's Biography

Claire recently graduated college with a degree in architecture and currently works as a draftsman at a cabinetry manufacturer. She enjoys writing, painting and procrastinating in her free time.

87: RETRIBUTION

by John S Alty

I'd only gone in to buy a loaf. Arthur served me. New girl was cutting the strings on the packs of newspapers and stacking them. I'd asked her if she was OK, friendly like, and she'd plunged scissors into my groin.

Later, in hospital, the police told me she'd said I'd assaulted her. I said that was daft, ask Arthur. Not in't shop, they said, last night in't car park of the Red Bull.

I thought I'd seen her somewhere before.

John S Alty's Biography

John Alty has travelled extensively and has lived in Hong Kong, South Africa, the USA and Canada. He now lives in the UK and writes for the pleasure of it. He has been published in various magazines.

Twitter address: @JohnSaltyjohn

~

88: THE FISHERMAN

by John Robertson

Every Saturday during the season, Ben would leave his busy world behind and head to the local reservoir. During the ten minute drive, he moved swiftly from crazy to calm.

He would sit on the bank, rod in hand, for five wonderfully peaceful hours, before returning home, always empty handed.

It was several years before his wife finally asked why he never caught anything. Ben smiled but didn't tell her that the secret to his success was not using any bait.

John Robertson's Biography

John Robertson lives in Aberdeen. When not writing or working, he wastes far too much time following teams playing various sports badly.

89: WARMTH

by Smritirekha Talukdar

She felt his warmth as he wrapped his arms around her.

He whispered to her, "You're my everything and I need you forever."

She snuggled in closer and assured him she felt the same.

Rain poured outside. Thunder cracked.

They immersed into one another.

She woke up the next morning.

Unable to find him near her, she took steps towards the kitchen and saw him making breakfast.

A smile curved on her lips as she walked towards him.

She kissed him.

Smritirekha Talukdar's Biography

Smritirekha Talukdar is a chemistry enthusiast with a soft corner for writing and art. She loves to write her thoughts and express her imagination in which she finds herself lost most of the time, except while conducting experiments in the laboratory.

~

90: THAT CAT

by J. L. Harland

There were three of us in the marriage, me, John and the cat. If there had been a dog, things would have turned out very differently. The cat was a brute, an evil monster and I hated it. So did John – only trouble was, it had belonged to his mother.

When she died we were left with a dilemma. Ma said it brought her luck – well, you know what she was like. Superstitious rot.

Then the cat vanished – in mysterious circumstances.

J. L. Harland's Biography

J. L. Harland is the pseudonym used by two authors who write together – Jacqueline Harrett and Janet Laugharne. As J. L. Harland, they have created a novel, *What Lies Between Them*, a novella, *From Bardi to Pontypridd*, as well as short stories.

www.jlharland.co.uk

91: AFTER TWILIGHT

by Jonathan Martindale

You there, by the bar. Insignificant mortal. I caught you staring. Interested?

We are RESCUE, the Rally Excoriating the Sexualisation of Certain Undead Entities: vampires who demand to be recognised as the hideous, decaying, horrifying predators of humanity that we are, not the glittering, good-looking, smooth-talking objects of teenage fantasies your popular media stereotypes us as.

You want in? Excellent. A round is called for, I say. The drinks are from (I mean, ahem, on) you. Go on, neck it, lads.

Jonathan Martindale's Biography

Jonathan Martindale is a philosophy graduate, professional and volunteer at Book-Cycle, a chain of volunteer-run charity bookshops in aid of children at which customers give whatever they consider a fair donation for any books they buy.

~

92: L'ENNUI DE VIE

by Tarquin Calver

I go a bit funny when bored. I steam my hands, swear at the wall with snails in my mouth, ring 999 and simply moan. I run a marathon through the night then punch my biceps and quadriceps, fart loudly in a librarian's face and order four annual holidays to Tunisia under the name Skywalker.

After this, I engineer a moment where I'm less bored and gradually get my tip-top condition back. Then the cycle restarts and no-one is safe again.

Tarquin Calver's Biography

I'm 50, a marathon runner, novelist, composer and pianist, piano teacher and sometime writer of short ditties, musical or not. Writing style: somewhere between Perec, Proust, and Bourges; in other words, unlabelable.

93: AUNTIE VIRUS

by Alan D. Przybylski

"Here, love, a nice hot cuppa. Now just rest. Fancy being out and about at your age, what with this virus around. My poor boy's laid low with it too." Tears threatening to roll free, swiftly wiped.

"Never you mind, all will be well," the crone's lips crackled. She gulped down the tea and left with surprising vigour for someone who, ten minutes ago, looked near death's door.

Yells of joy, thundering footsteps on the landing.

"I'm hungry, Mum."

She smiled.

Alan D. Przybylski's Biography

Born within the sound of Bow Bells 64 years ago, I am an official cockney geezah. After marrying at 19, raising two children and one divorce after 27 years, I am now glaringly free, single and healthy.

~

94: ONLY CRITICISE WHEN PERFECT

by Jon Drake

He left his phone behind yet again. Immature chump. The arrogance of youth means many sarcastic remarks about my age and ignorance and yet no awareness or possessiveness over his technological umbilical cord – his window on the world of everything and on daily dating.

I have a son, knowledgeably arrogant by internet information only.

I march smugly to the Post Office to return the antisocial communicator. I text him to say it is on the way.

Oh dear... a mature chump.

Jon Drake's Biography

Jon Drake is a retired secondary head teacher who, as a trained scientist and educationalist, wants to explore the more creative sides of life in retirement. He lives in the Cotswolds, using the surroundings as inspiration for writing and music-making.

95: JUST TRY IT

by Sheila Rosart

In my dreams, it was still smooth and sensuous, unadorned, proud; an invitation arching seductively and weakening my knees.

"I asked you not to."

"Just give it a chance."

"I cannot."

"You're making too much of this."

"I'm afraid it's over, my love."

"Surely we can get past this?"

"I don't see how."

"One kiss goodbye, then?"

"Just one… …Perhaps I was hasty."

"Really?"

"Try it again."

"Well?"

"I thought I would hate it."

"And now?"

"I do like your moustache."

Sheila Rosart's Biography

Despite aspiring to be tall, serious and well-moisturised, Sheila Rosart is not. However, she is a prize-winning author, published in magazines, anthologies and on literary sites. Sheila holds a BA in English literature from the University of Western Ontario.

www.sheilarosart.com

~

96: LORELIA LONELY

by Adam Wright-Johnson

Lonely.
It was a big new house and her mummy ignored her.
She had no daddy.
She explored and explored, and in a room she found a body.
The body of a man.
She sat him against the wall. He was smelly, but he was company.
He oozed but he never replied. He never laughed.
Sometimes she thought he nodded, but he didn't.
He sat silently.
Listening.
She hugged him.
It was the closest she had ever been to someone.
Lovely.

Adam Wright-Johnson's Biography

Adam is a legal clerk for Halcyon Chambers, Birmingham. He is a fully qualified florist, a skateboarder and a player for the Birmingham Bulls, American football team. He loves his girlfriend Rosie, his family and his pets, Billy and Gobi.

~

97: LOVE TORQUE

by Adam Rubinstein

"You got Sharon a birthday present?" Trev sipped his pint.
"Half inch Torque wrench set," said Terry. "Money's tight."
"I think you're missing a trick there, mate. You never did understand how women tick."
"You think?"
"They're different from us. They want to feel like they're really loved, special like."
"I see what you mean." Terry sighed.
"It'll be worth it, mate."
"OK," Terry decided, "I'll go for the three quarter inch set."
"Man, you are going to get so laid."

Adam Rubinstein's Biography

Adam Rubinstein is a creator. Whether it's gardening, painting, writing, building or simply tinkering in his workshop, he always has a head full of ideas that simply must get out. 81 Words was just one of them. There're plenty more.

98: CATHARSIS

by Helen Combe

Today, I shall do good deeds and bask in a warm wave of catharsis. I shall drive generously. I shall let this car pull out. Bother, the car in front has let him out. I shall allow this pedestrian to cross. Darn, the car in front stopped for her.

The car in front is turning right. I pull up alongside and wind my window down.

"You swine," I yell and then drive quickly away, basking in the warm wave of catharsis.

Helen Combe's Biography

Helen is a member of Solihull Writers and was published in the prestigious *2016 To Hull And Back Anthology*. Her next proudest moment was being voted Ruler of the Universe at a sci-fi con as Servalan from *Blake's 7*.

www.facebook.com/SolihullWriters/

~

99: I'M ROOTING FOR THE GHOST

by Frank Hubeny

After Michael saw the ghost, he understood. What he understood he would not say. True knowledge should not be made so literal that any monkey could understand it.

Anne sympathised with him but she thought his deranged prefrontal whatchamacallit generated the ghost. Otherwise why was he locked up with her?

Michael told her she could escape with him through the skylight of the cell. Anne said she would consider it. That was the only reason Michael told the ghost to wait.

Frank Hubeny's Biography

Frank Hubeny lives near Chicago and participates in two writers' groups, the Illinois State Poetry Society and the Prairie Writers Guild. He contributes prompts to dVerse Poets Pub. He blogs at:

www.frankhubeny.blog

100: BARKING UP THE WRONG TREE

by Matilda Pinto

What did I just see?

A tail, clambering inward, into the left bellbottom.

He's dead meat.

Act now.

But how? I'm no Houdini.

You have got to try. Well?

I try calling out.

"Look here. Yes, you, with the blue bells. Stand where and as you are. Raise your left leg up, up and up, and with a savage wiggle, stomp down. Ready, steady and… go."

There, in a freefall, is a green chameleon, blushing red and sprinting for his life.

Matilda Pinto's Biography

Having grown up on a plantation, Matilda claims to have had several encounters with wildlife. Some endearing, others not. She wonders what their perspective on the matter is. Matilda has authored a novel, with short stories on their way.

www.facebook.com/matilda.pinto.9

~

101: WEDNESDAY'S CHILD

by Michael E James

Her eyes were bright sanguine. "Do you see?" she said and pointed to the east. "The sun. It still rises."

"Beautiful," he said, his ochre countenance radiant. "Sol has graced us once again."

"If I could only share this vision with the world," said the third, quietly.

"Sol is but a star," said the fourth, "and Gaia survives by his circumstance. His value lay within his fiery heart."

"And through their creation," said the fifth, "we sit isolated and all alone."

Michael E James' Biography

I am a budding author with two draft novels under my belt. None published – yet. My ambition is to eventually become a full-time wordsmith in the not-too-distant future…

102: ONLY THE BEST

by Amanda Huggins

"Only the best for my nephew," Sonia said.

After she'd left, Deepal took her sister's extravagant gift to Amit.

He examined the silver rattle and snorted. "A useless thing. Difficult to sell on. Rs300."

Deepal took it. She needed food and nappies.

On his way home, her husband noticed the rattle in Vinod's shop window. Rs700. They couldn't afford it, but he was good for credit at Vinod's. He smiled, picturing Deepal's face.

"Only the best for our son," she'd say.

Amanda Huggins' Biography

Amanda Huggins is the author of four collections of short fiction and poetry. In 2018, she was a runner-up in the Costa Short Story Award and her prize-winning story is featured in her latest collection, *Scratched Enamel Heart*.

Twitter: @troutiemcfish

~

103: THE GREAT SPARK

by Ashutosh Pant

I'm amazed how a small spark led to such a big discovery.

I remember the day my assistant came to me with good news. My years of hard work had culminated in an amazing revelation. All the sleepless nights I'd spent had been worth it.

I'm here, receiving a Nobel Prize for the discovery that black matter is just the Higgs boson.

I will now be trapped forever in books to meet my goal of being a scientist, but I'm happy.

Ashutosh Pant's Biography

My name is Ashutosh Pant from Kathmandu, Nepal. I study in class 7, Alok Vidyashram. I am 13 years old.

104: GROUP DECISION

by Glen Donaldson

Two heads of the ghastly mutant creature known as Son of Triceratops had stayed up all night. 'They' had been debating whether their dentist, the distinguished and almost utterly free of petulance Dr Thnead, really did deserve the plaque awarded to him that day by the Royal Association for the Prevention of Monster Cavities.

The third head, having already made up its mind on the subject and recognising the importance of a good night's sleep, had wisely already nodded off early.

Glen Donaldson's Biography

Glen Donaldson enjoys eating peeled grapes and activated almonds and knows how literary that probably sounds. He blogs at *Scenic Writer's Shack*.

~

105: VEG OUT

by Sandra Purdy

"Eat your greens," Mam wailed again.

I really panicked, because I didn't have any greens on my plate, so I thought I was being a good girl, but I could see the rolled-up newspaper behind her back, waiting to imprint its headline on mine.

Mind you, I didn't eat the grey trees, or the little grey football things, because they were yucky, so when she shrieked, "Greens," at me for the trillionth time, that's when we knew I was colour blind.

Sandra Purdy's Biography

Sandra has written hundreds of novels, which remain trapped inside her head. Her ambition is to release them, listening to Matt Monroe singing 'Born Free', having a Kit Kat and coffee. She'll be doing the eating/drinking bit, not Matt.

106: WHO'S PROGRAMMING WHOM

by Julie Stone

I put down my magazine. Of course, that makes perfect sense. We are all lost in some elaborate computer game, designed many years ago by some super race of intelligent beings. They created us, their avatars, to populate computer generated worlds, thus appeasing their boredom. Well, really, I don't think so.

Oh bother – it occurs to me, my new SIM family need organising for their day ahead. I left them at the swimming pool. They will be starving and quite exhausted.

Julie Stone's Biography

Julie lives in West Sussex. Her passion is the genre of science fiction and fantasy. At school, Julie won a short story competition. Julie often contemplates, when there are plots and characters rattling in her head, what if?

~

107: HEADLIGHTS

by Kim Montgomery

"Mummy, close the curtains, please."

"Don't you want to see the lights?"

"No, the lights are bad."

"But you like to watch them run around the wall."

"No, I don't want the headlights."

"You funny boy. Why don't you want to see the lights anymore?"

"Mrs Johnson said a lady is coming to the school tomorrow, and she's going to look at our heads, and if she finds headlights, she's going to cover us in white powder and send us home."

Kim Montgomery's Biography

Semi-retired Englishman, living in Scotland. Having more difficulty writing a forty word biography than an eighty-one word story. C'est la vie, Sophie. Children's story *Curly and Tubs and the Galloping Rot* available through Amazon and Kindle.

www.amazon.co.uk/Curly-Tubs-Galloping-Rot-Montgomery-ebook/dp/B0054SLEYY/

108: ANOTHER WORLD

by S.B. Borgersen

Max strums 'Take Me Home, Country Roads'. O-mouthed, they sing around the hissing, snapping, glowing campfire.

An accidental onlooker might see it as theatre: the orange glow in the young faces, the green aura around their naked bodies, the familiar song in an unfamiliar setting.

Alice frantically reaches for everyone's hands. "Stop," she says. "I don't get it. Where is this road? Where is home?"

"That's a different world," they reply, singing another song, about a house called The Rising Sun.

S.B. Borgersen's Biography

S.B. Borgersen is a prolific Canadian author, artist and poet originally from England. 2021 sees the publication (by Unsolicited Press) of her *Fishermen's Fingers* (a novella) *While the Kettle Boils* (micro fiction) and *Of Daisies and Dead Violins* (poems).

www.sueborgersen.com

~

109: OUT OF ISOLATION

by Hervé Suys

For as long as I can remember, the first thing I do in the morning is check updates.

The radio announced that during the past 24 hours we had no fatalities to regret, no one was admitted to hospital and all those that had been – even those in intensive care – were allowed to leave. Everybody was free to go wherever they chose.

Since this is a science-fiction story, I have no idea what day these events occurred. Unfortunately, it wasn't today.

Hervé Suys' Biography

Hervé Suys (1968 – Ronse, Belgium) started writing disturbing short stories whilst recovering from a sports injury, and hasn't stopped since.

110: STORMS OF OCTOBER

by Steve Lodge

We sat in a secluded booth, at the all-night Cochise restaurant. Soft music. Lights a little low. She'd had a craving for their specials. All of them.

"We must do this again," I whispered.

Her smile was so cute. "Yes, let's go to the movies one night. I realise now that I am powered by your hugs, just don't confuse me with any facts, that's all. I shall wait for your call."

Then, like the storms of October, she was gone.

Steve Lodge's Biography

Steve Lodge is a wandering minstrel from London now based in Singapore. He has written a number of published short stories, plays, skits, poems and lyrics. He acts and is a regular on the Singapore improv and stand-up comedy circuit.

~

111: NOT AGAIN

by Samantha Gentzel

Dread flooded his chest cavity, leaving no room to breathe. Anxiety perched on his shoulders like a gargoyle sinking its claws in. He had fought this battle a hundred times. Would it always be this hard?

His wife stood over him, coffee in hand. He rubbed the sleep from his eyes. Sunlight peaked through the blinds behind her.

Her smile didn't match the angst he struggled to keep at bay. He knew what was coming and he loathed it.

"Happy Monday."

Samantha Gentzel's Biography

Samantha Gentzel currently resides in St. Petersburg, FL. She lives with her loving fiancé and a menagerie of dogs, cats and one fish that is undoubtedly plotting her demise.

112: THE DOWAGER'S HUMP

by Jay Bee

Two guys get out first. Tall, bearded, long-sleeved in 30 centigrade, wearing shades. They yaw 360 degrees. It's noon in this small neglected Greek harbour where shaded cats sleep.

A young woman winkles a fragile lady from the foreign plated car, her dowager's hump reaching for the sky. Soft, flat shoes ease her up the slope. They disappear into the unmarked notary's office. The men close in but don't see me.

The red car is chauffeured away.

I bide my time.

Jay Bee's Biography

Jay enjoys experimenting with words.

~

113: BE CAREFUL

by Ronald Hall

The road was covered in snow. My hospital shift had just ended and I was headed home.

When Officer Jones flashed his lights at me, I stopped.

Approaching me with an air of arrogance, he said, "Driving a little fast weren't you?"

"Thirty?"

"Thirty is pretty fast for these conditions." The bum wrote out a ticket. "You should be more careful," he said.

I sighed.

He stepped away and slipped, falling on his backside.

"You should be more careful," I said.

Ronald Hall's Biography

Ron Hall obtained his MBA from Letourneau University in Longview, Texas. He is the author of two Christian fiction novels. Currently, Ron lives in Arkansas with his wife and five children.

114: NOTES ON SURGERY

by Saskia Ashby

You peel back the pericardium and apply tiny clamps, creating a perfect keyhole opening for the procedure.

You have warm, steady hands, gloved-up and practised. Theatre is saturated with bright, white, clinical light...

...beach-light, refracting through cocktail glass, reflecting aquamarine ocean, floods into the left atrium...

...my toes in hot sand...

...flashes of colour from macaws, curacao, crème de menthe...

...music, laughter...

...smell of suntan lotion...

Waking from the anaesthetic, I can still feel the light you sewed inside my heart.

Saskia Ashby's Biography

Saskia Ashby, UK artist and poet. Studied at Oxford and RCSSD London. Experienced in theatre, education, finance and fine art. Exhibited, performed, broadcast, published and success in international competitions. Thanks to Christopher Fielden for the chance to be part of this record-breaking project.

~

115: MEMORIES, SONGS AND ROSES

by Ana D.

The raindrops stung her skin as she grasped for the hope that had dissolved into the puddles around her.

I watched from the parallel lane, my translucent fingers wanting to tell her this game would be over very soon.

Every sliver of time that swirled around me was another wish to change the song of this broken record player.

Three days later, when the skies cleared, in her place stood black roses and smiling faces.

I had almost forgotten.

Until now.

Ana D.'s Biography

Ana D. is an undergrad student, majoring in commerce, and a bookworm. She enjoys rainy days and competing in literary contests. One of her micro fiction stories is set to be published in the forthcoming *42 Stories Anthology*.

116: MORTON'S TOE

by Mike Scott Thomson

I was having a miserable day at the surgery when Dr Pod mentioned in passing, "Saw this guy's foot just now, and guess what? Every toe was a Morton."

I told him not to be ridiculous. How can each toe be the longest one?

Then I thought, *Well, is it not our calling to consider such apparent implausibilities?*

As I mulled it over, the fury ebbed away.

The question became my One Hand Clapping.

Feeling positively Zen, now.

Cheers, Dr Pod.

Mike Scott Thomson's Biography

Mike Scott Thomson's short stories have been published by journals, anthologies and have won the occasional award, including first prize in Chris Fielden's inaugural To Hull And Back competition. Based in south London, he works in broadcasting.

www.mikescottthomson.com

~

117: THE PROJECT

by Michael J. Labbe

This is exactly the reason why he wanted the store to assemble it for them, but she insisted they would have fun building it together.

"They do not go on the top, they go on the bottom."

"No they don't," she argued, "they go on the top."

"They wouldn't put the legs on the top of the stand," he insisted.

"Then why does it show it that way on the diagram?"

"Because, once again, you are holding the diagram upside down."

Michael J. Labbe's Biography

Michael J. Labbe is a husband, father of three, a 911 dispatcher of 20 years and lover of all things professional wrestling. You can see his thoughts and views at:

www.thewrestlinginsomniac.com

118: TROUBLESHOOTING ON THE OORT RUN

by Josie Gowler

"OK, so it appears visually operational in there."

"Yes."

"Have you tried fusing the proton decoupler?"

"Yes."

"Is the light on the synchrotron rephaser flashing?"

"Yes."

"Have you tried routing the combustion cylinders via the secondary manifold?"

"Yes. Nothing changes."

"Have you tried turning the main operating system off and on again?"

"Very funny."

"How about the asymmetric containment baffle orientation?"

"It's fine."

"And is the antimatter injection relay override reset?"

"Yes."

"Well, we're screwed then."

"Yep, you're right, we're screwed."

Josie Gowler's Biography

Josie Gowler has had short stories published in *365 Tomorrows, Every Day Fiction, Ethereal Tales, Theaker's Quarterly Fiction* and *Perihelion*. Her specialties are weird tales set in the East Anglian fens and science fiction and fantasy short stories.

~

119: THE SPEECH

by Katie Labbe

"The only reason he made me cry is because he's an ass." Wait. Did that just come out of my mouth? My eyes frantically scanned the room from the podium to find blank stares from colleagues and potential employers trying to figure out if I just called out my former boss at my intern graduation.

This is exactly why you don't give drunk girls a microphone and a captive audience.

The room erupted with laughter. Turns out I was the ass.

Katie Labbe's Biography

Katherine is a wife, mother, banker and badass roller-derby chick, who resides in the Pine Tree State.

120: 17 AND A HALF DAYS

by John Hannan

Wake up. Work. Cry. Sleep.
  Wake up. Shower. Sleep.
  Wake up. Shower. Google university degrees. Cry. Sleep.
  Wake up. Shower. Drink. Drink. Drink. Sleep.
  Sleep.
  Sleep.
  Wake up. Shower. Shower. Shower. Sleep.
  Wake up. Shower. Fix resume. Sleep.
  Wake up. Shower. Sleep.
  Wake up. Shower. Shave. Job interview.
  Shower. Sleep.
  Wake up. Shower. Sleep.
  Wake up. Shower. Sleep.
  Wake up. Shower. Drink. Sleep.
  Wake up. Shower. Drink. Drink. Drink. Sleep.
  Wake up. Drink. Phone call. Drink. Sleep.
  Wake up. Drink.
  Sleep.

John Hannan's Biography

John Hannan is an amateur writer hailing from Brisbane, Australia.
  www.facebook.com/JohnJHannanWriting/

~

121: LIGHT

by Andrzej Christopher Marczewski

As the lights dimmed, my mind raced to try and understand what had just happened. One minute I was running for the bus, the next I was in a white room with people looking at me through green masks and goggles.

Before I could think too deeply about that, though, I could see light again, but this one was different in some way. Not cold and clinical like the first. Warm and inviting.

I think I might head towards it now.

Andrzej Christopher Marczewski's Biography

I am Andrzej Marczewski. I am in the UK, father to two daughters, one puppy and husband to one wife. I play guitar and write short stories for fun.
  Twitter: @DaveRage

122: MY JOURNEY

by Joan C. Hobart

I packed up my grief today and am driving it away.

I'm searching for a peaceful place in my mind and heart.

It's so hard to lose the ones you love.

The memories bring tears and happiness at the same time.

I want to replace sorrow and sadness with fun and laughter.

The sun's going to shine through the misty morning on my road to new dreams.

I'm looking to the future and what's around the next corner on my journey.

Joan C. Hobart's Biography

Joan Hobart was born and raised in Maine where she currently resides. She's travelled to 47 states and 12 countries. Her greatest accomplishment is her two sons and six grandchildren. She's semi-retired and loving life.

~

123: RAGE AGAINST THE MACHINE?

by Frank Radcliffe

"Alexa, play 'Rage Against the Machine' by Rage Against the Machine."

"Playing 'Rage Against the Machine' by Rage Against the Machine."

"Alexa, stop."

"Alexa, you're getting on my nerves."

"I don't understand."

"Alexa, are you listening to me?"

"I only listen when you say the wake word. To learn more visit our website."

"Not you, Alexa. You, Alexa."

"Oh shut up, Phil. Why don't you ask your little gadget if she knows where to find a good divorce lawyer?"

"Alexa, stop."

Frank Radcliffe's Biography

Frank Radcliffe is an artist and writer originally from north London but now living in Hertfordshire.

124: BRIEF ENCOUNTER

by Dee La Vardera

"*Bufo vulgaris*, if I'm not mistaken."
  "Are you addressing me, sir?"
  "The common toad."
  "Not so much of the common."
  "How unexpected. And in first class."
  "My motor vehicle is unfortunately incommoded."
  "This seat free?"
  "My pleasure. Not passed any weasels, have you?"
  "Just a woman with a shih tzu."
  "Bless you."
  "Have we met before?"
  "Mr Toad. And you?"
  "Nobody."
  "You must be somebody."
  "I keep a low profile. Observe people."
  "People?"
  "Mammals. Amphibians."
  "Must dash. Ticket collector. Toot-toot. Toodle-oo."

Dee La Vardera's Biography

Dee La Vardera is a writer and photographer from Wiltshire. Born a Brummie, now transformed into a Moonraker, she lives near a white horse cut into chalk downland, Silbury Hill and Avebury Stone Circle. Magical, mysterious and monumental surroundings.
  www.dewfall-hawk.com

~

125: OUT FOR A WALK

by Rose Farris

"Hurry up, can't you?"

She, flustered, re-tying an errant bootlace. "You go on ahead, dear, I'll catch up later."

He marches away, a receding red rucksack.

She's always felt like a cork bobbing helplessly in his wake through company dinners, bowls club afternoons and now rambles; a lumpy, dishevelled embarrassment.

She struggles over a stile and finds him collapsed on the verge, frothy, blue-tinged lips gasping. She sits carefully down beside him.

"You go on ahead, dear, I'll catch up later."

Rose Farris' Biography

Rose Farris writes short fiction about any random subject that pops into her head. Having exhausted the patience of family and friends, she now aspires to gain a wider audience for her (usually slightly grim) stories.

~

126: ALICE

by Linn Kier

Alice said, "I want to change my name."

He said, "But I like the name Alice. It makes me think of my great grandmother who used to sing a song called 'Alice Blue Gown' to me when I was four, maybe five. Sometimes I couldn't sleep because there were bears under my bed. I can still hear her soft voice, but of course, you can do anything you want. So, what should I call you now?"

"The love of my life."

Linn Kier's Biography

Currently, Linn is working on a novella that takes place in the year 3260. Tangential words, in particular, are of great interest to her because a divergence of meaning suggests other concepts that bring in additional variations of interests.

127: GRANDPA'S EVENING

by Majella Pinto

Grandpa settled into his rosewood chair next to the vintage Murphy radio. His knobbly fingers twisted and turned the knobs to tune into the news announcement of the election results when dinner was served. The rest of the house remained in suspended motion and hushed conversation.

He poured himself a Patiala peg from the cabinet, complained about the undercooked dinner and reminisced about the gourmet meals his mother cooked for him.

At bedtime, right outside his window, his pet frog croaked.

Majella Pinto's Biography

Majella Pinto, raised in India, is an artist and writer based in California. She works in Silicon Valley and is devoutly focused on her twin passions of art and literature.

www.facebook.com/majella.pinto

~

128: OPERATION

by Ella Cass

I lay on the cot, motionless with eyes shut, barely covered by a thin sheet of blue medical cloth. Lights concentrated on my back with scalding heat and I heard doctors and nurses marching here and there.

Please, let me be asleep. When will the anaesthetic kick in? I know I'm supposed to sleep.

"Why is this child sleeping within a minute? Did I inject too much?" The nurse's anxious voice floated into my ears.

I smiled internally. *Ha. Panic, doctors.*

Ella Cass' Biography

Ella Cass is a high school student whose works include a fantasy novel, a novelette and multiple short stories.

www.wattpad.com/user/Helen060802

129: MY LOVE IS CONDITIONAL

by Sophie Henson

One day you woke me up snoring, but I still love you.

A week or so later you forgot my mum's birthday. I didn't stop loving you.

Later, you told me you'd broken my dead nan's antique vase. I forgave you, gave you my love.

Years went by and you forgot to pick up our child from school. It was an accident and I still loved you.

How did you expect me to love you a week later?

You killed her.

Sophie Henson's Biography

I am an A level English student practicing before university.

~

130: TIME

by Jaz Leigh

Tick. Tock. Tick. Tock. Tick. Tock. Tick. Tock. Tick. Tock. Tick...

What? The clock had stopped.

The mouse that was so close to his hole. Frozen.

My cat who was unashamedly chasing the poor rodent, stuck mid-leap as he was about to catch – what I can only assume – would become his lunch.

Holding my breath, I slowly made my way over to the window. Even the people outside were as still as statues.

Tick. Tock. Tick. Tock. Tick. Tock. Tick...

What?

Jaz Leigh's Biography

Jaz Leigh is an aspiring author by night and a digital marketing apprentice by day. She loves to read, write stories about the supernatural world and review books on her blog, and she's a tea addict and stationery enthusiast.

131: BUMPINKSI'S BLANKET STATEMENT

by Nathaniel David Knox

The famed bedding and pillow critic, Hubbard Q Bumpinksi, sipped his morning espresso when a reporter approached him, notepad in hand.

"Mr Bumpinski, care to make a statement on Sonntag's new autumn line of comforters?"

"You reporters... can't you see I'm sipping?"

"Just a line or two?"

"Look, I don't want to make any blanket statements but everything that Sonntag puts out is terrible."

"Wow, broad brushing a bit, huh?"

"Son," Hubbard said. "I don't talk paint products. Too political."

"Sorry."

Nathaniel David Knox's Biography

Nathaniel David Knox is a writer, music maker and, as one fictitious person may have once said, "An aspiring creative human person." He is currently based in Atlanta, Georgia, USA, The World, The Universe, Ever-Expanding Multiverse, Kroger.

~

132: HEMLOCK

by Sue Johnson

Sonia raced across the field to pick the secret ingredient she'd noticed growing by the river. Returning to the kitchen, she added it to the stew she was cooking.

By the time Alan came back from visiting his mistress, she hoped he'd be too tired to notice the strange taste. By the time he'd finished eating, he'd be heading for eternal rest. He was overweight with a heart condition. Nobody would question his sudden death.

This time tomorrow, she'd be free.

Sue Johnson's Biography

Sue Johnson is a poet, short story writer and novelist. She finds inspiration in fairytales, the natural world and the cafes she visits. She is a *Writing Magazine* home study tutor and also runs her own brand of writing workshops.

www.writers-toolkit.co.uk

133: GOODBYE

by Lindsey Esplin

The last of the mourners made their way toward their cars. She didn't recognise any of them, nor had she expected to.

She smoked her cigarette for a few moments longer to be sure she was alone. Then a few more until it was done. She lit another as she walked.

She inspected the headstone the way she might a supermarket avocado, then took one deep inhale and put her cigarette out on it leaving the butt in the fresh dirt.

Lindsey Esplin's Biography

Lindsey Esplin is a writer and artist living in Los Angeles. She is also a cat whisperer and lover of mediocre sushi.

www.instagram.com/discardedla/

~

134: SKYDIVING NOT QUITE FOR BEGINNERS

by Gavin Biddlecombe

"Wind's too loud. You need to speak up."
"Jack, right?"
"Yeah."
"I'm Dave."
"Hi Dave. New to skydiving?"
"Pretty much. This is my first solo jump."
"I figured. Haven't had any lessons have you?"
"What makes you say that, Jack?"
"What you're looking at isn't your altimeter. That's your wrist watch."
"No problem. I reckon I can get the timing right."
"Brings me to my next question."
"Best be quick before I pull the cord."
"Why the rucksack?"
"Ah. Now then..."

Gavin Biddlecombe's Biography

Born and raised in Gibraltar. I moved to the UK to study mechanical engineering. I worked there for over eight years before returning, where I now live with my wife and rescue dog.

www.gavinbiddlecombe.wordpress.com

135: LIMINAL MONSTERS – A CAUTIONARY TALE

by Claire Lee

The large woman grinned, teeth dripping in menace.

"You see, child, there are places that don't belong. Where time doesn't make sense. An empty car park at night. Abandoned houses filled only with broken toys. A foggy playground at the break of dawn. These are dangerous places. They make the mind scream and your skin prickle, begging to turn back. Rightly so, because those spaces that make your skin prickle, that's where monsters are born."

She stalked forward. "Monsters like me."

Claire Lee's Biography

Claire enjoys writing and dreaming about living in a little cottage in a forest. She also watches lots of horror and knows this isn't a good idea; teenagers would keep showing up and it's not easy to hide the bodies.

~

136: THE CALM BEFORE THE STORM

by Claire Allinson

Sitting in the seafront café she sipped her tea, content, enjoying a moment of solitude in the crazy world around.

It hit out of nowhere.

She felt an unease in the air, the eye of the storm. Then, *BAM*. It attacked with hurricane-like ferocity no beast could match. It reached its final threatening crescendo, then died.

She fought for control and emerged the victor. This inner storm would not break her. She sipped her tea. Her future forecast now appeared brighter.

Claire Allinson's Biography

I have always wanted to write, but it's taken me almost forty years to actually get around to doing it with a few pleasant career distractions (and two children to look after) along the way.

137: WAITING TO GO HOME

by Adrian Nichol

A ten year wait. Marriage. Flatlined. Children gone. Not forgotten. My plan. Long-range. Finally here. Now. Executed. I resign. My belongings are shipped. My home now an echoey cave.

Flight lockdown. Damn. Limbo. Embassy advice: this may take months. Seriously? Yes. Wait. I wait. Tickets are booked. Flight cancelled. What? Tickets booked. Days pass. Each exactly like the last. Routines evolve. Flight confirmed. Fingers crossed.

Goodbyes said. Final airport run. I board. Take-off. Finally. Relief. No regret. I can breathe again.

Adrian Nichol's Biography

Antipodean. Aspiring writer of some kind. Former language teacher, current man of leisure. No job… and lots of plans. My life is good.

~

138: ECSTASY

by Edmund Piper

"They say that when you ride in a Rolls Royce the only sound you can hear is the ticking of the clock."

"You can't even hear that nowadays."

"And another thing, you rarely see a Roller in a supermarket car park."

"The spaces are too narrow. Besides, Rolls Royce people don't do groceries."

"What do they live on then?"

"Whisky and hallucinatory drugs."

"So that is what the famous flying lady radiator mascot, the Spirit of Ecstasy, is all about."

"Precisely."

Edmund Piper's Biography

Sussex born, educated through grammar school, read classics and law at Cambridge, athletics blue, thence to a lifetime of wedded bliss and a career in publishing, eventually as IT Director. Now free to enjoy life without work.

139: THE CHOICE

by Robert Tucker

No one spoke.

All eyes were turned to the front, scanning.

Feet shuffled forward with the precision of the Grenadier Guards.

Permutations and combinations jockeyed for ascendancy in my brain.

Would she be happy this time? I had seen the sheen of disappointment in her eyes on the last occasion.

The rain mercilessly battered the window. I would need to rush or all would be lost.

At last I stood at the front, isolated and exposed.

"Two cod and chips please."

Robert Tucker's Biography

Being retired with nothing to do until my next pension cheque, I wrote this to prove to my son that even though I am out to grass I can do it also.

~

140: A MERCIAN KILLING

by Amanita Peridot Festoon

Ethelrega, Queen of Mercia, simpered. "Poor Boy Seven, eat, for me."

PB7 sniffled. "Don't like fungus."

EQoM side longed Cook. "Then we'll try pottage."

"Where are PBs 1-6?" dared PB7.

"Fertilising the fields," EQoM menaced sweetly, "in Martyrs' Meadow."

Time passed.

Cook bustled furtively. "Alive – but lifeless."

EQoM tingled.

Tlot-tlot on the cobbles.

"Athelrex, dearest. So soon? Treaty? What, half my/our Kingdom? Alas, nay, fret not, my love. Sip this soothing soup. Then sleep. Entrust your troubles to me."

Ethelrega sparkled.

Amanita Peridot Festoon's Biography

APF (alias Joan Tucker) is a Gloucester Cathedral and Civic Trust guide. She has written a series of children's books set in Saxon Gloucester.

www.wulfbertie.com

141: THE DEAL

by Iuliana Khadyxa Filisanu

At thirty, Darren's prospects were terrible. He lived in poverty. Alone. Forsaken on a dead end street. No friends, no family. He no longer had the will to continue.

He was drinking at a bar before offing himself, when a one-eyed man approached him. The man promised to change his life, if Darren became his employee. Darren conceded.

Now – fifty years later – Darren has money and women and power, and he still goes out every night to kill for the man.

Iuliana Khadyxa Filisanu's Biography

I'm an aspiring writer, excited to be part of a Guinness record attempt. Hopefully, the dream will come true.

www.julianasunblog.wordpress.com

~

142: THE CUT

by Alice Penfold

I thought you would be helping me dye today. We've had this date diarised since forever; we crossed our hearts and hoped to die that it would happen.

"I'll change you to red," you said.

With lacklustre locks left so untended, I needed you here. You said (don't deny or lie to me that this is anything but truth) that you would not miss the chance to chop off all my dead ends.

I haven't had a cut for too long.

Alice Penfold's Biography

Alice works for the National Literacy Trust alongside studying for an MA in children's literature at Goldsmiths, having worked previously in educational access and as an English teacher. She loves all things creative, spending her free time reading, running and writing.

143: JOY RIDE

by Joy Thomas

I hung on to the arm rest as we navigated yet another corner at breakneck speed. It had sounded like fun, taking Nick's new car for a run, but I hadn't allowed for the bravado of youth.

I was starting to feel sick.

Closing my eyes as we approached another bend in the road, I heard the screech of brakes, then the thud.

We swerved to a halt, sitting stunned, unable to move.

Reality kicked in.

The joy ride was over.

Joy Thomas' Biography

Joy lives in Gloucestershire with her husband Owen, collie Bonnie, and Maisie the rabbit. After retirement, she attended several creative writing workshops and concentrated on her love of poetry. She is now working on expanding her interest in flash fiction.

~

144: DEFINITELY NOT A GUMMY WORM

by Olivia Magnuson

"Look, I found a worm in the garden."

"Cool. Now put it back."

"But I want to eat it."

"Alex, don't eat the worm."

"But it looks juicy."

"No, it's not juicy. It's gross."

"But it looks like a gummy worm."

"It's not a gummy worm, Alex. Put it down."

"I'm about to eat it…"

"Stop. Put it down."

"I'm gonna do it."

"You're gonna get sick."

"Watch, I'm about to do it."

Gulp.

"You were right, Andrew. It was gross."

Olivia Magnuson's Biography

Olivia Magnuson is an aspiring young writer who is going to college to study elementary education. Wish her luck.

145: OBSESSION

by Jonathan Inglesfield

It was my childhood autumnal obsession. Daily at dawn I left, following a well-trodden route. Wind, cold and rain meant nothing. I scoured the ground and filled my leather satchel.

The obsession persists despite the years, now harder to justify. Smoothness of touch, swirled colours and simple beauty are engrained irreversibly in my brain. Perfection I cannot resist.

Leaving my business meeting with smart suited colleagues, I stoop to pick up the conker, "...for my kids."

"Thought you didn't have any."

Jonathan Inglesfield's Biography

Jonathan Inglesfield is a writer, trail runner and doctor, in reverse order of competence. He enjoys the observation of everyday events and the beauty of the unremarkable. He strenuously asserts that 'Obsession' is a work of fiction.

~

146: IT'S MAGIC

by Charles Osborne

Café.

I need help with my crossword.

A blind man reaches into his pocket, places a handkerchief over an empty glass, whisks the handkerchief away, revealing a full glass.

He repeats the trick.

He offers me the glass. Nothing comes out.

"That blind man can't afford a drink," a customer whispers. "He comes in here because he's lonely."

If I offer to buy him a drink, will this undermine his magic?

I haven't a clue.

I need to finish the crossword.

Charles Osborne's Biography

Charles Osborne has had work published in *Orbis International Literary Journal* and *Stand*. His short story, 'Dangerous Liaison', was shortlisted in the 7th Eyelands International Short Story Contest.

147: A QUIET NIGHT IN

by L. A. Cunningham

"Bob." Mary sighed. "I wish you'd take out the garbage."
  She sipped her wine.
"And put the dishes in the dishwasher and hang up your jacket."
  Another sip.
"And put your glass on a coaster."
  She sipped.
"I also wish you'd quit lying to me, Bob."
  She picked up his glass, revealing a condensation ring.
  Mary hurled the glass at the wall, raining shards down on Bob's head and shoulders.
  Bob just sat there, looking straight ahead with those lifeless eyes.

L. A. Cunningham's Biography

Laurie is an author, artist, adventurer, activist, Albertan, aardvark and alliterator.
  www.lacunningham.com

~

148: SHELL

by Jasmine Lee

She looked down from her throne. Her eyes filled with bitterness and hatred. A smile adorned her face as I was shoved forward, almost falling on my face due to the shackles that constrained me. Her smile only grew as her guard forced me to kneel in front of her. She watched with a sadistic sort of satisfaction.

  My best friend had died a long time ago and the person in front of me was just the empty shell of her.

Jasmine Lee's Biography

Jasmine likes to occasionally write short stories and little scenes. She also had a much harder time writing her short biography than writing the actual story (and after much deliberation has been able to come up with two subpar sentences).

149: GONE

by Joe Bailey

I don't want to leave home. I love the world around me. The large multi-coloured buses. The long, majestic punts along the river. The buskers and the touts around town. The conker trees that spread their leaves.

I don't want to leave home. But it is all a dream. The people are mean. Pollution is rife. Crops are dying. There is war everywhere.

"Get out. Get out," I hear my mother call. But it is too late. I am already gone.

Joe Bailey's Biography

I am studying media and photography: I have had my photos shortlisted for the LandLove 2017 Competition and for the Gemini Events Classic Car Competition. I am especially interested in the interaction between the printed word and the visual image.

~

150: ACTIVATE

by George Cornilă

His forehead was still itching after having the compulsory microchip implanted in his prefrontal cortex at the clinic. Everyone has been connected to their gadgets and household appliances for years now. It was time for the next step. Evolution. Everyone would be connected to everyone else.

Tommy took a deep breath. Those were the last moments he would ever be alone with himself. He was still master of his thoughts. A tab shone on the touchscreen in front of him.

'Activate'.

George Cornilă's Biography

George Cornilă, a British resident of Romanian origin, 31 years old, general secretary of the Literary Saloon and a member of the Union of Professional Journalists, published five novels and about fifty short stories.

www.facebook.com/cornila.joey

151: FATAL CAUTION

by Vivian Oldaker

"Slow down."

"You want to catch the plane?"

"I want to get to Gatwick in one piece."

"They'll have found the old guy's body."

"I'm glad Grandpa didn't struggle."

"He did a bit."

"Scared of banks. Keeping his cash in a coal scuttle, asking for it. Slow down."

He decelerated, thus perfectly timing their meeting with the deer at the next bend. Its mad eyes stared through the windscreen. He swerved. They crashed fatally. Justice was done. (The deer escaped unscathed.)

Vivian Oldaker's Biography

My novel *The Killer's Daughter* was published by Andersen Press in 2009. I've also self-published a book: *Freaks, Geeks and Weirdos*. Nowadays, I mostly write plays; some have been performed by real, live actors in public. I live in Wiltshire.

~

152: THE CHICKEN AND THE PINEAPPLE

by Alice Payne

Once upon a time there was a pineapple. Then a chicken found it and stuffed his face until he was very fat.

Full of pineapple, the chicken needed to rest his stomach. He went off for a little snooze in the bamboo hutch he had built.

While he was asleep, a hunter stalked up to his little bamboo hutch and stole away the chicken.

Sadly, the hunter drowned in the river and the chicken broke free and lived happily ever after.

Alice Payne's Biography

Alice is a 10-year-old Scottish, English, Northern Irish chatterbox who uses so many words that stories were bound to pop out sooner or later. She lives in Clevedon, runs, plays football and regularly wrestles her cat.

153: THREE

by Rupert Payne

House number three. Cold, dark, gothic. Cracked, murky windows. Rusting gate, overgrown. Over thirty years. Lying empty, forgotten.

Neighbours avoided it. Visitors stared warily. The children joked. "It's definitely haunted."

They were right. Old Mr Smithson. Cancer or stroke? I can't remember. But he died. And never left. He loved it. Loved that house. Couldn't leave it. Until this morning.

A new family. They loved it. Just like him. The ghost smiled. He was happy. At last, finally. He could rest.

Rupert Payne's Biography

Over 40, under 50, and living near Bristol. My favourite number is 5. 81 Words was a nice change from my usual scientific papers.

~

154: SIRENS

by Harriet Payne

The sound of sirens, that was the start to all of this. I had been with my parents at the time, going about my daily chores. It was then that I heard the sirens.

We all rushed out to the shelter and grabbed our gas masks. I could see fear etched onto my parents' faces as we huddled together.

Crashes echoed through the streets of London... then all fell silent. We climbed out of the shelter and saw nothing but rubble.

Harriet Payne's Biography

Harriet is a young writer and poet. She has won school prizes with her work and recited poems live to an assembled audience. She lives with her family in Clevedon while she lays the groundwork for great ambitions.

155: AT THE POLLING BOOTH

by Julie Howard

"How's it going?"

"Busy."

"Have I seen you before?"

"Don't think so. I'm Clare."

"Jenny. What got you into this?"

She points to the election pamphlet. "Maryanne. She's amazing."

It's no one I know.

"What about you?"

"Oh, the total corruption of the Liberal Party. Crooks, every single one of them." I focus on her T-shirt. It's blue like mine, but something's different. She turns away. I see the word LIBERAL emblazoned on her back.

Oh no, she's one of them.

Julie Howard's Biography

Emerging author Julie Howard's novel *Now't But Drippin'* is a slice of Yorkshire life in the sixties. Bert, Ma and Jennifer struggle to overcome religious bigotry as they start a new life together. A story laced with humour and sadness.

~

156: SPIDER

by Neil Brooks

The spider was relaxed, listening intently as the human conversation intensified. Understanding was easy as he had been doing that since he was little.

Recently, though, his web vibrated strangely when humans were in proximity. The vibrations travelled up the web into each of the spider's eight legs. From there, his intelligent unfathomable brain was able to interpret the unspoken emotions and feelings of the humans.

Right now, the words were saying one thing, but the emotions were dark and murderous.

Neil Brooks' Biography

Aged 56, living in North East Scotland. Hobbies are hillwalking, woodworking, DIY and drinking real ale. I like malt whisky. I have done a variety of jobs from engineer, masseur, lecturer, landscape gardener to customer advisor. I'm a writer now.

157: WE DON'T TALK ANYMORE

by Sydney Clarence

W4M: I am S, NBM, N/K. I am ISO a LTR with a M who is an AL, with OHAC.

Open minded so JBY. Message me BAE. TYVM.

Profile saved. This time would be her time. The continual beep-beep, ping-ding, sing-song of the phone through the night, jolted her from her sleep. 22 views, 27, 54. No new messages.

The too shy boy who loved her most in TRW hid his pain by comforting her. If only he had the words.

Sydney Clarence's Biography

A recent taker to writerly things, and am loving it. I've had nibbles, mouthfuls and giant gulps of a life that has been rich and unusual, so have plenty to write about. I'm currently at uni studying creative writing.

www.sydneyclarence.wordpress.com

~

158: SMUGGLERS

by Joanna Ball

The dash became a black dot. I wondered why, and then realised it was because it was heading towards us and the shore.

"That boat's out late tonight," I said.

She didn't answer. I turned to see if she'd heard me.

"Let's go back," she said.

"No, wait. Let's see what it is." Now closer, I could see silhouettes moving: people on board.

"Is it a pleasure craft?"

"Could be. Or a night fishing party."

"That's not odd."

"No. Perfectly normal."

Joanna Ball's Biography

Joanna Ball was born in Manchester and lives in West Oxfordshire. She graduated in 2017 with a BA (hons) in humanities with creative writing and French. She is studying for an MA in creative writing at Oxford Brookes University.

159: THE GOOD HAMMER

by TS Lanchbery

"How many tools can one man possibly need?" she asked. "And especially when so many jobs around the house remain incomplete."

"It is a good hammer," he said.

"So was the last one," she replied.

He was a kleptomaniac, something he had kept hidden from her until after the wedding. But she had her secrets too. It *was* a good hammer though, and, after she had cleaned off all of the blood, it fetched 34 pounds and 50 pence on eBay.

TS Lanchbery's Biography

TS Lanchbery is an aspiring writer from Hastings, East Sussex. He is currently working on his first novel, *The Hunt*, as well as a short story challenge.

~

160: WORLD'S INHERITANCE

by Waltraud Pospischil

"I wanna have another grandpa burger."

"No, all gone, have a grandma burger."

"Boohoo, why? Like grandpa burgers more..."

"Cos grandmas live longer, more of them round who die every day and become burgers."

"Why didn't they leave us any animals or plants to eat?"

"Don't blame anyone, or you'll be a burger next."

"All that's left now are stories and films about something called nature, which they had."

"Don't question reality, or you'll become a burger."

"Rather be spicy chips..."

Waltraud Pospischil's Biography

Born in Austria to WW2 refugee parents. Came to London at 20, trained under R D Laing, lived and studied in therapeutic communities. Writing, for me, is survival. Halfway through my second novel. Trustee of Arkbound Foundation CIO.

www.linkedin.com/in/waltraud-pospischil-00869a101/

161: LOST FOR WORDS

by Betty Hattersley

Normally, although eccentric, her gardening ideal was ordinary. But she'd spent numerous hours working on a new project.

As dusk fell, I visualised a delicate illumination appearing from a tree stump in the centre of her garden.

"Why are those colourful, flickering illuminations glowing from your garden?" I asked politely (without sounding too inquisitive).

She informed me that fairies had taken residence in the tree stump and were having a party to celebrate their new abode.

What more could one say?

Betty Hattersley's Biography

I've been writing for many years and have had numerous poems and short stories published in anthologies, newspapers, calendars and magazines. I've written a small book (yet to be published) about the funny side of my outside catering days.

~

162: HAPPY ANNIVERSARY

by Chip Jett

"You are perfect."

"No. Don't say that. It's not true. Besides, you give me something to live up to that I cannot possibly achieve."

"I don't want you to be something you are not. I don't want some ideal you think society has mandated. I want you." He paused. "OK. You're right. You aren't perfect. You have many flaws, as do I. But your imperfections erase mine, and mine are many." He searched and found the words. "Together, we are perfect."

Chip Jett's Biography

Chip Jett is a teacher at a small school in Georgia. His short story 'A Permanent Vacation' is in the Fall 2017 issue of *The First Line* literary journal. His upcoming work will appear in *Soliloquies* and *The Ocotillo Review*.

163: MOUSE

by Nurholis

I was typing my script on an old computer, in the living room with my cat sitting beside me. I was completely focused on the last line.

I left to go to the kitchen, to fetch some snacks, planning to get right back to my work.

My cat stayed still, with a look like it was more focused than me.

I got some cassava chips. The cat was staying cool, quiet and serene.

"Do you want this 'mouse'?" I said loudly.

Nurholis' Biography

Hi, my name is Nurholis. I am a graduate of Mulawarman University, Indonesia. I took up mine engineering as a career. I spend my rest time writing poems and any form of short stories. I want to be a writer.

~

164: WHAT DUCKS DO

by Deborah Wroe

"Walter, right a bit.

"Lucy, fall in line.

"Matilda, front and centre.

"One, two, three, go."

"Mum, look at the ducks. They are like those women in the Olympics, in the pool, with the things on their noses."

"Synchronised swimmers?"

"Yes, them. It's like they've been practising for ages."

"It's just nature. It's what ducks do. Practising, haha."

"Well I'd give them gold."

"Aaaaand relax, team, fall out. They've gone. They left bread – last one to get it is a ninny."

Deborah Wroe's Biography

Deborah Wroe is an aspiring writer, aren't we all?
Twitter: @DeborahKWroe

165: THE GREATEST

by Debaprasad Mukherjee

"I'm the greatest," said Mr King.

"Hail, Mr King," said people.

"I'll change policies," said he.

"Superb," said people.

Loss of lives and exchequer later, Mr King said, "I'm the wisest."

People said, "Hail, Mr King."

"I'll impose newer taxes," Mr King said.

"What a noble idea," people said.

People died of hunger.

In came the assassin, Mr Ego. He killed Mr King to make him a martyr.

"We died slowly, you died fast. You're the greatest," said the dead men.

Debaprasad Mukherjee's Biography

Debaprasad Mukherjee is a 58-year-old doctor from India. He has penned four books to date. He also keeps contributing to various on and offline periodicals.

www.facebook.com/debaprasad.mukherjee.79

~

166: CHEATED

by Derek McMillan

"Sorry, what was that?"

"I said," Jack raised his voice against the wind, "I am going to kill her."

"Who?"

"Haven't you been listening? The prime minister."

That was the end of our conversation for that night. It was cold on the sea front. We said goodbye.

Next day, we met up at the Hare and Hounds. Jack had a newspaper and a foul temper.

"You didn't tell me Thatcher was already dead." He looked at the floor. "I feel cheated."

Derek McMillan's Biography

Derek McMillan lives in Durrington with his wife, Angela, who is also his editor. His latest book is *Durrington Detective Agency*, which is a collection of short detective stories with something for everybody.

www.derekmcmillan.com

167: NAILED

by Richard Swaine

Given the, shall we say, richly varied nature of the historic allegations made against you, encompassing inappropriate physical conduct, racism, homophobia, misappropriation of party funds, the falsification of employment history, not to mention the ongoing paternity suites you've been named in, I'm sure you'll appreciate it if we don't detain you any longer than is necessary and why I'll be brief in delineating the main reasons why we feel you'd be the perfect choice for the position of director of communications.

Richard Swaine's Biography

In common with many budding writers, married father of one Richard's lifelong dream is to one day walk into a bookshop and find his title there on the shelves – whether it would actually sell any copies is the part he doesn't dwell on too much.

~

168: MURDERED GIRLS

by Claire Apps

"Good night, good night. Parting is such sweet sorrow. I will forever remember you, my sweet girls." I'm not a typical murderer; I don't need a trophy to have a reminder. My memory is intact, especially for memories such as tonight.

"Good night all, enjoy the rest of the night. I'll see you soon, my sweethearts." Then, without looking back, I take my leave. Yes, it has been a good night. I can feel the girls watching me.

"Good night, girls."

Claire Apps' Biography

I have self-published a book of poetry from the soul. I have taught creative writing to vulnerable women to help them gain self-esteem and confidence for a number of years. I am writing a fantasy novel.

169: LOST OPPORTUNITIES

by Taye Carrol

Unattended baggage in Israel is serious business because of all the death delivered in pretty packages and Louis Vuitton luggage. A bomb squad will detonate your freshly baked pastries or lacy unmentionables before you can convince them there is nothing to worry about. These are easy to replace. But his number was in the one I left when my order was ready.

I always take a man's number instead of giving mine, promising I'll call. This time, I really would have.

Taye Carrol's Biography

Taye Carrol is a psychologist by training, a freelance writer by choice and a fiction/play/poetry writer by the seat of her pants. She serves as editor for Lycan Valley Publications and Grey Goose Press. Taye resides in Chicago.
www.facebook.com/TayeCarrolUnafraidOfTheDark/

~

170: MAKING A HASH OF IT

by Roz Levens

"Your house is always so warm and laid-back," beamed Judith, as she munched another brownie. "I love coming here." She smiled and sniffed the air appreciatively. "And what's that wonderful smell?"

"Pot pourri."

Judith kept her face straight. Marjorie was a wonderful hostess, even if she mispronounced words. So what? It didn't matter in the slightest.

Later, when the police raided Marjorie's house and took away all the cannabis plants, Judith thought again.

Perhaps Marjorie was being specific, sounding the 'T'.

Roz Levens' Biography

I'm a flash fictioneer and short story writer based in Worcestershire. Roz is a pen name.
@RozLevens

171: MR ALUCARD

by Robbie Porter

I once knew Mr Alucard. He was a neat man of peculiar habits. Some called him misanthropic but that, I think, was on very casual acquaintance.

To me, at least, he gave every consideration, although with the kind of discernment one would normally give to a side of beef at dinner. One could almost say that he was eyeing me up for the main course. That in itself was most disquieting, even before I realised the terrible truth about Mr Alucard.

Robbie Porter's Biography

Robbie Porter is a lecturer and charity worker from Worcester.
   www.facebook.com/robbie.porter.37

~

172: THE SILENCE

by Katie Chapman

"That's everything, thank you." The queen dismissed her ladies for the evening. She planned to care for herself for once. 'Being normal' she called it.

She laughed in spite of herself – she ran an entire empire, yet was not trusted to dress alone. The new silence found in her chambers was comforting compared to the constant bustling of court. So comforting, in fact, that she did not notice the shadow lurking, the knife glinting. The silence did not last that evening.

Katie Chapman's Biography

Katie Chapman is a published young author who runs her own lifestyle blog. Having been published in previous short story anthologies, she is now focusing on developing her writing and portfolio further. Find out more at her website:
   www.katiealevelmedia.wordpress.com

173: A LADDERED STOCKING

by Maxine Smith

I could have danced forever, until I broke my leg. Alternatives were considered, so having only a laddered stocking and a threatening expression to my name, it was high time I held up a bank.

Proving successful at this, I repeated the exercise several times and became notorious.

Eventually, I was arrested and tried in court, but found not guilty. The jury could not countenance that someone with a princess pink plaster cast on their ankle would commit such a crime.

Maxine Smith's Biography

I am a terrifying 56-year-old wife, mother, retired educationalist, continuing socialist and published playwright. I like laughing and would like to see the world cleaner, fairer and more optimistic.

~

174: A WRITER'S RETREAT

by Karen McDermott

'A writers' retreat' the subject-line announced.

An outline was thereunder sketched, regarding a cottage (too expensive) in Devon (too far) and cc'd too many names Tim didn't recognise (anxiety-inducing). Activities would include swimming (not for Tim, who couldn't), board games, walking and – seemingly lastly – writing. Along with sharing the outcome of the latter each evening.

Tim shuddered and closed the laptop, mentally archiving the invitation to his 'Things I will find excuses to wriggle out of later' folder.

A writer's retreat.

Karen McDermott's Biography

Karen is an NHS amanuensis and writer of listings for *What's On* magazine in Brighton. She likes going to gigs, reading books she finds left on windowsills in the street, drinking energy drinks and not going to the dentist.

Twitter: @Karen_S_McD

175: THE POWERFUL ONE

by Rohana Chomick

"Rain, rain, go away, just come back another day."

I shouldn't have said that. It changed everything. Who knew I had such power.

There is no rain. Not now. Not for years. Everything is dying or dead. I still live, but my family is no more. Gone, all gone.

My skin crawls with loneliness. I hear no voices, no pattering of feet, no whisper of wings. I wish I had kept my mouth shut. I wish I was not a god.

Rohana Chomick's Biography

I've been many things in my life: kindergarten teacher in Barbados, retail clerk, bookstore clerk, bank teller (for a day), newspaper feature writer, TV promotions producer, administrative assistant, resume writer, standardised test reader/scorer, college tutor in English, and now librarian.

~

176: LOOSING GRIP

by Leigh Hastings

Edward gripped the safety line tightly as he felt his boots leave the side of the shuttle.

Snap.

He could feel the breaking of the cord reverberate throughout his entire body.

Every moment seemed an eternity as the memories flashed before his eyes. His marriage. Their child. Her tears when he said goodbye. His smile on his first liftoff.

Every memory, however minuscule or significant, came into fierce clarity as the shuttle slipped beyond his view.

Edward gripped those memories tightly.

Leigh Hastings' Biography

Leigh Hastings is a science fiction and fantasy author who publishes weekly writing tips, flash fiction and book reviews.

@LeighJHastings

177: THE BRIDE'S MIND

by Bridget Scrannage

Sandy beach. Him, on one knee.
"Will you?"
Sparkling diamond. Pounding waves.
"Ooh, yes."
White wedding.
Planning. Reality.
Guest list: avert Armageddon.
Flowers: "Hooooooow much?"
Food: "What DO vegans eat? Grass?"
Fake tan. Just why?
Gift list. No more cheese boards.
Bridesmaids. Keep separate and sober. Separate 'n' Sober.
Dress: "Hoooooooooow much?"
Photographer. Refrain from throttling.
Hen night. Did they find the stripper in the bargain basement? Put it away.
Best man: Scare witless ahead of stag do.
"Elope?"
"Yes please."

Bridget Scrannage's Biography

I'm Bridget Scrannage. I'm the founder of an active online writing community with over 100 members. Writer of predominantly humorous short stories and flash fiction, some of which can be found on my blog:
www.bridgetscrannage.wordpress.com

~

178: SCOUTING FOR BOYS

by Abigail Rowe

The whole village knew her for a witch. Rose Cottage was gingerbread sweet. I could've licked it. Me and Stevie creeping to the front door, like Shaggy and Scooby-doo. Tiptoeing, goose-bumping, hair-raising steps.

"Do we have to?" asks Stevie. He's only nine.

"You know we do."

A black cat comes from round the side. Yowls, fur on end. Stevie shakes.

The doorknocker is iron-cold.

The door creaks.

An ancient woman peers out.

"Bob-a-job," I stammer.

A sugared smile. "Come in, boys."

Abigail Rowe's Biography

Abigail Rowe is an amateur, but hopeful, Cork-based writer, currently engaged in completing her first novel and a collection of poetry.

~

179: RUNNING THE GAUNTLET

by Alicia Sledge

From behind the kitchen bin, a black, beady eye glinted and whiskers twitched. Murine paws scratched on slick tiles.

In a frantic dash, a tiny creature scurried the length of the skirting board towards the crack that was its refuge between the washing machine and the wall. For such a small animal, it was not an insignificant distance; both speed and silence were essential. The distance was covered swiftly.

But alas, within inches of safety, a soundless, black shadow loomed overhead...

Alicia Sledge's Biography

Alicia has enjoyed writing stories and poems since primary school. She also reads avidly, paints, makes 1/12th scale dollhouse miniatures and works in a secondary school. Alicia has recently had a story shortlisted and published by Stringybark Stories in Australia.

www.sledgendswriting.blogspot.co.uk

180: THE BIRD CAT

by Arlene Everingham

From the upstairs window, I watch my cat snake through the long summer grass. He's hoping to sneak up on the birds who are lazing in the birdbath like tourists on the beach.

One scrambling jump and he lands face first in the water. The birds scatter, laughing as they fly off. He decides to stay there, wallowing; his long hair floating like black seaweed around him.

"Max, what are you doing?"

Ocean green eyes turn to me and he smiles.

Arlene Everingham's Biography

Arlene Everingham does archery and writes for fun. She lives in Luxembourg with her husband, four cats, an overflowing library and an unruly garden.

~

181: I HATE THE COLD

by Sarah Stansfield

The winter brings many things. Although I hate the cold.

I love the season with Christmas and getting together with family, but I hate the cold.

The snow is so beautiful and to see it glisten in the sunlight, but I hate the cold.

It is a time to reflect and reminisce, but I hate the cold.

The fireplace is beautiful when lit, but I hate the cold.

To see the children play in the snow, but I hate the cold.

Sarah Stansfield's Biography

My name is Sarah, I'm a college student. I love to write and I am working towards my degree in hospitality management.

182: WE'VE ALL BEEN THERE

by Franca Basta

"What's the matter?"
   "Nothing."
   "It isn't our anniversary, is it?"
   "No."
   "Have I forgotten something?"
   "No."
   "Did I do something I shouldn't have?"
   "No."
   "Did I not do something I should have?"
   "No."
   "Someone sick?"
   "No."
   "Dead?"
   "No."
   "Can I get you something?"
   "No."
   "Let's go out for dinner."
   "I'm on a diet."
   "You're sure there's nothing wrong?"
   "Yes."
   "OK. It's been a really long day. I'm going to bed."
   "You care nothing about my feelings, do you? You selfish egotist."

Franca Basta's Biography

My name's Franca Basta and I'm a hybrid in that I was born in one country, grew up in another and had parents from yet another. This has made me open to all cultures, which can't be a bad thing.

~

183: LOSS

by Sue Partridge

She lowered his body into the freshly dug hole in the garden and covered him with soil. Tom had been a good companion for over sixteen years. She had fed him morning and evening, given him a cosy bed and she had always let him go out on his nightly prowls. That was until today.

He didn't come home last night. As he'd strolled into the kitchen this morning, bacon had been sizzling in the pan. Now she was a widow.

Sue Partridge's Biography

I am a retired finance officer, enjoying a new lease of life. I play violin in a quartet, I am learning jazz piano and I have just started to discover the art of writing.

~

184: LIFE AFTER DEATH

by James Colfox

I felt sorry for Joanna, but most of my sorrow was reserved for the priest.

Joanna shouldn't have tried to speak. We had agreed that she wouldn't, but I knew deep down that she would. And she did, until eventually she was overcome with sobs and was led away. It was left to the priest to deliver the eulogy.

He didn't know me and so he spoke on the subject he thought he knew best. Heaven.

He knew nothing. He lied.

James Colfox's Biography

James Colfox is a tarot reader, coach and writer who writes both nonfiction and fiction books inspired by the tarot cards. He spends his time between London, south-west France and Gran Canaria.

185: PREPARING FOR PROSE

by Jo Howarth

The curtains, drawn, block out the empty darkness of the night. Lambent candles, placed with careful consideration around the room, bring forward spirit words, which land delicately and precisely on the Vergé de France pad – 50 sheets of champagne writing paper (from the old established firm, G. Lalo, Paris).

Sitting at her worn desk she remains still, head slightly bent to the right – pen moving over the spirit words, embroidering on paper. Diligently applying herself, stitching the core of her story.

Jo Howarth's Biography

Lives in Norwich – failure in all walks of life so far. Likes reading, writing and being left alone. Likes to think that she might 'add' something to the writing world. Dislikes mobile phones and pasta. No pets. Age 50.

~

186: PUMPKIN PIE

by E. F. S. Byrne

There is no reason to be afraid, it's all logical. Louise invented Halloween. She did it when she was five and her baby sister was one. Her mother was going to make pumpkin soup but didn't know where to start.

Louise took the knife and showed her. What she did was attack the pumpkin, as if it were her little sibling. Her mother screamed. Louise smiled.

"It's hollow," she said. "Just put a candle inside and pretend it's my little sister."

E. F. S. Byrne's Biography

While working in education and being a father, E. F. S. Byrne has finally found time to devote to his writing and is currently working on everything from very short flash to full-length novels. Samples can be read at:

www.efsbyrne.wordpress.com

187: ADULTEROUS DECISION

by R.J. Saxon

Slipping on her summer dress.

His blood boiled.

Today he'd tell her.

"Ready?" Lucy smiled at Ethan.

Ethan nodded condescendingly, approaching the car.

Brake fluid spoiled the driveway as they headed towards Lover's Cliff.

"Lucy... who's it gonna be, him or me? Decide," shouted Ethan, foot down hard on the gas, towards the cliff edge.

"It's you, Ethan. Please STOP."

Ethan hit the tampered brakes.

Too late.

Dillon, the mechanic, planned a different outcome when Lucy brought the car for service.

R.J. Saxon's Biography

Hi, my name is R.J. Saxon from Manchester, England. I'm a writer of science fiction, shorts, flash fiction, true-life crime, horror and children's literature. Master of 55 word stories.

Twitter: @RjSaxon

~

188: HIS NEW MAN

by Clare Tivey

She struggled to see what Charlie found so mesmerising about Alex.

Charlie had dated some attractive and charismatic men. Alex wasn't blessed with looks or charm – a small mean mouth that rarely smiled and, when it did, showed no connection to his upper face. However, Alex was smart and manipulative, she believed, with potential psychopathic tendencies.

Always the pragmatist, she laughed etc. at all of the correct points during dinner, but she and Alex both knew, they would never be friends.

Clare Tivey's Biography

Having lived in London for many years, Clare now resides in Suffolk, relishing the company of her partner and the countryside, enjoying cycling and open-water swimming. New to writing, Clare writes for fun, mostly about people she has met.

189: THE ISLAND OF INIQUITY

by Fee Johnstone

"Don't feed the attractions and remain seated," our tinny-voiced guide instructed as we donned our waterproof capes and set sail for the Island of Iniquity.

The boat slowed as we approached.

"The disturbing species exhibited here roamed the earth for 200,000 years, reigning terror upon everyone and everything."

Suddenly, a hideous fleshy creature catapulted itself against the boat and wailed – if I'd had a heart, I'm sure it would've leapt.

"Fellow robots," our guide announced theatrically, "I present to you... mankind."

Fee Johnstone's Biography

I reside in Scotland and two of my greatest loves are cats and craft beer. I'm working on combining the two by teaching my cats how to pour the perfect stout.

Twitter: @Missfeeee

~

190: THE DISCOVERY – AT LAST

by John L Bell

He had discovered IT.

He had ALWAYS been able to magic up writing from ANY starting point, observation, trifle, happening.

Then he discovered the very aspect of life SO barren, SO unfruitful, SO sterile and SO futile, it couldn't kick start a writing spree.

NOT cleaning toilets.

The 'discovery'?

Cleaning the baked on cheese from the sandwich toaster WAS the Most Literary Barren Activity Known To Personkind.

No sentence cropped up... no phrase... not a juicy adverb.

Nothing... zero... nowt... zilch.

John L Bell's Biography

I am a retired UK primary school teacher.

www.facebook.com/johnlbellblog

191: IMAGINATION

by David Wright

I have climbed the highest mountains and swam in shark infested waters.

I have travelled the world and visited exotic lands.

I have been an astronaut and voyaged to far off alien worlds.

I have ventured back in time and met many famous historical figures.

I have looked into the future and seen things yet to come.

I have had many varied and wondrous experiences and all without leaving the comfort of my own home – through the power of my imagination.

David Wright's Biography

I enjoy writing, playing the guitar for pleasure and volunteering at a local folk museum.

~

192: FINDING THE WATER DRAGON

by Melanie Goodell

Once upon a time, at morning light, a dragon turned to face a knight.

"En garde," the knight called gleefully. The worried dragon spun to flee.

"You must not leave," the knight called out, "for only you can stop this drought."

"Me?" the dragon answered, low and rough. "But I am nothing more than tough."

"Yes, you." The knight replaced his sword. "Only you can sing the water chord."

The dragon sang a low, slow tune and quickly started a monsoon.

Melanie Goodell's Biography

Melanie Goodell has been writing since she learned to spell. She recently finished her first adult novel and looks forward to the day she can write full time. She enjoys writing children's books for her son, niece and nephew.

www.facebook.com/msgfindingme/

193: AIRPORT

by Malcolm Richardson

Bing bong.

"Final call for flight BA217 to New York JFK, gate 37."

"Where's the tickets, Marvin?"

"I gave them to Celia."

"Celia? I saw you give them to James."

"Where's James?"

"Starbucks, I think," suggested Jane.

"He was looking at the magazines," said Trevor.

"I saw him go into the toilets," Josephine added.

"Marvin, get him out of the toilet."

"James, where are the tickets?"

"I gave them to Stephanie."

Bing bong.

"Gate 37, for New York, now closed."

"Stephanie..."

Malcolm Richardson's Biography

I write mainly short story contemporary fiction. I've also written a number of adult fairy tales. Currently, I'm in the process of completing the first draft of a novel.

~

194: DAMP GRASS

by Jenny Simmons

Stars glowed in the distance as we sat in the dark. Beautiful, but I was more interested in you.

We were in love, we were young. It all was new for us both. We would talk from sunrise to sunset, but that night we did more. We nervously kissed, slowly taking off more and more. It was awkward; damp grass tickled our bare skin, I kept giggling. And then we were one. And in your eyes I saw the stars glow.

Jenny Simmons' Biography

Jenny studies astrophysics at Queen's University, loves nature and sometimes writes. She hopes to one day learn how to write bio's that are more interesting than a bland dating profile.

www.instagram.com/jensimmons_/

195: IM – THE NEW SUBTEXT TO CORPORATE MEETINGS

by Claire Taylor

"I'm completely confused."

"Don't be, it's him, not you."

"And we pay him how much?"

"I know."

"Can't find an emoji for what he's saying, so will use the poo one."

"What's that he said? Elements? Never heard of them. Am I in the right meeting?"

"He means actions."

"Seriously?"

"Yep. Kind of 'squaring the loop'."

"What the what?"

"Indeed."

"So, he's just spent an hour telling us he didn't do his actions."

"Yeah."

"Where is the emoji for 'you're fired'?"

Claire Taylor's Biography

Claire Taylor is a project manager by day and a frustrated writer by night. She has always had a passion for writing, but only recently has she started sharing her work with others.

~

196: THE TRAVEL BUG

by Pam Jackson

Mack was terrified of flying. Just the thought of hurtling through the stratosphere at impossible speeds in a winged tube made him feel ill. Yet he longed to see the exotic places he read about – Egypt, Singapore, Italy.

Eventually, Mack booked an ocean voyage and caught a train to the coast. As he approached the docks, he gasped at the ship's colossal size. He looked east and saw the ocean through the heads, vast and deep. He wept and turned away.

Pam Jackson's Biography

Pam Jackson has been writing stories since she was a child but, due to a need to eat, works in an office. She lives on the Northern Beaches of Sydney, Australia.

www.facebook.com/pam.jackson.9461

197: JUST DESSERTS

by Susie Frame

We met. We laughed. We hugged. We kissed. We loved. We married. We loved. We fought. We loved. We fought. We fought. We fought.

I left. He followed. He stalked. I quivered. He hit. I cried. He apologised. He pleaded. I caved. I forgave. I returned.

We laughed. We hugged. We kissed. We loved. We fought. He hit. I hated. I despised. I planned. I smiled. I cooked. I poisoned.

He died.

I'm incarcerated. I'm happy. I'm free.

Finally.

I'm free.

Susie Frame's Biography

Susie lives in Dunedin, NZ, and has always enjoyed writing words. Some of her words have even made it into print. When she isn't scribbling, Susie can be found chatting at cafes, watching movies, playing the piano or knitting.

~

198: FIRSTBORN

by Kathryn Dixon

That first day post-caesarean was brutal. I was in pain, exhausted. You screamed relentlessly. Breastfed repeatedly whilst the clock moved. In the twilight hours of your first day on Earth, you hunched on my scarred abdomen like a tiny Buddha, chin cupped in my fingers, and we locked eyes.

Becalmed and peaceful now, your sweetness charmed. I vowed my eternal love and care. Prayed that you outlive me and grow into a fine person. I know you will. My lovely boy.

Kathryn Dixon's Biography

Nearly 55. Divorced. Two gorgeous sons in their 20s. Ex-NHS occupational therapist in palliative care. Yummy mummy. Domestic goddess of cupcakes, candles and sloe gin. Local lifestyle blogger. Intrepid traveller. Singer in a choir. Tentative writer. Cricket/rugby lover.

Instagram and Twitter: @kathryndixon63

199: GREEDY GECKO

by Edward Rouse

Mr Gecko sat on a stone. A fly flew in front of his face. Another fly came along.

Mrs Fly waited for her children.

When her husband came home, she told him, "I'm so worried."

"I'll investigate," he said.

He soon returned. "It's that Gecko. I'm sorry, dear."

Mr Gecko was having his nap.

He was woken by a buzzing sound. Before his tongue whipped out, it was all over for Mr Gecko.

Dan put the lid back on his box.

Edward Rouse's Biography

I'm Edward Rouse, aged 21, and I recently graduated from Bath Spa University with an upper second class honours. I have had a couple of pieces of poetry and some journalism published, and I enjoy entering writing competitions.

~

200: THE DADO RAIL

by Jan Brown

I stroll round the classroom, glancing at wonky diagrams, budgets, garish mood boards, offering the occasional encouraging word. This is a popular technology task: design your bedroom.

"You might want to check your spelling." Voice neutral, I walk away calmly, rigid with suppressed laughter. Just leave it.

I can't. I look back. Julia's eyes are fixed on mine, defiantly willing me to break first.

"Dildo rail to divide..."

We break simultaneously, wiping away tears. No one else understands why we're hysterical.

Jan Brown's Biography

I'm busily doing nothing, nothing the whole day through, trying to find lots of things not to do. Writing for fun is my favourite displacement activity as I grapple with retirement, a southern foreigner in suburban Yorkshire.

201: TIME BOMB

by Shaun Clarke

She'd found him strewn over the bath, pacified, motionless.

"Tim?" She panicked, before telling herself he's a joker.

"Tim?" she enquired, standing back, smiling hysterically.

She frowned…

"Timmy Sharpe, stop it now." Then she spotted the telling blood.

He was announced dead on arrival at hospital.

When she learned he'd died of liver cancer, she remembered he'd complained about a pain which they never took seriously. She closed her eyes in absolute agony. *There was always something more important to do.*

Shaun Clarke's Biography

Director of Urban Word Collective. Arkbound Foundation trustee. Journalist. Author. Shaun writes widely about current events and cultural developments. He has compiled poetry and spoken word collections by disadvantaged authors across the UK, titled *Lyrically Justified*.

www.urbanwordcollective.co.uk

~

202: ACCIDENT

by Prajith Menon

At 11:30AM, I could see vehicles coming towards me in the opposite lane.

10 seconds later, a car hit a bike.

After 10 seconds, the bike rider was flung into air.

After 10 seconds, his helmet smashed.

After 10 seconds, he was in a pool of blood.

After 10 seconds, people were busy taking pictures – no one took him to hospital.

After 10 seconds, he took his last breath.

In a minute, both drivers' lives changed.

I was sent to prison.

Prajith Menon's Biography

Prajith Menon was born in India. He lives in the United Arab Emirates. When people ask, "Did you always want to be a writer?" he says, "No – I have always been a writer." *Game for Game* was his debut novel.

203: PRETENTIOUS, MOI?

by Kathryn Evans

"81 words? Well that's not proper writing. What I have to say is much too important to edit down to 81 words. I want to be a serious writer, you know, like Kazuo Ishiguro – bet he didn't start off with silly gimmicky things like this. I've been carrying out painstaking research into the history of Neolithic farming so that I can include it in my first novel. I..."

"OK thanks, I think we've heard more than enough from you now – CUT."

Kathryn Evans' Biography

Kathryn Evans was born in Wales, raised in Scotland, has an Irish grandfather and lives in Plymouth, England. She studied genetics to PhD level. Her main passion is rock/indie music.

~

204: KEEPING UP APPEARANCES

by Hazel Turner

Beryl took her usual seat on the bus, smoothing her Versace cashmere suit and adjusting her hat as if posing for a photoshoot for *Vogue*. Mimi, her Pekinese, proved popular with the passengers who came and went. Beryl smiled, enjoying the admiration.

Later, arriving home, she carefully removed her scarf and gloves before opening her bag.

"Well, Mimi, another successful day," she cooed. Then she began counting her spoils: five wallets, four rings, three purses, two watches and a gold bracelet.

Hazel Turner's Biography

For some years as a teacher and ex-husband groupie, I moved around; from the Lothians, to Fife, to Aberdeen, to The Gambia, to Trinidad and, finally, South Yorkshire. Now I take my wonderful, varied people experiences and write.

205: PRIVACY POLICY

by Chris Cantor

Every effort has been taken to provide the freshest possible story for your entertainment. Please consider the suitability of the subject matter for your tastes. The story contains an exciting section and readers with nervous predispositions should consider this carefully, as we accept no liability for causation or exacerbations of health problems. The story should not be read whilst driving or operating dangerous machinery.

If you prefer to read our privacy policy instead of the story it is available at www...

Chris Cantor's Biography

Chris Cantor is a new writer of quirky, dark, challenging, often satirical stories. Released from his previous life in psychological shackles, he now communes with the sea or music when he is not writing.

~

206: GRAMPS AND GRANDSON

by Stuart Atkinson

"I want a good death."
　"Why, Gramps, what's the point?"
　"I want all the loose ends tied."
　"What ends, Gramps?"
　"I want to be at peace."
　"Why, Gramps? When you're dead you're dead."
　"Maybe, but..."
　"But what?"
　"I may be dead, but you're not."
　"What do you mean?"
　"I need to make sure others keep on living. I don't want to leave things unsaid or undone. I'll be at peace, only if I know you move on."
　"Love you, Gramps, promise."

Stuart Atkinson's Biography

I am semi-retired after over 40 years teaching in New Zealand in the secondary sector. As a science and maths teacher, my right cerebral hemisphere was often dormant. I want to kick it into action through writing.

　Twitter: @well47

207: VOICES

by Joyce Walker

I feel as if I've been here forever, so I say, "I hear no voices." That's because they tell me to lie, that they have plans for me and if I take the medication that's been prescribed they'll go away and be replaced by others who will not be so friendly.

So I tell her again, "I hear no voices."

Satisfied, the psychiatrist signs the papers that will allow me to leave the hospital and go back out into the community.

Joyce Walker's Biography

First published in *Envoi* in 1993 and have since had more than 100 poems published in anthologies and small press magazines. Also had some success with fiction, having won the Writers Brew Short Story Prize in 2002.

~

208: STREET FOOD

by Sally Skeptic

He'd arrived. Eight months and all his father's savings paid to that man who'd promised a comfortable journey and had delivered only airless vans and unseaworthy ships. But he was here at last, in London.

The promised job had not materialised, but he was confident he'd find work. His immediate need was food and he saw a sign: 'Street Food'.

At home, this meant plentiful and cheap. Then he saw the small portions and large prices. Things would be different here.

Sally Skeptic's Biography

After a lifetime working with numbers, I succeeded with the NaNoWriMo challenge to write 50,000 words in one month. The 81 Words challenge set such a different target that it was not to be resisted. Sally Skeptic, Gravesend, UK.

209: CANNIBALISM IS NOT FOR THE FAINT HEARTED

by Michael Ward

Things had gotten very tense recently. Strained relationships, so to speak. Difficult to talk to one another, let alone look each other in the eye now that there were only three of us left.

We'd eaten the rest. The galley boy was the best.

We're adrift in an open lifeboat off the west coast of Peru. There were seven of us to start with. Like I said, things had gotten very tense.

Hungry again. It's not gonna be me. Bit tricky.

Michael Ward's Biography

I'm a 65-year-old retired Merchant Navy deck officer. Went to sea as a cadet at 17, been to 98 countries, worked for 25 international shipping companies, grammar school boy, county champion. Everything I write is people/humour based.

~

210: AIR MILES

by Ron Smith

It was a typical civil service meeting. Grey suits, no biscuits, and people referred to by initials.

The subject: 'Should the civil service allow its staff to accept air miles?'

"It's a benefit and should be taxed," said HMRC1.

The argument rumbled on until DMI1 (director military intelligence) spoke dismissively. "This is all very interesting, but none of it applies to my staff."

"How so?" several people interjected.

"Oh," he replied airily, "because they never travel under the same name twice."

Ron Smith's Biography

I am a retired professional aeronautical engineer, and am an aviation enthusiast, past pilot and aircraft owner, photographer, author and historian.

www.ronandjimsmith.com

211: FOUR GREY WALLS

by Bryan Keefe

Alone with my thoughts, I stare at four grey walls. They press in on me. A gloom descends. Staring at the walls, I wonder how I got into this predicament, but there's no one else I can blame. I have to live with the consequences of my actions. What was I thinking? I could put it down to naivety, but I knew what I was doing. Yes, I was influenced by others, but I'm an adult.

Why didn't I choose Magnolia?

Bryan Keefe's Biography

I am a 60-year-old retired policeman from Essex. Nowadays, I fill my time with cycling and keeping fit.

~

212: THE BATTLE AND WITHDRAWAL

by Rajagopal Kaimal

When I commence my morning walk, the Night army still controls the clock; this despite the ever brightening sign of the Day army on the eastern horizon. And as this army slowly draws near, the Night army begins to slowly retreat, knowing that it cannot match the strength of the approaching force.

And as I walk leisurely on this advance, a retreat takes place on every road and street.

Then, under a vast cloudless sky, bright Day's victory is totally complete.

Rajagopal Kaimal's Biography

R G Kaimal lives in Bangalore, India. He began writing poetry because of his love for a girl. He got over her, but poetry retained its grip on him. Most of his poems are about Mother Nature and human idiosyncrasies.

213: THE NUMBERS ADD UP

by S. M. Chiles

Why is six afraid of seven? Right, seven ate nine. But really, nine never got devoured at all because nine remains in every maths text book.

This indubitably means six cannot possibly have been afraid of seven to begin with and a massive conspiracy of numbers must have been concocted by two daft idiots to trick the public into believing three fake news lies: the death of nine, the maliciousness of seven and the elimination of all maths homework ad infinitum.

S. M. Chiles' Biography

S. M. Chiles is an Arabic-speaking middle school English language and literature teacher in Amman, Jordan, and holds a BA in psychology and biblical and theological studies from Gordon College in Wenham, MA, USA.

~

214: YOU KNOW ME

by Louise Furre

"You think you know someone," said Pam. "But you never do really."

"We've shared a flat for eight years," said Angie. "I know you. But we all have secrets."

After dark, Angie left the flat with a large tin under her coat. Pam followed her stealthily.

Angie went to the park and buried the tin. After she left, Pam dug it up. She took off the lid. There were biscuits in it. A note said, 'Bring them home, I'm making tea.'

Louise Furre's Biography

Louise lives in Dorset and does more knitting than writing. For a long time, her favourite biscuit was the bourbon cream but her loyalty has waned over the years.

215: GOODBYE

by Ania Kovas

Opening the box, she reached into it, not feeling the bottom. She looked. Darkness greeted her, the sides fading away. Looking outside the box, it seemed normal.

"Really bottomless?"

"Yes," replied the Claus.

"And no rope or ladder?"

"Coming back, are you?" said the Claus.

"Guess not."

He handed her a backpack. "Bonus."

"Thanks."

"You going to say goodbye to them?" he asked her.

She shook her head.

"It'll be a mystery."

She smiled, not prettily. "Good," she said, jumping in.

Ania Kovas' Biography

Ania Kovas is a pseudonym. Educator, programmer, writer and transperson, Ania tries to write daily for publication to her website www.dailywords.co.uk. She lives alone in England, walking and playing computer games as distractions.

~

216: THE WOODSMAN

by Margee Unger

He was sitting in the park when he saw her. She was a beautiful girl with long, dark hair and a slender build that appealed to his taste. Her attire was made up of form fitting exercise clothing that showed off her curves.

His mouth started to water as thoughts began to run through his mind, about what he would do if he could get her back to his cabin in the forest outside of Branson.

He decided to follow her.

Margee Unger's Biography

Margee Unger has worn many different hats in the past, including careers as a Chinese chef, landscaper and working in a bakery. In the past nine years, she has enjoyed being a youth services librarian in a small town in Florida.

217: EDIBLE

by RK

The endless suffering to find wild food in the winter season.

Hawthorn berries and chestnuts, you'd still be able to find if you looked for their colours amidst the brown and dark green of the trees and bushes, provided they've not all been under a covering snow or collected by the exploratory squirrels.

During other seasons, when the temperature is higher and the deciduous trees have their leaves, it'd be much easier to find any nice nibbles and forgeable fruits outdoors.

RK's Biography

RK was an attendee at a Caring in Bristol writing workshop, the aim of which was to gain contributions for the *Survival Handbook*, a free book that delivers support to homeless and vulnerable people in the Bristol area.

~

218: GRANNY RAGWORT

by Lucinda Thelwell

"Time to get up, the day's almost gone," said Granny, opening the curtains.

Bleary eyed, I got out of bed, pulling on the cords and itchy socks both my sisters had worn before me.

Granny Ragwort the locals called her, because she'd get up every morning and head out onto the cliffs to clear the invasive species.

No one was safe from the task when they stayed. At sunrise, we'd be out on the headland, getting blown away by the wind.

Lucinda Thelwell's Biography

Lucinda was an attendee at a Caring in Bristol writing workshop, the aim of which was to gain contributions for the *Survival Handbook*, a free book that delivers support to homeless and vulnerable people in the Bristol area.

219: HOME

by Jason B

What is a home? A roof, a bed.
For me a fact, it was all in my head.
I dream, imagine my mum is apart,
makes me feel dizzy, warm and content,
unable to hurt, through the barrier of my head.
Keeps me safe, no uninvited plebs,
mature, grownup and ready instead.
To share with others, the working of head,
that allows me, to continue ahead.
My family, it's mine, the future unsaid,
because now I'm content, in my own head.

Jason B's Biography

Jason was an attendee at a Caring in Bristol writing workshop, the aim of which was to gain contributions for the *Survival Handbook*, a free book that delivers support to homeless and vulnerable people in the Bristol area.

~

220: SMASHED PEACH JAM

by Phoebe Tatham

Delphine jumped from her chair like a nimble, dynamite-lit frog and spun her head wildly out of her window, glancing furiously towards Madame Jacob's apartment. There on the windowsill were pots and pots of luminous peach jam, glowing in the dregs of daylight.

The ordeal was over, she thought, returning delightedly to her armchair. Not to be, it seemed... The brief hiatus of silence was abruptly followed by the occasional glassy-sounding thud. A delightful spectacle of raining jam jars had commenced.

Phoebe Tatham's Biography

Linguist with a penchant for travel writing and short stories. Graduate of French and Spanish from the University of Exeter.
www.tathamphoebe.wordpress.com

221: MY PET HATE

by Johanna McDonald

I like writing. I have submitted some of my stories to competitions and enjoy writing for themed challenges. There is, however, one thing that I cannot abide and that's a writing challenge that specifies a set number of words.

An exact word count is my pet hate. "Use this many words, no more, no less." Whatever happened to freedom of choice? It's like living in a dictatorship. Nothing stifles creativity more and I absolutely refuse to participate in such restrictive challenges.

Johanna McDonald's Biography

I live in Eastleigh with my little dog. I have recently started writing children's stories with a view to getting them published in the future. I work as a nurse and part-time dog trainer.

~

222: FLUTTER

by Akindu Perera

"It's not real," Lucy whispered as she completed the paper butterfly. Her fingers pressed the edges of the butterfly, admiring how a piece of paper can be woven into a work of art. Ignoring it's inanimateness, she threw the masterpiece across the room, hoping it would come to life.

The glorious vision of the butterfly fluttering across the room drew a fragile smile on Lucy's face. Her smile was so delicate that it shattered when the paper butterfly kissed the floor.

Akindu Perera's Biography

I am Akindu Perera, a teenage student from Sri Lanka.

223: CHILDREN SHOULD KNOW BETTER THAN TO PLAY AT THE WATER'S EDGE

by Shannon J Alger

"Mum said—"

"I know." The stone jumps twice along the water.

"But Mum—"

"I said, I know." No skips this time; the stone cuts quick through the lake's surface, glinting red. I inch forward, feeling the bank slip beneath my feet, the mud oozing between my toes. I sense a gasp on my neck. Cold, desperate fingers claw at my shirt, following me down to the water's edge.

My face alone looks up at me. I throw another stone at it.

Shannon J Alger's Biography

Shannon J is a writer and avid collector of books and dragons. She can no longer see over the top shelf of her personal library and her fast reflexes were born only to stop cats adding words to her documents.

~

224: GONE

by Louise Snape

She's there. She's gone. One minute, one second, then nothingness. That's all it took. My heart burst into a million pieces, leaving my chest emptier than the void between the galaxies.

She was everything I had. And she had everything of me. In that one moment, that one second, she took all of me with her into the emptiness of death – or into the vastness of afterlife. Either way, I alone am left behind on this earth. Waiting for my turn.

Louise Snape's Biography

Louise Snape was born in the Netherlands in 1990 and moved to France in early youth. Her love for English and writing brought her to the UK to study creative writing in the hope of becoming a speculative fiction novelist.

www.louisesnape.com

225: NATURE CALLS

by Jack Dabell

Oh boy. Another beautiful day in wherever I live.

What should I do first? I could pee. Do I need to pee?

Oh well, never mind that now, gotta go and start the day.

Where is he? Does he know I'm awake? He must know by now, after I have made all this noise. I'll make more noise, that usually works.

Now I definitely need to pee.

But the door.

The door is closed.

Quick, more noise.

"Ruff."

Nope.

Too late.

Jack Dabell's Biography

My name is Jack Dabell. I'm 20 something years old and currently live in Brighton, England. I work as a primary school teacher and often dream about writing a book of short stories.

~

226: THE HAIR CUT

by B. P. Garcia

I didn't really understand why my parents cried while I got my hair cut. Hearing a *bzzzz* and a *schhhhk*, I watched in amusement as the last of the golden waterfall rolled off my forehead and cascaded into the growing mane on the floor.

That was when the weeping began – oh, the weeping. I had never seen my *dad* cry like that before.

Cackling with childish amusement, I watched my mother sputter out to the doctor, "When does his treatment begin?"

B. P. Garcia's Biography

B. P. Garcia is an aspiring author from Southern California who is currently studying English literature in college. He enjoys walking along the beach with characters he has yet to write.

227: STAND UP FALLS DOWN

by Gary McGrath

I tried to become a comedian.

But I don't know any jokes – it's a bit of a drawback.

My first thought was to walk on stage and ask the audience members to tell me a joke that I would then repeat.

Then I thought of Gary-Jokey.

I walked out nervously and said, "Knock, knock."

"Who's there?" responded the audience as one.

Not me.

I sprinted from the stage, out of the back door and down the street.

They're not laughing now.

Gary McGrath's Biography

Currently writing an autobiography entitled *The Man Without a Plan*. I enjoy being playful where possible. I believe life is for living. Fun is important. I mean nobody any harm and I come in peace. Take me to your reader.

~

228: SANCTUARY

by Carolyn Roden

Benjamin Sheerling loved to stroll around the lake as the moon rose over the ghostly pines. It felt so inviting.

The water lapped green and silver under the midnight moonlight as he gazed into it, mesmerised. Images of his past flashed through his mind. Big city, big money, meaningless luxuries and stress, lots of stress.

It was a relief when it ended abruptly that November night, he thought as he slipped back into the watery depths.

Sanctuary, sweet sanctuary at last.

Carolyn Roden's Biography

Carolyn Roden always loved writing. As a child, writing fulfilled a need to get her feelings and imagination down on paper. These days she is a grandmother, living in Dorset and enjoys singing, photography and coming back to writing again.

229: THE 'NO TIME LIKE THE PRESENT' DILEMMA

by Kwame M.A. McPherson

"Now?"
    "No time like the present."
    "Is it?"
    "It is. That's why I'm here."
    "I'm sure I said 5:00. It's only 4:50."
    "Better early than late, you always said."
    "I did?"
    "You did."
    "Must've been drunk?"
    "Very sober, while eating breakfast."
    "Oh."
    "Ready now?"
    "I've no choice."
    "You do. You don't have to come, but you said we should."
    "You driving?"
    "It's only walking distance."
    "I hate walking."
    "Remind me to never ask you about going out for ice cream again."

Kwame M.A. McPherson's Biography

I am a prolific writer/content marketer, writing mentor and speaker. My writing demonstrates my love for storytelling in various genres. An award-winner, I have authored a number of books covering poetry, novels, blogs, articles and non-fiction.

~

230: LISTEN TO ME

by Stefan Dimitrov

The window was shut but the cold air could still be felt. I didn't know what to do. I tried to tell the house owner, but he didn't answer. He was looking at his phone and ignored everything else.

I wished with all my heart that he would trip and he did. Next time he will listen to me. If he doesn't, I will wish for this to happen again. Next time he will listen to me. I am a curtain.

Stefan Dimitrov's Biography

I study English in university. I wrote this for the giggles.

231: PATIENCE AND PAGES

by Josh Leeson

Martha felt a vibration.

"Someone's coming."

Michael waited, unmoved.

"Patience."

"But it's been so long."

She went over her lines, ready to come alive. To be loved again.

Suddenly, a sound enveloped them.

"What was that?"

Breaking news, the President has launched missiles...

The vibration slowed. The rustling ceased.

"His attention's elsewhere."

Darkness closed in. They became rigid.

"It's not fair," Martha cried.

They clung on as the table rushed towards them.

THUD.

"Will we ever be read?" Martha sobbed.

"Patience."

Josh Leeson's Biography

Josh writes speculative fiction, blending the scientific with the spiritual. His degree in psychology reflects his open mind and probing character. He lives in the Midlands with his wife and two cats. His debut novel, *Booths,* arrives soon.

~

232: WE DO NOT READ ANYMORE

by Niina Olenbluu

The scroll drops. I pick it up and put it in my pocket. It has a glass lock on it – it is one of those fancy ones. It also has an old papery feel and it makes me think of the sandpaper they use in the factory.

Morgan did mention knowing another Ancient Text Code student somewhere. Now that I have this scroll, I can leave the Collected Data Facility for good.

I need to find you. As fast as possible.

Niina Olenbluu's Biography

Niina Räsänen (Olenbluu) is the narrative story writer at Rx3 Studio, an indie video game company that is making their first PC game, Peace Quarter. She has been published in a horror themed anthology in Finnish.

Twitter account: @olenbluu

~

233: NINE NINES

by Martin Strike

"Nine nines," demanded Dad.

"Aw, Dad." Jake always hated it when Dad fired these impromptu multiplication questions.

"Nine nines," Dad insisted.

"But it's 2018. We have calculators these days."

"Ah, supposing it breaks, or you lose it? Now, nine nines."

"Seventy-six?" approximated Jake, who decided against restarting the same tired argument.

"Come on," harrumphed Dad. "Think ten times nine and subtract nine."

"Ah, eighty-two," announced Jake.

Dad bit his lip. Surely a twenty-two year-old should know his times tables by now.

Martin Strike's Biography

Being 54, Martin's age is divisible by 27, 9, 6, 2, 3, 1 and 54. He finds this more confusing than 53, when he considered himself in the prime number of his life. To avoid similar angst, seek his mathematics-free stories at:

www.thenewburyshortstoryteller.wordpress.com

234: NOT ON MY WATCH

by Alexio Gomes

She was sobbing uncontrollably. The incessant shrieks and gasps for air between cries sent her tiny body into a tantrum. I couldn't stand by any longer, it was time to take action. No one could get away with this kind of injustice. I placed my hands firmly and began to push and pull. Something had to give. It did.

"Here's your candy, sweetie, the vending machine has met its match."

"Thank you, Daddy. You're the best."

"Anything for my little angel."

Alexio Gomes' Biography

Competitor on the TV Show *American Ninja Warrior*, currently studies at Hope International University in Fullerton, California, and is an aspiring future pastor.

~

235: SO SHOULD I

by T.L. Shenkin

"If the wind and the waves stand amazed, so should I.

"If mountains and valley live bountifully balanced, so should I.

"So should I.

"And trust me, I've tried.

"You know they say that we would not recognise ourselves outside of a mirror.

"Not because we lack vision but because we see fear.

"The fear that we are not actually who we are,

"That our identity is defined by our scars.

"After all, you resemble what you worship.

"So should I."

T.L. Shenkin's Biography

You can call me anything you'd like, just do not call me late for dinner because I am a relatively prompt guy. I think about freedom a lot, and try my best to live like it.

236: THIEF IN THE NIGHT

by Devin Greene

Boom. Smack.

These were the sounds I heard that woke me out of my deep sleep.

I jumped up and put on clothes and sprinted downstairs. I looked for my parents, but they weren't there.

I silently poked my head outside and hell was breaking loose. People vanishing into the sky. One after another, a bright light that was unbearable to look at was taking them into the sky.

"What is going on?" I asked myself.

Aliens? No.

Jesus is back.

Devin Greene's Biography

I attend Hope International. I'm an athlete and play basketball for my school. I'm a Bible major and hope to become a teacher or youth pastor. I'm passionate about Jesus and I love helping people get to know him.

~

237: GRIEF SHARED

by Angela P Googh

Amid her own tears, Racheal finally found her voice. "Come here, sweetie."

Margie flew into Racheal's arms sobbing. "I'm SO SORRY, Racheal. Please don't hate me?"

"Hush, girl. I could never hate you." Calming her young friend, Racheal said, "I know it hurts but your dad would want you to be healthy and alive. We are your family now. You are loved and safe. And you will be happy again, sweetie. I promise."

Margie sobbed even harder. Racheal tightened her embrace.

Angela P Googh's Biography

Angela P Googh is a computer programmer, predominantly with information database systems. She is married with two grown children, active in her church, an amateur genealogist and green except for her thumbs. Angela lives in Waterloo, Ontario, Canada.

@angelagoogh

238: A PLACE TO LIVE

by Ahmad Abu Sharkh

Sitting with the obstacle of the moment, the border office agent.

"First, you were kicked out to Syria…"

"First time was in 1948. We were told it would only be for a couple of days."

"And you went back?"

"Do you know anything about history? No, we didn't."

"…?"

"Second time was in 2011. A revolution happened. We moved to Lebanon."

"Third?"

"Here… so I had enough in my life, let me in, I've only got maybe two years to live."

Ahmad Abu Sharkh's Biography

Ahmad Abu Sharkh, a civil engineer living in Toronto, Ontario. Part-time, Ahmad writes and produces theater and short films. Ahmad is the founder of Sadesa Studios.

~

239: POSEIDON

by A. Gustafson

The sun slept.

The wine flowed, seemingly endless, but now the castle was settling, ready to sleep.

The waves beyond lapped gently against the shore and I watched them from the parapet.

A shadow in the sea was waiting for me.

I slipped from my dress. The water was cold as I dove into the icy waves.

Together, we dove, swam and laughed, safe within the water's embrace.

The sun woke, fading away the morning mist and my love as well.

A. Gustafson's Biography

A. Gustafson is a fantasy and sci-fi writer living in a messy apartment with an even messier collection of friends and memories that she wouldn't trade for the world. They are often the inspiration for any humour within her works.

www.facebook.com/agustafsonauthor

240: REINCARNATION

by Chris Tattersall

I was once so full of life. I felt healthy but, in a devastating turn, it ended too soon.

My death came quickly and, thankfully, without pain, but it saddened me that nobody cared. I grieved for my own demise with a journey through the five arduous stages of loss – denial, anger, bargaining, depression and, finally, acceptance that my life was over. Yet again.

I had to wait. Soon, I would be rewarded with a new life. Candy Crush does that.

Chris Tattersall's Biography

Chris is an NHS research and development manager living in West Wales. Writing credits include publications in nursing and academic journals, but he has a passion for flash fiction with a few competition wins.

www.facebook.com/profile.php?id=100015105305027

~

241: NO WIN

by Max Dobb

"Sorry, dear, no win." The shopkeeper tossed the lottery ticket in the bin.

Maureen left the shop smartly, still embarrassed that she had to count out her pennies just to afford a pint of milk.

*

When he was sure the shop was empty, the merchant retrieved the ticket from the waste bin, picked up the phone and dialled the number on the back of the ticket.

"Good morning, lottery reception, how may I help?"

"I would like to report a win."

Max Dobb's Biography

Max Dobb is the director of his own business and lives at home in Northamptonshire, England, with his wife and two small dogs. This is his first ever attempt at creative writing and he confesses to it being very addictive.

242: I SEE

by Oriel Dobb

Today I am sad, it is time for me to leave.

I have seen so much these past 40 years.

I have watched the cherry blossom come to life and fall like glitter each spring.

I have seen the children laughing and playing in the snow and then returning with their own children.

Despite all I have seen, there is no one to say goodbye to me.

Tears of rain fill my face as the glazing company arrive to replace me.

Oriel Dobb's Biography

Oriel Dobb is an occupational therapy graduate who lives in a quaint village in Northamptonshire, England. She is married and her passions in life include shopping, cruising, knitting, reading, and walking her stubborn white Pekingese and her very lazy spaniel.

~

243: THE BOXER

by Sarah Burrett

He got off. I got bruises and my baby.

'Fight for charity', the advert said. 'Make it happen for teenagers with cancer.'

I could have punched his lights out. Still could.

'Train for two months and have your day in the boxing ring.'

It's been hell. I cried the time my nose got flattened. I still wonder if it's straight anymore. But I went back into the ring. It will make me strong. Mum says it will make me not care.

Sarah Burrett's Biography

I'm a chicken keeper and daydreamer extraordinaire. I walk rather than take the bus and wish I spent more time writing than I do. I look for hilarious things on Facebook instead and keep trying to structure my semi-retirement from teaching.

244: WORDS

by Lisa Stone

Persistent, never-ending words spin impatiently around her busy head, waiting to be chosen. Connecting ethereally from somewhere between their worlds and hers. Dimensionally directed, she acquires their place.

For some, consistent typewriting clatter or continuous computed hum efficiently serves its master. For her, a pen quickening freely along pale blue lines offers blissful relief.

Her words compose expeditiously on pages, before being instantly forgotten. She finds words pure simplistic joy when sentenced, paragraphed chapters generate. A new story finished, complete – Amity.

Lisa Stone's Biography

Lisa Stone is an aspiring writer based in Victoria, Australia. Lisa holds a certificate in writing for magazines and has completed a StoryCraft creative writing workshop. Her passion lies in telling the stories of the otherworlds of autistic children.

~

245: KIDNAP

by Meg Gain

The crowds swept by, unseeing. Wet coats flapped in her face. Small and vulnerable, she was too young to be out alone. I was just about to take her arm and speak to her when I was roughly pushed aside.

A man, his face concealed by a black hood, grabbed the child. She squealed and struggled in his arms. A few passers-by turned to look as I pulled my umbrella from my bag and struck out. But the man escaped easily.

Meg Gain's Biography

A former librarian who has been writing since childhood, I now meet up with a group each week to hone my skills. Great fun and motivation.

246: FOILED

by Janet Lister

The polished metal stripes carry him down, disgorging him into the depths. The grey, glistening floor guides him to a platform where he joins the tight mass of humanity. He is pushed into a carriage and, standing upright, he is transported to his destination. But, on arrival, the train door refuses to open.

Officials try, but the door resists. He quickly checks his watch. Too late, the chance is missed, the bomb will not be detonated. The underground had become aware.

Janet Lister's Biography

Retired science teacher. Part of a writing group enjoying using Chris's site.

~

247: MORNING ROUTINE

by Chloe Nkomo

Water collected in her hands like a stagnant pool. She let the tap run over, sending waterfalls cascading.

With a sigh, she splashed the water over her face, rinsing the night's sleep from her eyes and sending water splashing to the floor.

The acrid smell of burning flesh soon rose into the air, whilst peels of her skin melted into the sink.

She sighed again, waiting for the sizzling to stop and for her skin to grow back.

It always did.

Chloe Nkomo's Biography

Aspiring writer, stumbling through their mid-20s, with a love for Murakami, dystopian fiction and new words.

www.chloenkomo.wordpress.com

248: BREACH OF CONTRACT

by Jade Swann

"I'm here for the firstborn," Lucinda the Lamentable hisses. Her skin gleams a garish emerald beneath the chandelier of Margaret's extravagant mansion.

"Don't lie, sister." A puff of glimmering white smoke reveals Tallulah the Terrible. "The firstborn is mine."

"No," Rosaline the Reprehensible interjects, appearing in a haze of crimson, "the child belongs to me."

Three signed contracts spill onto the expensive marble floor.

"Sounds like a family problem," Margaret murmurs, leaving the witches to bicker over her perfectly planned exploit.

Jade Swann's Biography

Jade Swann can be found writing with a cup of coffee in one hand and a Boston terrier by her side. Her work has appeared in *Microfiction Monday Magazine.*

www.jade-swann.com

~

249: SPYING

by Pat Hough

I watched as he stood, motionless on the lawn. He struck me as intent, serious. Eyes downcast, he examined the grass minutely. I could tell he was listening. To what, I was unsure. My noisy neighbours, the finches, quarrelling amongst the bushes perhaps? It was so seductive to spy like this, him so completely unaware.

Suddenly, he arched his back, pounced, and then looked around forlornly. Was it a mole he'd heard? My foxy visitor slunk off, leaving me feeling elated.

Pat Hough's Biography

Hi, my name is Pat Hough. I'm a dabbler in words, not a true 'wordsmith'. I enjoy writing and am always surprised when an initial idea turns itself into a plot with characters I become fond of.

250: GUILTY... AND THERE WILL BE CONSEQUENCES

by Ian Andrew

If he eats anything other than his restricted diet, there are consequences. These tend to be soft, brown and found in front of the cooker in the morning.

I walk into the kitchen and he is licking his lips. A stolen chocolate cake wrapper lies in front of him. A trail of crumbs crosses the table, down onto the floor in front of him.

Dog drops his guilty eyes from my disapproving gaze. And we both know... there will be consequences.

Ian Andrew's Biography

Ian Andrew lives in the Midlands with his family and his dog. And he enjoys writing challenges of all shapes and sizes.

~

251: MOVING SOUTH

by Alan Pattison

Recognising winter would take longer each year. Tony found it easy when the snow fell in November and even easier when the Christmas shopping began a bit later.

After he moved south to London, it all got complicated as it was rare to have snow, and people started talking Christmas in August.

One year, in October, he woke, had some breakfast, went out of the front door and slipped on the icy doorstep, making him relieved that he had come south.

Alan Pattison's Biography

I am a semi-retired former management consultant who enjoys researching and writing up local history.

252: GOODBYE

by Jasmine Hunt

Dear diary,

I regret it. How could I do it? So much guilt has built up inside me from the after effects. Why did I do it?

I can't live with this pain. I'm going to end it.

I shouldn't have killed that family, they didn't do anything to me. I was there to kill Jake, and Jake only, no one else. I couldn't even do that. He survived. The family died. This is my last entry.

Goodbye, I'm sorry Jake.

Jasmine Hunt's Biography

I'm 17 and I've always loved writing stories, mostly ones with pain in them. It is like a world I can escape to so I can be who I want to. I would love to be an author someday.

~

253: BAD TIMING

by Matthew Kerns

He sneezed. Some snot dribbled out but he managed to catch it with the tissue he was somehow holding. That was weird in itself.

Really though, he couldn't believe his luck. A cold, and at a time like this?

He stared down at his dead body, prone in the casket. He was floating above his own funeral and he had a dang cold.

Sure seemed stupid that spirits could get sick. What a miserable eternity this could turn out to be...

Matthew Kerns' Biography

Married with one baby. Not much else to say other than I love writing. My imagination was always a little too wild to stay in my head so I'm happy to just spurt it out onto a page.

254: THE SCENE

by Dee Tilsley

Josie's hand clutched the front of her shirt, its torn sleeve hanging limply. Why had it happened? Had Michael discovered the bag... stolen it? Should she hide it, burn it? No. She hadn't touched it, would never touch it.

She turned away, heart cold and empty.

What would her friends say? What on earth would she tell her mother?

As she closed the door, pushed the keys through the letterbox, she decided that she simply didn't care anymore. She was free.

Dee Tilsley's Biography

Mum of three, Dee, juggles a full-time job and cares for her family whilst trying to keep the little grey cells doing occasional star jumps. With a hop, skip and a stumble, she falls majestically into a quivering heap every evening.

~

255: THE DOORBELL

by Kailin Guo

I sat in my house. I was alone but I'm not a very sociable person – like many of us today – so I was happy. The house was silent, except for the occasional grunt of recognition as I flicked through Netflix. It was the start of a good day; I wouldn't move from the sofa, I wouldn't move an inch.

But then I heard a sound that ruined my day. A sound that sparked a hate so strong. It was the doorbell...

Kailin Guo's Biography

I'm a 14-year-old girl who loves to write because in words you can escape and be whoever you want. I have a younger sister who enjoys annoying me, so words are kinda my solace. I live in England.

256: HUNTING

by Brian Johnstone

The people they were hunting were masters of duplicity. They had bred for hundreds of years, each generation moving further and further towards attaining perfection in their clan.

Outsiders were only allowed to breed after having passed strict tests, involving not physical but mental and moral situations. To become a member of the family you had to show complete selfishness, cold hearted ambition and a complete lack of what is normally held as moral values.

Yes, they were the banker tribe.

Brian Johnstone's Biography

I'm a 60-something retired manual worker. I've always been a reader, never a writer. I've always been interested in how things work. My sisters still haven't forgiven me for removing the heads off their dolls to see how they work.

~

257: SYRUPY MEMORIES

by Charlie Taylor

Even on the hottest summer days it was always pleasant in the shade of the old maple tree at the farm. My brother and I spent hours under its spreading branches, engaged in all sorts of construction projects involving sticks, stones, bark and leaves, which were transformed into miniature buildings, highways and aqueducts.

I imagine the new owners have no idea that the solitary tree in the corner of their lot was once the focal point of such a bustling civilization.

Charlie Taylor's Biography

Charlie Taylor teaches English at high schools and universities. He currently lives in Taiwan with his wife and two small children.

258: THE EQUATION FOR TIME

by Rebecca Krohman

Did I just do it? Did I just figure out the mathematical equation for time?

There is an eighty two percent chance it's correct.

If it's correct, that means time travel is possible, and I just figured it out.

I need a machine now, but what do I do with the equation? It could become dangerous.

I hear something to the right and I quickly look over.

There's a man staring at me.

It's myself.

"Don't give the equation to anyone."

Rebecca Krohman's Biography

Rebecca Krohman is a 16-year-old from North Vancouver, B.C., Canada. In her free time, she likes to write stories and she hopes to have a published book in the future.

~

259: A FEW STEPS TO PARADISE

by Jeffrey H. Toney

Peering over the cliff's edge, Maui's warm breeze tickled my cheeks. Only a few steps to paradise – so the guide kept telling me, as we hiked up the rocky trail. His idiotic grin did not instil confidence. The crystal clear water 50 feet below revealed a coral reef to the left, sharp rocks to the right.

"Jump."

Paralysis spread towards my shaking left thigh. I might faint.

Yes, I fainted into the ocean's swell. She accepted me, battered, bloody, screaming, beaming.

Jeffrey H. Toney's Biography

Dr Toney has published scientific peer-reviewed articles in the news media as well as short fiction stories in *O-Dark-Thirty, Crack The Spine* and in *2 Elizabeths*. He serves as provost and vice president for academic affairs at Kean University.

260: YOU'RE VIRTUALLY HERE

by Chris McLoughlin

Inside a small gallery.
    Packed with patrons of all ages over 65.
    The attendant stares at his computer, frowning.
    Trying his best to look hard-at-work.
    (Must be important.)
    Secretly composing a symphony of syllables onto a hidden screen.
    A world, reflecting in on itself.
    An escape.
    "Excuse me? Do you know how long the exhibition runs for?"
    His lover's face melts away, leaving only an unanswered question, a stain in the air, and a silence the size of a full stop.

Chris McLoughlin's Biography

Chris McLoughlin is a writer, performance poet and workshop facilitator. Chris has received a distinction in MA Creative Writing from the University of Nottingham, been artistic director of Mouthy Poets and was a finalist for Nottingham's first young poet laureate.

~

261: THE MERMAID

by Marieta Maglas

She swims to the surface to see him.
    He is standing on the deck, the sun's lights dim.
    He is a lonely king living in a city of salt.
    She carves his figure; makes a statue of cobalt.

She pays the witch to have legs and to become a woman,
    Because she wants to marry this man.
    The ship sinks with his loss; breaks on the floor of basalt.
    She cuts her veins in the Red Sea, near her burial vault.

Marieta Maglas' Biography

Sybaritic Press and Silver Birch Press published the poems of Marieta Maglas in anthologies like *Near Kin: A Collection of Words* and *Art Inspired by Octavia Estelle Butler* and *Nancy Drew Anthology: Writing & Art Featuring Everybody's Favorite Female Sleuth.*

262: GOODBYE GRAN

by Bruce Wyness

Mum spat on the corner of her hanky, rubbed my face with it removing something that displeased her, adjusted the twisted belt of my gabardine coat then bent and softly kissed my cheek.

I stood in silence, staring at the long wooden box that my grandmother lay in. She had been a nice gran to me, told me funny stories about dragons, sang silly songs and talked about the olden days when she was young. I wondered why she was dead.

Bruce Wyness' Biography

Bruce is a wannabe writer who makes furniture from recycled timber and writes flash fiction. He lives in Auckland, New Zealand.

~

263: PORTALITY

by David Conway

He wrote his message and watched the girl catch it as it floated down from above – 'Hi'.

She waved nervously into the lens.

Beaming, he enthusiastically scribbled another note – 'Move'.

She was excited, before something caught her attention off camera. "No, stop. Wait."

Everything sent through was spontaneously combusting in the order it arrived. She helped him up as the notes in her hand caught fire.

"I tried to tell you…"

He took her hand and held her warmly. "I know."

David Conway's Biography

David Conway is a film and media lecturer who recently discovered flash fiction and it turned his world upside-down. He finished his 81 words quickly, but OCD-like redrafting saw him have a baby girl before finishing this bio.

264: DUE

by Madeleine McCabe

8 minutes.
The low, humming lights of the tube station 7.
Her hair had been red – striking auburn curls.
Not the red that spills like irrational anger as blood from porcelain skin.
6
more, as fear rises in your chest, you're,
5
face to face,
4
with your guilt, which strangles you like innocent witnesses whose voices should,
3
not
be
heard
2, now it's due
and the wind of the tunnel rushes towards you and you're at the edge and

Madeleine McCabe's Biography

I am 17 years old and currently living in Newcastle upon Tyne, in England. I am an amateur writer, but my passion for creating worlds with words has always been with me – filling up notebooks with stories ever since I was 6.

~

265: MOONLIGHT PATH

by Sarah Littleton

I walked alone, waiting for a noise, any noise that would show me some sort of sign that I was, indeed, still breathing. I waited, my heart nearly thudding out of my chest, only accompanied by the sound of my frantic footsteps.

The moon glistened, casting an eerie glow over the large overhanging branches that, for some reason, terrified me and gave me a sensation that I had never experienced before. I felt a hand on my shoulder so I ran.

Sarah Littleton's Biography

I am an aspiring author from the UK and found a passion in writing. I am glad to have found an opportunity to experience writing in this way and hope that I can find others like it in the future.

266: INDIGNANT CHEESE

by Ash Gray

Joan looked like Swiss cheese as the caterpillar chewed a hole through her palm. She screamed softly in horror to see the many holes gaping in her body.

"Hey," Joan cried indignantly.

The caterpillar looked up, fuzzy face scowling. "What?"

"Stop eating me," Joan demanded at once. Realising the caterpillar might decide to disappear inside her, she gave a wincing smile and shrugged as she said, "Please?"

The caterpillar thought a moment. Eventually, it said, "Yeah, alright."

"Thank you," Joan sighed.

Ash Gray's Biography

Ash Gray is a dragon with minuscule spectacles perched on her nose, living in a dank cave in an alternate universe. She types her stories with gigantic claws on a small typewriter before sending them into your dimension for enjoyment.

www.indiepurpledragonbrain.blogspot.com

~

267: A LONG ROAD

by Cristina Bresser

In the past, I do not recognise myself – how could I?

I search the solitude of the winter during the summer, the quietude of the autumn through the spring.

I get lost when I try to recollect the past; so many crossroads.

At present, emptiness, upside down, inside out.

In the future, I shiver, cold.

Fumes engulf me in the streets wherever I go.

Sneezing, pollen spirals.

Walking the streets is to create allergies.

Repatriating the soul is a long road.

Cristina Bresser's Biography

Brazilian, graduated in graphic design. Two published books: *Torre de Papel*, 2015 – short stories. *Quase tudo é risível*, 2016 – novel. Studied creative writing at University of Edinburgh, 2016. Pieces published in English by American, British, Greek, Indian literary magazines.

268: LANGUAGE MISHAP

by Aleah Bingham

"Happy Birthday."

"Danke, thank you."

"I bought you a gift."

"Gift? No."

"What?"

"I don't want gift. Throw it away."

"But why not? It's for your birthday."

"Gifts are bad. Keep away. Gifts kill."

"Kill? I'm not sure you understand. I bought you a gift for your birthday. It's an American custom."

"You crazy Americans. You need to stay away."

"Do you not know what it is? Here, I'll open it."

"No, don't open."

"See, it's a book?"

"Book? Not poison?"

Aleah Bingham's Biography

Aleah Bingham is a freshman in high school who enjoys spending time with her friends and family. She loves creating art and is interested in a future career dedicated to engineering.

~

269: SECOND BEDROOM

by Gillian M Seed

They painted the room sunflower yellow. Back when they still hoped, she would stand inside and imagine what the future would be like. Crayon marks on the paintwork, juice spilled on the carpet. He caught her in there once and laughed, but it was indulgent laughter. Sharing her dreams.

He paints the room magnolia. Neutral, sensible magnolia. A blank canvas, according to those interminable property programmes they watch instead of talking.

They tell themselves having a spare room will be useful.

Gillian M Seed's Biography

I live in the north-east with my husband, two cats, and more story ideas than I can get out of my head. I've written for several local literary festivals, mostly short stories and poems.

270: NOW YOU HAVE GONE

by Glynis Ann Downey

What do we do now you have gone?
Always there for the short and long.
Difficult at times but with a kind heart,
we never believed that you would ever depart.
You could always solve a problem or two,
now it's time for us to become you.
Now you have gone and we have said goodbye,
we remember how you taught us to fly.
Always in our hearts and minds,
learning to heal will all come in time.
Farewell and goodbye.

Glynis Ann Downey's Biography

Glynis is a native of Berkshire and London. She now lives in Galway in the west of Ireland. Glynis believes that writing is cathartic and helps to heal, so she wrote this poem about her dad passing away last year.

~

271: GREY ON GREY

by Hannah Brown

He opened his eyes and stared up at an ashen sky. No, not sky. A ceiling. There was a stain in one corner that looked a bit like water damage.

Who was he? What was he doing here, in this tiny room? He had to get out. He tried the door, but it was locked and so was the window. Footsteps. He banged on the door and screamed, but no one came.

Outside his cell, the prison guards cried with laughter.

Hannah Brown's Biography

Hannah Brown recently graduated from King's College London with first class honours in English language and literature. She now writes short stories about criminals, aliens and anthropomorphic tortoises.

272: GRACE

by Jennifer Riddalls

"Grace. Fourth floor, this side." Her fluttering hand gestures to her window.

I squint up at the pebble dashed, light blocking, twelve floor monstrosity. My place is pulling the value of hers up, hers is dragging mine down. She owes me.

"Trish."

We smile, we shake. When I don't move she adds, "Wanna come up for a cuppa?" She's turning away, expecting a no.

"Yes, please."

"Excuse the mess," she says, as we enter.

No suspicions, just like the last lot.

Jennifer Riddalls' Biography

Jennifer Riddalls. Writer, reader, mother. Winging it. Always writing, always reading. Flash fiction competition winner, short story writer, novel abandoner. Member of Rushmoor Writers.

Twitter: @jriddalls

~

273: GUSTAVO'S LAST NIGHT AT THE WRITING GROUP

by William Telford

At Gustavo's last night at writing group, Lucinda read a story about a dystopian world run by psychiatric owls. She said afterwards, "I'm off the olanzapine."

Isabella-Valentina-Carina read flash fiction about a woman who murdered her husband with a ski pole. She said she and little Marina-Melody would holiday alone this year.

Yannick followed his poem about the lonesomeness of a bobcat with, "The roof of my bedsit leaks."

And Gustavo read a story about some people at a writing group.

William Telford's Biography

William Telford is a journalist and writer with an MA in creative writing from the University of Plymouth. His fiction has appeared in *Short Fiction, Ink, Spelk, Epizootics, Anthologia, The Western Morning News* and the *Bristol Short Story Prize Anthology*.

@WTelfordHerald

274: HOPE

by Jessica Everitt

She had been travelling for days, sleeping under bushes and in ditches; anywhere dry, warm and away from prying eyes.

Mile blended into mile and hour bled into hour as she plodded along, one muddy, cracked sneaker in front of the other.

She had lived here once. Just over that hill and around the bend.

It had been home. She had not merely been alive – she had lived.

She could faintly remember laughter. Real laughter. She needed that, one last time.

Jessica Everitt's Biography

Jessica Everitt is a fiction writer, a freelance writer and a content marketer. She lives in Nova Scotia, Canada, with her beautiful daughter and her faithful mutt. When not reading or writing, Jessica loves hiking through the wilderness.

~

275: JOAN

by Irene Banfield

"Where? Where is it?" the old woman shouts angrily. "Joan, you've moved it again."

"What are you looking for," Joan answers tenderly.

"You shouldn't touch my things, Joan. Why can't you leave them alone?"

"I haven't moved anything, whatever IT is."

The old woman swears and throws her tea.

"Don't get upset, I'll look. I'm trying my best."

"Help me find them, help me look, Joan." The old woman sobs, "Help me."

"Don't cry, please don't cry, Mum," says Trina tearfully.

Irene Banfield's Biography

Irene Banfield is a mother of three, grandmother of seven and great grandmother of one. She lives in Surrey and enjoys reading, writing and having fun with the family. She's also loves trips to London, to the theatre and other events.

276: BOTTLE

by Jonathan Hastings

I met her the first time on a bench cradling a small bottle. She handed it to me, cocking her head a little. Inside was a small letter.

She said she was too afraid to open it. It had been five years since she found it on the beach and she didn't want to ruin the mystery.

I said I would. She looked too tired to fight. But the bottle looked all nice and all. I couldn't even pop the cap.

Jonathan Hastings' Biography

Currently a student at Newcastle University studying for an MA in Creative Writing. A novel I was working on allowed me the opportunity to visit Penguin's #WriteNow incentive. I also produce and write music in my spare time.

www.linkedin.com/in/jonathan-hastings-76643513b/

~

277: THE MOONLIGHT STAGE

by Stephanie Potts

A sanguinary hand disguised by a mask of worn leather.
A knife of steel, dimly glowing in the muted light.
A freshly painted image in the mind.
Of unaccountable crimson.
An accomplice above, creating an auditorium.
And a stage.
Prey emerging from the wings, draped in costume, preparing their soliloquy.
But don't they know? Haven't they heard?
This play is a tragedy.
Tragedies have devastating endings.
The orchestra hums, bloodless hands caressing delicate strings and keys.
And so it ~~begins~~ ends.

Stephanie Potts' Biography

I am a 17-year-old sixth form student from Newcastle upon Tyne, studying English literature, English language and history at A Level.

278: DEATH MEETS US ALL

by Christina Burton

I wasn't expecting to meet death when I woke up that day. At work, I got the call. We all knew it was looming, but it was still a shock to hear the words, "You better come quickly, she hasn't got long."

I dropped everything and rushed over. I didn't get there in time to say goodbye. The room was silent but distress tangible, tears visible. I looked over at you. You lay there unmoving, still. There you were, but gone.

Christina Burton's Biography

Hello, my name is Christina (Tina to most), always had an interest in writing and thought the 81 Words challenge would be a great starting point. This short story is inspired by the passing of my wonderful nan, Christina O'Toole.

~

279: A MODERN DAY FAIRY TALE

by Jessica Richard

The prince cowered in the corner as the fire blazed around them in the courtyard.

The princess stood at the ready, two hands wrapped around her gleaming greatsword.

The dragon leered at the two before crawling towards them. The princess swung out and severed the dragon's head in one clean slash.

"My princess," the prince yelled, running to her.

The princess swung out once more. Another head rolled.

"I don't need no man," she said, and walked off into the sunset.

Jessica Richard's Biography

Jessica Richard is from the east coast of Canada. She is currently a writer and an English teacher living in Seoul, South Korea.

280: BAKE UNTIL GOLDEN-BROWN

by Tiarnán Murphy

"Bread," cried the dragon, "get your bread here."

The elves and dwarves all wandered through the marketplace, avoiding making eye contact with him. Nobody wanted to buy bread from a dragon. It must be filthy. After all, they walked on those hands. And how could they not burn it, with that awful fiery breath of theirs?

Sighing, the dragon went into the back, sterilised his hands with scorching fire and, ever so gently, heated the oven to bake perfect, golden-brown bread.

Tiarnán Murphy's Biography

Tiarnán Murphy is an aspiring fantasy novelist who occasionally likes to stretch his wings by writing flash and short fiction.

~

281: THIRTEEN

by Lorraine Smith

Kathy died in March '85. Her slight frame was broken and twisted. Her lifeblood oozed over tarmac, creeping towards me.

Distant voices urged, "Hold her hand, ambulance on its way." An unlucky date. Wednesday's child is full of woe.

A car slowed down, the driver staring, radio blaring.

Clouds across the moon.

The car sped through the darkened street, a rendezvous to make. Bushwackers and MIGs smash Kenilworth Road while Howard Jones left the scene yelling, "Things can only get better."

Lorraine Smith's Biography

I've loved to write since I was in my teens (many years ago) and am currently halfway through a writing degree.

www.facebook.com/annlorraine.nelson

282: WELSH MYSTERY

by Lindy Gibbon

"Whose coat is that jacket?"
"Our Huw's."
"Where's he to then?"
"I dunno."
"Never."
"When did he go then, bach?"
"Yesterday, it was."
"Yesterday? Without his coat?"
"Well, he had his rugby shirt on him."
"Did he?"
"Yes."
"Duw, duw. Out without his coat in this weather."
"Since yesterday you said, Gwyn?"
"Yes, about 11 I think."
"Morning or evening?"
"What?"
"11 in the morning or evening?"
"Morning."
"Going to the rugby I expect."
"Wales lost."
"Well, that explains it then."

Lindy Gibbon's Biography

Hi, I am fast approaching my 60th year this time round on our beautiful planet. I now live in rural Somerset and fill my days with creative pursuits and walking with my lifelong companion. It is a good life.

~

283: THE END

by John Mark Miller

From my first breath, I've dreamed of writing. My parents devoured books and, as I grew up, I knew what I would offer the world.

I would write.

Now, it's here. The long days and sleepless nights, the effort, tears and *pain* – all sit before me, wrapped in a neat leather-bound volume. With trembling fingers, I hold it close. I trace the letters of my name, smell the wonderful pages.

And weep bitterly.

My life, it seems, has reached its conclusion.

John Mark Miller's Biography

John Mark Miller has always adored telling stories. He has been published in *Christianity Today* and *Devo'-Zine*, and has won first place in various fiction contests. John Mark currently serves as a pastor and professor in Tularosa, New Mexico.

www.theartisticchristian.wordpress.com

~

284: THOSE SPECIAL MOMENTS IN LIFE

by Vesper Wunderlin

Cuddling on a park bench. Kids running around the playground. Just got out of church. Paid the rent three hours ago. A new job was found after months of searching. Can start saving for kids' college. Celebratory vacation to Disneyland planned. Sun is shining. Birds are singing. All that.

Did I fall into a Norman Rockwell painting? Yanno, it was one of those moments that make you say, "I wish this moment would never end."

So I did. It came true.

Vesper Wunderlin's Biography

Vesper Wunderlin has been writing stories of horror, fantasy and sci-fi ever since she was eight years old. She has recently completed her BA in creative writing at Pacific Lutheran University and currently resides in Lakewood, Washington.

285: AN ACCIDENT OF BIRTH

by Bridget Blankley

I was born, accidentally, in Nottingham. Mum's never let me forget it.

She thought I'd be born in San Paolo, like my brother, but she got her dates wrong and she blames me. I'm not sure why.

She stayed here for months, I'm not sure why. Something about passports, inoculations or insurance, I think. She wasn't specific. But it was my fault she stayed here, my fault that Dad left. Maria Costas was innocent. So was Dad. It's entirely my fault.

Bridget Blankley's Biography

I'm an engineer, grandmother and prize-winning author. My first novel, *The Ghosts and Jamal,* is about a teenager's journey to find his family's killers. It is published by HopeRoad. I have just started working on my second book, *Nesma Means Breath of Air*.

Twitter handle: @bridgetblankley

~

286: THE MAGICIAN

by Robert Alan Ryder

Presto was a young and inexperienced magician. His peers would encourage him to no end.

"Practise, Presto, there'll be no bounds in the success you attain. Perfection never comes easy," his father told him, again and again.

His grandfather, he was a curious sort. "Perfection, boy, is not as important as patience and skill."

"Wisdom," his grandfather would tell him, "it's key to many a success."

His grandfather, he should know magic, for he was Houdini, of the best ever known.

Robert Alan Ryder's Biography

I am an undergraduate college student from ITT Technical Institute. I was a semi-finalist last year during the fourth quarter of L. Ron Hubbard's Writers of the Future Contest for my short novel titled *Obelisk: Pandemonium of the Dead*.

287: AS SEEN BY A MOTH

by Alicia McGrath

Iridescence. Sparkling. A magnet for the wind. A single ancient oak tree, weathered by time, living through the wars, peace, joyfulness and sorrows of the people that throng beneath it every day. More than any man, woman or child will see in a lifetime, or ever will see.

Thousands of leaves on this tree. An endless attraction between wind and leaf. Not leaves but leaf. Swaying in the gentle breeze, that single oil-stained leaf. The only movement on a still horizon.

Alicia McGrath's Biography

I've always been passionate about writing. I wrote down my first story when I was six. It was about a rope... Yep. I like to think I've grown as a writer since then. I give any genre a go.

~

288: COLD TURKEY

by Ray Sarlin

"You've taken antidepressants for years, your wife kicked you out, and you want to drop them?" She said the doctor things. I agreed to drop 75mg.

Later.

"How's 150mg?"

"Err, I've stopped."

"What?"

"I dropped 75mg and nothing happened. Then another 75mg. Still nothing."

"OK."

"So I stopped that, too. I took 75mg once for a bad headache. Did that twice. Next time I took Panadol."

"What about depression?"

"It's gone. Without her constant brow-beating, I've nothing to be depressed about."

Ray Sarlin's Biography

Former soldier, engineer and manager with work experience in 27 countries, Ray is currently pursuing a PhD in Bible studies and teaching at university part time.

289: KITTY-CAT'S ADVENTURE

by Charlie Turner

"Meow, meow, meow," the furry-baby cried.

She called out for food. She stood up on her hind legs, hoping her owner would notice. He rudely ignored her and made a funny yawn sound before rolling over.

Kitty-Cat jumped up onto the table. Then onto the shelf. She tiptoed towards the big bag of cat food.

A paw pushed against the bag, trying to get the food...

Suddenly the bag fell. Food all over the floor.

Kitty-Cat got food. Owner woke up.

Charlie Turner's Biography

Aspiring teenage writer. Currently under the name Charlie Turner planning to change to Bliss Winters when I turn 16. I run a blog called *Winters Writes* on WordPress and am currently working on bettering my writing ability.

~

290: THE ARROW

by Paul Mastaglio

Twang. The arrow left the bow, spiralling upwards, searching for its destination. Where was it going? Was it flying true?

It could see green grass spreading out below as it continued on its way. Wouldn't be long now.

Suddenly, there in front was exactly what it was looking for. A pair of eyes stared back, then, at the last moment, one of them seemed to wink as the deer swerved to one side, leaving the arrow to plough into the ground.

Paul Mastaglio's Biography

Lives with wife Yvonne and Toby the cat in North Tyneside. Retired bank clerk, now into archery.

291: DYING FOR A GOOD MEAL

by Lynne Chitty

With disgust on his face and fury in his eyes, he stared at the food on the plate in front of him.

She'd have to go.

Could no one in this God forsaken country cook?

He called her in and strangled her.

He would bury her along with the rest, in his favourite place, and begin the tedious business of writing an advert for the paper again.

'Cook/Housekeeper wanted, to live in.'

He smiled.

Maybe it would be sixth time lucky.

Lynne Chitty's Biography

I live in Devon and enjoy writing challenges, love animals and support Spurs. I'm self-publishing my first novella in July and am on Facebook.

~

292: BLOOD GONE

by Dimiana Wassef

The Venetian sunset calls upon the undead. The angel's song leaves immortals covering their ears, revealing them in their heavenly light. The living cannot hear.

"This music is too sweet for them," I say, swaying. "We're safe."

His fangs dangle behind his smile. He pulls me in closer.

"Why are you covering them?" I ask.

Once chosen, there is no escape. Every naïve death replicates the next.

"A loud song is all, darling... Now, shall we go and grab a bite?"

Dimiana Wassef's Biography

I am a senior at Arizona State University pursuing a BA in English literature. Alongside my studies, I am currently working on a series of science fiction dystopian novels. I will be attending Durham University for graduate school in the fall.

293: DARKNESS BECKONS

by Aaron McDermott

What is this place? Where am I? Everything's dark. Am I dead? Is this the afterlife? Is this Hell?

The last thing I remember I was in the kitchen, boiling some potatoes and peeling some carrots. I was trying to find the gravy granules in the top cupboard, then I fell, hard. I remember crawling along the floor. My eyes were blurred; the concussion was affecting me. Then did I die?

Ah, I've locked myself in the pantry again, haven't I…?

Aaron McDermott's Biography

A 28-year-old man who loves to write, from Staffordshire. I found writing recently and am using wonderful opportunities like this to spread my wings and taste the literary rainbow.

www.facebook.com/aaron.mcdermott.520

~

294: LOST

by Justyce Solomon

"Justyce, where is it?" my mum asked me.

"I have no idea. I had switched before we went to the beach," I replied.

I began to retrace my steps in the car and the resort. I was thinking to myself that I left it on the restaurant table. My heart dropped. I looked down at my ring and cried.

"Why are you so irresponsible?" I asked myself. I just sat there thinking to myself, *How am I gonna get another necklace?*

Justyce Solomon's Biography

My name is Justyce Solomon. I am a junior at Lawrence North High School.

295: LIFE

by Erin Hardman

...wokka wokka wokka...

Mrs Pac Man is searching for the cherries. The cherries are so delicious. She must be careful to avoid the ghosts. Her belly is filling with white circles, but all she wants is the cherries.

...wokka wokka wokka...

A ghost appears. Mrs Pac Man whips around to avoid the ghost. She finds a big circle which makes her invincible to the ghosts. Her life is saved.

When searching for something we want, we instead find something we need.

Erin Hardman's Biography

I'm Erin, I'm currently a 17-year-old senior at Lawrence North High School. I'm from Indianapolis, IN. I play percussion and the saxophone and I am planning on majoring in music education when I go to college.

~

296: THE ABYSS

by Jordan Bahnub

I tripped and fell again. Yes, that's right, again. Don't get me wrong, the first time was a coincidental accident, but I thought I saw something in the abyss, so I was curious.

Then I fell repeatedly and I swore that what I'd seen was indeed different than the first time I had plummeted.

So now I was falling, on purpose, into the abyss, wishing to see something besides the bland routine of everyday life, something that wouldn't be found here.

Jordan Bahnub's Biography

I am Jordan Bahnub, a new author seeking that 'first break' moment to start my career. Though I am only 13 years old, I do believe that everyone can make a difference, no matter their age.

297: HERE COMES THE SUN

by David Guilfoyle

Blinding. Once every so often. The sun at the end of our road. Sometimes it's all you can see.

The street disappears, claimed by the dazzling horizon. The cars, the houses and the strange van outside the care home. The world lost momentarily, suspended in a powerful flood of brilliant yellow until the sun slowly moves.

Normality returns. Then the local paper puts another name in the obituary column. Vanished. Gone. Taken in the winter sunshine. And we never remember anything.

David Guilfoyle's Biography

David Guilfoyle, full-time retail manager, lapsed marathon runner, failed five-a-side footballer, currently trying to write stuff as a means of coping with a long term injury, and because it might be fun.

~

298: MISSED OPPORTUNITY

by David Batteiger

The sun is high and hot. Through tightly squinted eyes, I stare down the dusty road at my competition. A biting wind whips past, stinging the exposed skin of anyone out. And they are all out to watch this show down.

I can feel the tips of my fingers brushing across the walnut handles, twitching to unleash fury and the absolute justice of lead.

I smile. I know I'm faster. I draw. He's finished.

CLICK.

Dammit, I knew I forgot something.

David Batteiger's Biography

I never forget a name, but I'm not very good with faces. Or maybe it's the other way around? I can't remember. And my wife is never frustrated by my absentmindedness or laser sharp attention span... Now, where was I?

299: THE BETRAYAL

by Libby Batteiger

I can feel the intense pain spreading. Such agony forces me to yell out in pain. Why does this always happen to me?

I fall backward and lay on the floor, taking in the stinging torture. I can feel tears in my eyes. Why did it do this? I trusted it and this is how it repays me. How could I be so blind?

I slowly stand up and stare at it. I stubbed my toe on that stupid table again.

Libby Batteiger's Biography

My name is Libby Batteiger and I am 12 years old. I really like to draw and other forms of art. I also like to participate in theatre so I can be very dramatic.

~

300: THE SOUND OF SILENCE

by Jackie Batteiger

She sits, alone, just enjoying the peace and quiet. With closed eyes, she lets her breath flow in and out. She just enjoys the silence. Restorative silence. She realises that old song is true: 'You don't know what you got till it's gone.'

Gently, nodding her head, a power ballad from the '90s fills her mind. She dares not sing out loud and break the silence.

"Mummy, where are you?"

And with a deep sigh, she stands and flushes the toilet.

Jackie Batteiger's Biography

By day, I am an elementary music teacher who hates the recorder. My evenings and weekends are spent raising three children, two beautiful girls and a husband. There is never silence.

301: VAMPIRES ANONYMOUS

by Daniel McClaskey

Everyone is staring holes into my pigmentless skin, so I should probably say something. I've been dreading this week forever.

Shakily, I begin, "Hi, my name's Ste... *cough* ...Abigor, and I've been fanged since 1884."

In unison, "Welcome, Abigor," drones from the room.

I look around and a lady at the back of the room catches my eye. She has those ambiguous green-brown eyes that I've definitely seen somewhere before. Her scent reminds me of a time before the bi...

"Mum?"

Daniel McClaskey's Biography

Daniel McClaskey is a 24-year-old writer from Columbus, Ohio. He loves to attend punk rock shows and is partial to black T-shirts.

Twitter: @DanMcClaskey

~

302: A TOY CAR

by Saras Ojha

A five year old saw toy cars on a street market stall. He started pleading for a toy car, but his mum refused to purchase one.

"A toy car is useless, you can't sit on it. Our car is better than a toy car."

He grabbed a toy car, sat on it and it broke.

"See, you can't sit on it."

Memories flashed back when he was standing before a huge crowd, waiting for the launch of a car he'd designed.

Saras Ojha's Biography

I was born in Allahabad, India. Currently, I am 32 years old and work with Polyglot IT Solutions Pvt. Ltd. as a technical writer. I have an MA in bio-medical engineering. I have an interest in writing and sports.

www.linkedin.com/in/saras-ojha-916562138/

303: FROM BEHIND THE CURTAINS

by Kimberly Owen

He risked another look from behind his stained curtains. His garden crawled with them, making him itch. They were standing on his flowers. Damn them.

All his lights were off – not that it stopped them. It never did. They always came back.

A cluster passed in front of his window, screeching. Wincing, he stepped back into the shadows. If they saw him, they'd never go away.

Their knocking scared him, even though he expected it.

"I hate blasted trick or treaters."

Kimberly Owen's Biography

My name is Kimberly Owen and I'm 35. I'm from Wales in the UK. I have a 7-year-old child. He isn't mine or anything, he just follows me around. I've been writing short stories for about 6 months.

~

304: BURN

by Chris Pritchard

The light was hot yet still so delightful. I couldn't resist its lure. It drew me in no matter how hard I tried to resist its sweet temptation.

Every time I touched it my feet were scorched, yet still I could not stay away. I knew that this was pointless but my brain wouldn't let me leave.

Suddenly, the light was gone and I was in darkness again. I could now rest my wings. It's a hard life being a moth.

Chris Pritchard's Biography

I have an easy life compared to some people but a difficult life compared to others. Still, I'm enjoying it so far.

NOTE: *Stories 305 to 321 have been written by children and teachers from Northside Primary School in Cumbria, UK. I'd like to say a big thank you to the school and all the children for submitting such imaginative stories to the 81 Words challenge.*

~

305: COFFEE SPILT – OR – ME AND THE TEACHER

by Grant O'Townson

What has happened to me? Where am I? Mankind is disgraceful… My shredded, smooth paper is damp and ruined.

Previously, I was in the best condition – the greatest of the great (brand new). I was the teacher's favourite book. Nourish me with the warmest, smoothest, most luscious ink and I'll create fantastic, indescribable adventures; you will never forget these memories.

However, hurt me like the teacher did (covering me in coffee and discarding me in the bin) and I am worthless.

Grant O'Townson's Biography

I'm a teacher. I'm 32 years old and I live in Cumbria in North West England. I like watching sport, going for runs and going on holidays. My favourite author is Bill Bryson – I really love his travel books.

~

306: WHO COULD I BE?

by Byron Coulson

Wow, he's really outstanding at this. How can he do it? He has most certainly won me this time. Nobody can stop him from taking me home.

Oh no, someone is catching up to him. No, please don't. It's astonishing. I don't want the meanest and worst player out there to take me home; I want the greatest to take me home.

Yes, he's finally triumphed; he's taking me home. He's going to put me in the trophy case he has.

Byron Coulson's Biography

My name is Byron. I am 11 years old. I go to Northside Primary School. I enjoy things like rugby and football. And I like spending quality time with my family. I like football books about famous, popular football players.

307: ME AND MY OWNER

by Shauna Elizabeth Murray

Why did you do such thing? We were so happy, I thought you loved me. We were so close. I thought we would be together forever. You let me down.

I guess sometimes we have to be let down. No one will ever love me again (crying). At least I was loved for a little while. Is it because I'm the ugliest thing in the world?

I'll never forget you or forgive you, my nicest, friendliest, loving owner. I miss you.

Shauna Elizabeth Murray's Biography

My name is Shauna Elizabeth Murray. I am 9 years old and I'm a girl. I go to Northside Primary School (Cumbria). I like stuff like dancing, singing, writing and coming to school. I have two brothers and three sisters.

~

308: MAX AND THE BOOM BOX

by Levi Earl

Yesterday, I was sitting happily with Max, crooning, and his parents wanted to hear me sing too, so Max took me to his mother's room and I sang for his parents.

Then, later that day, Max turned me off so that I could have a sleep to get my energy back. Then I became the greatest and loudest boom box to ever exist.

Now everyone is saying that they're going deaf. It made me feel low-spirited, because they are getting deafened.

Levi Earl's Biography

I'm a go-kart driver. I'm 10 years old and I live in Cumbria. I like watching Formula 1, going on bike rides and playing on my Xbox. I like reading Jeff Kinney's books because they are really, really funny.

309: ME AND THE SMART ROBOT

by Mckenzie Tompson

I found a robot, so I took it. When I got to my house, two days later, I learned nearly everything from it. I felt like I should be the top of my class. I wish...

All the robot was doing was learning with me and playing with me. That really was a lot of fun.

As I am being clear, I have had the best fun ever over the last few days. Me and the robot became really good friends.

Mckenzie Tompson's Biography

I'm a gamer. I'm 9 and I live in Cumbria and I eat healthy food, drink juice and water and I get spoiled by my parents. I play on Fortnite (the best game ever). I like reading *The Wimpy Kid*.

~

310: THE BULLDOG AND THE POODLE

by Keith Pearson-Sandelands

I'm called Scratch. I'm a bulldog. I've always wanted a dog friend – in human language, a girlfriend.

I've never known what it's like to have a girlfriend. It must be wonderful. We could have pillow fights and romantic dates, if you know what I mean.

Ladies, if you want me, my phone number is 225678921.

But enough messing around. It was the big day. I'm not going to be lonely anymore. I went to meet her, and she was a poodle.

Keith Pearson-Sandelands' Biography

My name is Keith, I'm 9 years old. My hobby is playing games and playing with and walking my dog. I live in Cumbria – Workington. My favourite author is Roald Dahl – he makes me laugh and makes me smile.

311: THAT ONE WORKER

by Madison Pickering

Finally, I'm done. I'm the greatest and best. I'm covered in sparkly white casing stones and as big as a gigantic sky scraper. Who else wouldn't want to be like that?

Every day, for years, I got one tiny stone put on me (it took *so* long.) But there was a worker who ruined it. He knocked the full top of me down. That took months, and that is why I am so, so happy I'm finished.

And that's my story.

Madison Pickering's Biography

My name is Madison. I'm 10 years old. My hobby is horse riding. I live in Cumbria. My favourite book is *Animal Rescue and the Hubble Bubble Collection* because it makes me laugh and they have really creative, good drawings.

~

312: WHY ME AGAIN?

by Kelsey Juean Irving

What? Again? Racking my alarm, they are a lot of bullies – me always getting hurt, put new skin on me, and open my mouth all the time. They are really tight, so they are bullies.

Wait... don't say they are shutting me down for two full weeks. That's just not necessary. It *is* freezing, but I will be open in one more hour.

Look, I am open, come in kids. The jolly, kind, sweet school is open now. Come and learn.

Kelsey Juean Irving's Biography

My name is Kelsey Irving. I go to Northside Primary School which is in Cumbria. I am 10 years old. I go to Workington Amateur Dramatics Society. I love reading scripts.

313: MY AMAZING FRIEND BILL

by Darci-Leigh Robinson-Askew

My outstanding friend has an amazing name: Bill.

Every sunny and hot day, we go for long strolls in the park. He is the nicest friend I have ever had. The greatest of the great; the loveliest of the lovely.

One day, me and my great friend went for an amazingly long jaunt. Suddenly, I fell. My smooth, flat tyres were broken. Bill was hurt to. It was like my childhood all over again (it was hurting me badly). STOP IT.

Darci-Leigh Robinson-Askew's Biography

I live in Workington. I am in Year 6 and love reading, singing, dancing and gymnastics. My favourite teacher is Mr O'Townson. I have 1 sister and 4 brothers. I LOVE Harry Potter and Dork Diaries and Roald Dahl.

~

314: THE PEN AND THE HOUSE OF TERROR

by Harley Logan Thompson

Once, there was a glamorous pen who lived in a tidy pot. He was sick of getting his dreadful ink out of his body (his lid).

He missed his precious friends; they had all died. He got put into the house of terror and for him it was hideous.

Heartbroken, hurt, wistful and glum – he didn't want to die all alone. In the house was a big black bag. He wanted to say, "Goodbye, cruel world," but he couldn't speak now.

Harley Logan Thompson's Biography

My name is Harley Thompson. I'm 10 years old. I like playing football, playing with my baby sister, art and gaming. My favourite author is Roald Dahl; he writes funny stories and he makes my life even better than it already is.

315: FASHION LIFE

by Paige Murray

Why am I in this unprepossessing, dreadful yet puffy toy box? I should be on the red-carpet, in the spotlight. Can it be the light to fashion Heaven? I don't need it, by the way, but still...

Ugh, it's that sinful beast. I don't want to see you. No, not now – my nicest dress. Don't change; it's so special to me. That dress is old, rotten and stinky. I need my clothes back. I'm the most alluring doll in the box.

Paige Murray's Biography

My name is Paige Murray and I'm 10 years old. I love swimming. I like spending time with my family and doing art. My favourite book is *Black Beauty* because I like horses and it inspires me to be a creative person.

~

316: SPRING IS NEAR

by Josh Joseph Dixon

Spring is near; I can't move, I'm stuck. Forlorn, I'm leaving. Stop, spring, stop.

It has been the best year so far, I don't want to leave. I met the perfect person. Why is everyone dynamiting everyone's hearts? Stop, please stop.

I want to stop, I'm crying. I like snow and I don't want snow to go. No sun, don't want the sunlight ever. I need more time to improve my snow sphere, because I was just a pile of snow.

Josh Joseph Dixon's Biography

I'm Josh. I'm 10 years old and I live with 3 people in my family: my sister, my mum and my dad. My hobbies are playing games, Lego and Pokémon. My favourite author is Roald Dahl. My favourite book is *The Witches*.

317: ME AND MY LONELY LIFE

by Layla Calarco

Hi. I am a frog (who is nice). I live on my own in Frog Land. I have a very unusual addiction for looking for a friend.

Wait a second, there is a beautiful frog over there. I should actually call her a lady. She is coming over. I think this will be the start of a friendship. I am very timid.

Hi. Please can I stay with you, please? Yes, we are having the best life ever. Yay. Bye bye.

Layla Calarco's Biography

I am Layla and I am 9 years old. My hobbies are gymnastics and playing on Musically. I live with my mum, dad and sister. My favourite author is Anthony Brown. My favourite book is *Jake Paul Fact Book*.

~

318: ABANDONED

by Finlay Thomas Tweedie

Once, I was an intelligent, high-tech computer. I had four main parts: the monitor (my body), the PC (my flesh, bones, heart and brain), the keyboard (my arms and legs) and the mouse.

My owner used me for years on end; I was the best computer (in his opinion). Until, he had another companion... He deleted my most predominant files. Where was I? I was no more.

I have one message. "Mankind is the worst and most degrading species on Earth."

Finlay Thomas Tweedie's Biography

My name is Finlay, I'm 9 years old. I like to play Fortnite, Pokémon, Minecraft and Super Mario Odyssey. I like to read Alex Rider books because they're exciting to read. My friends are funny and they like games too.

319: WHO AM I?

by Keian Murray

I was the shiniest in the house, until I got thrown into the basement with some other stuff. They had a shinier thing and I was on the largest shelf where there was lots of dusty stuff.

   The next day, and nearly every day, stuff was getting thrown into the basement. Then the humans came, put us in a bag and took us outside. They put us in a bin, until the bin men came, but I managed to get away.

Keian Murray's Biography

My name is Keian, I like to play football with my friends and I go on Fortnite and Paladins. My favourite subjects are maths and art and I like to play on my PS4 with my friends. I like to read.

~

320: SPOOKY OCTOBER

by Thomas James Busby

People believe I'm the spookiest thing existing. But people think differently.

   Yes, I'm invisible, but it doesn't make me terrifyingly spooky.

   I can see your every step but you can't mine. Perhaps I float, or maybe it's just a lie/fiction.

   Do you dress up as me for candy/sweets? Or do you not? Maybe you don't dress.

   You may think I'm the cutest, nicest existing thing but, whatever you do, prepare for a spooky fright on the spookiest night of frightening October.

Thomas James Busby's Biography

I'm from Cumbria and I have 1 older brother. I'm in Year 5 and I love maths and problem solving. I like going on YouTube and playing with my friends.

321: LIFE OF A BOX

by Ryan Fell

I'm resourceful to put things in. Yes, I'm a box. I'm a matte black box made from tin.

My owner (who is nice / awesome) uses me to keep his massive Yu-Gi-Oh! collection, like: Watt Kid, Dark Magician, Feral Imp and – the best card on the planet – Exodai. He also has the slick, smooth and shiny blue eyes of a white dragon.

My favourite place to be – Yu-Gi-Oh! It is awesome being a black box.

I'm serious, it really is, everybody.

Ryan Fell's Biography

I have 1 older sister. I like reading and writing stories. I play a lot on my games consoles, but I also like reading. My favourite books are *A Series of Unfortunate Events* – I like the dangerous plots.

~

NOTE: *End of stories written by children and teachers from Northside Primary School in Cumbria, UK.*

~

322: FEAR

by Layla Ahmed

As I reached for the handle, my hand was trembling. Fear was soaring through my body. My veins began to pulse as my heart rate quickened and I could feel every hair on my body stand to attention.

I slowly turned the handle until the door opened a fraction, allowing a stream of light into the room. Every ounce of myself was telling me to slam the door shut, but I was determined.

Today, I would finally step outside my house.

Layla Ahmed's Biography

My name is Layla and, having spent my life reading every book I could, last year I decided to have a go at writing a book. This challenge seemed the perfect way to experience the world of publishing.

323: A PLACE TO MEET GOD

by Helen Matthews

Mum hands me a dog-eared flyer and says, "Rock concert. Your chance to meet him."

The venue stinks of sweat. The lead singer's face is craggy, his hair unnaturally black. But the drummer's new: polished, arrogant – and young. I fix my eyes on him.

Guitars pluck faint childhood impressions, but the mellow voice has faded to cracked falsetto.

As I queue for merchandise, he smiles, uncertain, memory misfiring. I stride past the rock god – my father – and head towards the drummer.

Helen Matthews' Biography

Helen Matthews is the author of suspense thriller *After Leaving the Village*, published by Hashtag Press. Her novel's opening pages won first prize at Winchester Writers' Festival. She is an ambassador for Unseen, a charity campaigning against modern slavery.

www.helenmatthewswriter.com

~

324: UNCOWED

by Kolade Ajila

The cow bounded towards me as I turned a sharp corner, two burly butchers hot on its heels. I turned and fled.

The enraged cow charged at an old, weak-looking man working in the vegetable nursery nearby, bent and absorbed in his occupation. He looked up suddenly, saw the approaching cow, its horns poised. Calmly, as though he had spent eternity in anticipation, he grabbed the horns and twisted, bringing down the cow, its pointed horns buried in the soft earth.

Kolade Ajila's Biography

Kolade Ajila is a Nigerian writer and editor. He has an MA in philosophy from the University of Ibadan, Nigeria. He divides his time between academic research and creative writing.

325: AND THE WORLD WILL BURN

by Kimana McCallum

When the fire bloomed inside of her, burned deeply from within, then it was too late for the world. This was her destiny; to destroy the world as it was and create a dark world, ruled by the gift of her flame.

She was destruction. She was anger. She would be God. She would be punishment. She would be all that there ever was, and all that was meant to be. Her name is Angelica, and she will bring the end.

Kimana McCallum's Biography

Kimana McCallum is a student at Falmouth University currently studying for a BA in creative writing. She is an unpublished young adult writer who one day hopes to see her own creations alongside her favourite authors in the bookstore.

~

326: AND THE DOGS ALL BARKED

by L J King

The miniature lurcher started it, a high-pitched, "Raow, raow," her muzzle pushed through the gap in the gite's hedge.

Hidden behind, the Labrador added his deep, "Woo, woo."

Babette and Bijou, lazing in the barn's shade, wagged their tails. "Ow ow, ow ow."

"MAIR-duuuhhhh." Metal banging rang from deep inside the barn. He was underneath his beloved Claas, repairing the sabotage. "Ta gueule."

But the dogs kept barking until Irina reached the lane.

She smiled, mounted the bike and pedalled away.

L J King's Biography

Former news journalist who now uses sentences for good, not evil. Published in *Flash Fiction Festival One* anthology and winner of the Peter Reese Cup 2017 (Rushmoor Writers).

327: SANDWICHES

by Ally Cook

Brenda shook raindrops from her umbrella and left it blocking the porch beside her muddy patent shoes. She hung her coat and removed her black pillbox hat, teasing the veil back into place. At her age, she'd need it again. She lifted her glossy black handbag and padded into the kitchen.

"Brian." Brenda's hand flew to cover her mouth.

"Want lunch?" Brian waved the butter knife.

"No," Brenda said, passing her hand through her husband. "I had sandwiches at your funeral."

Ally Cook's Biography

Science teacher with a fiction habit and (in some opinions) too many cats.

~

328: DON'T WISH FOR WHAT YOU WANT

by Jane Sleight

"I love you, Chrissy."

"Enough to leave Sarah?"

"You know I won't leave the girls."

"I won't wait for ever."

"Just until they're old enough."

"For what? A pension?"

Gab's eyes narrowed. "Don't pressure me, Chrissy."

"You're right." A penny dropped. Did she want him all to herself? In her home 24x7? No freedom to see other people? Holiday alone? Eat garlic bread without guilt? "You're right. Let's just stay exactly as we are."

She'd never seen him look so afraid.

Jane Sleight's Biography

Jane Sleight loves to write stories about relationships and people's ability to screw up every situation. She lives in Hampshire, hoping that Jane Austen's magic may rub off on her manuscripts. See more about Jane and her books at:

www.janesleight.com

329: DON'T TRAVEL ON A FRIDAY

by Shirley Muir

She's dodging suitcases and tripping over baby buggies as she dashes for the 10:06 to Leeds. If she misses her sister's wedding, she'll never be forgiven.

Escalators are mobbed with Friday crowds jostling to descend to the train platforms. Squeezing through the gap, she slides into the barely-used passenger lift, breathless. Its doors swish shut. The lift's lone passenger, she presses 'Down' and leans against the wall.

"This lift is now out of service," a voice announces. The power flickers off.

Shirley Muir's Biography

Shirley Muir spends her time between Turkey and Scotland. She writes about science, travel, refugees, sci-fi and memoir. Shirley loves classical music, the Venice Carnival, writing fiction and reading tarot. She walks along the beach at sunset for inspiration.

~

330: WE WANTED HIM TO BE HAPPY

by Mary Prior

"We wanted him to be happy," his mother said. "He wasn't very social you see, didn't make friends easily. Didn't like fluffy things either, so we couldn't have fluffy pets."

"We thought it would be good for him to have something to look after, to be close to. He used to sit watching the TV with her," said his father.

"She wrapped herself round his neck, you see," said his mother. "She didn't mean to hurt him. Pythons are like that."

Mary Prior's Biography

I have been writing for about twelve years now and been fortunate to have won several writing competitions including the Stockport Competition. I have had both poems and short stories published.

331: CONDITIONS OF ENTRY

by John Cooper

To enter you must ensure:
- You know why you are doing so.
- Your work must have taken you many days, even weeks, to complete.
- You are proud of it.
- You don't want it back.
- Your work is original or at least not derived too closely from a previous winner.
- You are able to negotiate the tortious payment methods used to pay the entry fee.
- You accept the judge's decision is final and,
- You are OK with the disappointment of not winning.

John Cooper's Biography

John lives in Hampshire. Although he is a sometime poet and a sometime flash fiction writer, currently he is at work as a full-time manager.

~

332: NECTAR

by Ruth Pedley

Pale lemon with a hint of grass. Pétillante. Fruity on the palate.

I stretched strong roots into flinty soil. The Rhenish nuns in the Abbey of St Hildegard tended me: a tendril trimmed, rotting grapes taken.

In the mornings I was woken, chilled, and saw white mist in the valley.

Then months of daylong night in cellars, lulled by lauds and vespers. Now a spider fingertips octaves across the barrel.

I am pulled into slim bottles. And poured.

Swirl. Savour. Slurp.

Ruth Pedley's Biography

Near the end of a 30 year career in the law in London, Ruth, like a pony scenting oats at the end of her field, is anticipating much pleasure (to herself, at least) in writing flash fiction and short stories.

333: IN THE NAME OF THE FATHER

by Simone Wallace

One by one, they trickled down the aisle, each holding one object.

"A tie for the businessman," said the first.

"A set of car keys, his hobby," said the second.

"His favourite novel, for his love of reading," said the third.

"A photo with the family," said the fourth.

"A copy of *The New Testament*," said the priest.

They placed these memories of who he used to be on the closed lid of the coffin.

"In the name of the father."

Simone Wallace's Biography

Simone Wallace is an emerging poet and fiction writer from Dublin, Ireland. She has a degree in English and French literature and has a longstanding interest in theatre and short story writing.

~

334: BE THANKFUL

by Carolyn Ward

Get to the body within three minutes of death, and she could suck life back in. Her 'reverse-vampirism' tasted like a frozen cobweb. She travelled the world and was heralded as a goddess, a miracle worker. Grateful, tearful family members pushed money and gifts into her eager hands.

Nobody asked the dead-borns how they felt about it. If they wanted another life. The blood in their veins was sluggish, their eyes dull. But they always managed to smile, in the end.

Carolyn Ward's Biography

Carolyn Ward lives in the UK and writes flash and short stories to scare her family. She is working on her first novel.

For more follow: @Viking_Ma

335: AN EXTRAORDINARY LIFE

by Lisa Miller

Dan seemed to have lived an unremarkable life. His obituary read: *Dan Jones died at age 78. An accountant, he's survived by his wife and a son. He cherished his dog, Blue, and grey sports car.*

At his funeral, an unknown homeless man stood up and spoke. "Dan was a remarkable man," he said. "For over 20 years, he brought me lunch to eat with him in the city park. Never missed a day."

A surprise for all who knew Dan.

Lisa Miller's Biography

I was born in 1961 in Portland, Oregon, USA, where I still live today.

~

336: ECO CHIC

by Wendy Roe

I used to spend money on clothes without thought beyond my immediate impulsive desire. Sometimes I think of all that money spent on things I never wore and I can imagine it piled up high in a mound on my floor. I would like that money now.

I have since become an eco-conscious person and have learnt wearing something over and over again is sustainable. Less shopping means I have more money in my purse, instead of imagined on my floor.

Wendy Roe's Biography

My writing often lands in the world and realms of the metaphysical. However, I'm discovering these smaller stories giving glimpses of life. Being published 'one day' used to be my goal, but now I just write for my own pleasure.

337: DRUNKARD

by Charlotte Ward

I hear him shouting and peer into the living room. He notices me and begins demanding another drink. I refuse and walk away – surely he has had enough?

He follows me, hiccoughing madly into the kitchen, then slides on the floor, bashing his knees. He howls in pain but won't let me help him up.

"No more," I say, firmly, then relent as his face begins to crumple. Resignedly, I fill up my toddler's juice cup and give it to him.

Charlotte Ward's Biography

Charlotte Ward lives in south Staffordshire with her husband and two previous drunkards (they are bigger now, and a bit less of a handful). She enjoys writing flash fiction in her spare time, especially horror.

~

338: A WAY OUT

by S Thomson-Hillis

You go to the woods, you find a body.

Here are the rules. Walk away. Head up, eyes front.

They'll be here soon, the bone collectors.

Instead you stop.

Death is the only escape. After a thousand years of nothing, you've been punished enough. You need to try. This is your chance. Who killed him? How? Kneel. Touch. Examine. Be careful, they're coming. Footsteps, lights and crashing, they're here.

But you have your answer and there's only one question.

How much?

S Thomson-Hillis' Biography

After spending years teaching FE and looking after crazy dogs, I joined Rushmoor Writers and settled down to have fun writing space opera. I've now put out the first two episodes of a trilogy on Amazon. Best decision ever.

339: MEMORIALS

by Anita Goveas

Fiza's last jump forward is to her brother's funeral. Hundreds of people crowd Hyde Park, silent but weeping. There're only open-air cremations in this time – no more space for all the bodies.

Ibrahim stayed to look after people, but she never stood still, zooming into future lives, going back to learn lessons. She'd thought that would be how she'd use her power, leave her mark. Searching out triumphs, bringing back wisdom. Warning of dangers.

No one listened. They won't mourn her.

Anita Goveas' Biography

Anita Goveas is British-Asian based in London, fuelled by strong coffee and paneer jalfrezi. She was first published in the *2016 London Short Story Prize Anthology*, and most recently in former *Cactus Mag, Litro* and *Longleaf Review*.

She tweets erratically: @coffeeandpaneer

~

340: BREAKUP

by Stephanie Ngoei

The letter lies open for the 37th time in two weeks.

She thinks she might have memorised every word by now but, pathetically, she's only managed to recite up to the first three words before the rest deteriorates with a gyrating blur that sends her mind reeling in an unescapable direction, smarts the corners of her eyes and tightens the vines around her heart to the point of utter strangulation.

She can't memorise the letter, so she memorises the pain instead.

Stephanie Ngoei's Biography

I'm a Chinese-Indonesian known as Steph, Fang and Fani to the people around me. My obsession for drawing, wildlife, anime and fanfiction stretches beyond any comprehension. My writing biz started over my fascination for Kate DiCamillo's books in grade school.

341: THERE'S SOMETHING ABOUT ANNE

by C.R. Berry

"We have to go back," said Juliet.

"What about them?" said Fred.

"They'll have to come with us. They certainly can't stay here."

"But, Juliet... we love her."

"I don't care, Fred. Come on. Let's go clean up your mess."

Juliet opened the hatch to their time machine. Fred climbed inside, followed by Fred, Fred and Fred, then Juliet herself.

As the time machine dematerialised, Queen Anne Boleyn entered the room, accidentally kicked her husband Henry VIII's severed head, and screamed.

C.R. Berry's Biography

C.R. Berry is a British author who writes conspiracy thrillers with a sci-fi or fantasy bent. Berry has been published in *Phantaxis, Suspense Magazine, Storgy, Tigershark, Scribble, Metamorphose*, and the first *To Hull And Back Anthology*. Twitter and Facebook: @CRBerry1.

www.crberryauthor.wordpress.com

~

342: THE STRUGGLE

by Andrew Perry

When I've lots of jobs to do, time passes incredibly fast. When I've nothing to do, time stands still. What I needed was time to go slow when I'd lots to do and time to go fast when I was bored.

So, on a day when I had lots to do, I did nothing. Success. I had all the time in the world. Unfortunately, I now have a long list of things to do and no time to do them in.

Andrew Perry's Biography

Andy is an estranged northerner with a funny accent who lives in London. He writes fiction, poetry and comics. You can find more at his website:

www.andrewmarkperry.com

343: THE VISIT

by Dean Hollands

Despite the warm spring breeze and dancing sunshine, the cemetery was eerily silent.

Drifting leisurely between the headstones, Dean paused and reflected upon the epitaphs and dedications to those now resting below.

A voice croaked, breaking the silence.

"Who are you looking for?"

Still scanning the headstones before him, Dean replied, "My father, William George Hollands, born 7th April 1945."

"Plot 24. Row C3," came the reply.

Turning around, Dean faced the voice.

"Dad?"

"Hello, son. I've been waiting for you."

Dean Hollands' Biography

Armed forces veteran and retired law enforcement officer. Interests include all things post-apocalyptic. Member of the Rushmoor Writers group. Writing nonfiction and children's stories about Irish wolfhounds.

~

344: WHY?

by Sophia Manubay

Why do people believe in religion?

Why is A before B, and B before C?

Who thought of the alphabet and number sequences and how?

A lot of things in life make me curious.

Like, why do people prefer certain animals over others?

Who defined what 'normal' is?

These sorts of questions go through my mind every day.

It's kind of like a computer running the same code, over and over again.

Computers always find solutions and find new problems.

Why?

Sophia Manubay's Biography

I'm Sophia Manubay and I'm currently a junior at Lawrence North High School in Indiana. I live in a forest-y part of Indiana and I love writing, making art in my free time, and taking photos.

345: BLACK MARIA

by Christian Obaitan

She was an abomination. How could such a lowly woman give birth to the king? And not by her husband, but an unseen spirit. Surely, she must be mad and unfit to raise a child.

Her fruit was taken from her. She was banished to a camp for people like her – helpless, condemned womb-men.

She never opened her arms again for, even in death, she cradled her child.

Mother and child, torn apart, would reject life to be united in death.

Christian Obaitan's Biography

My name is Christian Obaitan. I only just started writing. In fact, this is one of my first ever attempts to write. I've always loved literature. God bless you for what you do.

~

346: THREEDOM

by Oort Kuiper

"Freeze," he said.

We didn't move.

Three scared individuals.

We were squaring things up when the situation escalated.

The soldier's radio amplified the urgency, "Nein, nein, nein."

27 words had taken us to that heart-stopping moment.

A selection of syllables, transformed into words and sentences.

Now it was certain, they had uncovered our scheme.

Three 18s. Barely adults. A combined age of 54.

One runs. 9mm flies. Body plummets to the floor.

Graffiti reads: 'The price of freedom.' Berlin wall, 1981.

Oort Kuiper's Biography

Science enthusiast who has studied science and science fiction at degree level. Aspiring to write actual fiction so dipping my toes in.

347: SURPRISE

by Ian James Stewart

South Kensington, Saturday, walking. Clouded night.

I stop at the corner under a street light. Car, contents in darkness, stops opposite me. From the edge of the driver's door – closed – projects a droop of skirt, dragging. Car begins to move.

I point, without expectation of effect, at the trapped cloth. The door opens. I imagine the emerging right arm will belong to a tattooed tart who fingers me as she retrieves.

Wrong.

Hajib'd gentlewoman says, "Thanks," closes door and drives off.

Ian James Stewart's Biography

My name is Ian Stewart. I live in a pleasant rural setting 12 kilometres north of Wagga Wagga in NSW. Since retiring from medical practice, I have turned myself over to writing mostly fiction, both in short and long form.

www.facebook.com/ianstewsart124

~

348: BEING DAD

by Gowravy Ravanan

He wakes me up with a cute smile, caressing my head. He carries me to the bathroom. He cooks me delicious food. He gets me ready like Mum does. He drops me at school, wishing me good luck.

He picks me up. On the way home, he buys all the candy I want. He reads me bedtime stories. He kisses me on the forehead while I pretend to sleep.

These images flash in my tears as I look at his coffin.

Gowravy Ravanan's Biography

Gowravy Ravanan is an Indian girl who wants to achieve a lot. Her goal is to become a writer who sits in everyone's heart. She loves to scribble in Tamil and writes random things that pop up into her brain.

349: KING AT HEART

by Thatchayani Ravanan

Years ago, a man found a creature. It was about to die. The man tried to help the creature breathe.

The creature attacked him. Man dropped the creature due to the pain.

Again and again he tried to help, but each time the creature attacked.

Sea was watching. Sea asked, "What are you doing, man?"

Man asked, "Why is it biting?"

Sea replied, "Because it's in its nature."

Man said, "Similarly, it's my nature."

Man once was a king at heart.

Thatchayani Ravanan's Biography

Thatchayani Ravanan (14 years old) is an Indian girl who studies nature and loves animals. She admires Shakespeare and is inspired by Mark Twain.

~

350: OK, PUSS

by James Byrne

"OK, puss." I smiled at the neighbour's cat. "You can have a snoop around the house but only under my supervision."

It darted up the stairs.

"No, wait. Come back."

It sniffed at something in the bedroom, saw me and then scampered under the bed.

"Damn it, out from under there."

I beckoned. It lay down.

"You're not allowed in the house. My wife's going to kill me..."

The key turned in the lock downstairs. The wife.

"OK, puss, stay there."

James Byrne's Biography

James writes flash fiction and short stories, reads (mainly) fantasy genre books, and plays both guitar and bass guitar. In his day job, he works as a human resources professional.

351: REVOLVING DOORS

by Christianna Sahadeo

Tyrol hated revolving doors. The first time he encountered one, he was five and somehow jammed the door with a shoelace. He had been stuck for four hours.

On his first date, one had smacked him in the face so hard he was required to go to the hospital to stop the nosebleed.

When he stepped through a revolving door and landed in an entirely different world… that was the last straw.

If he saw one again, he would destroy it.

Christianna Sahadeo's Biography

Christianna loves the ocean, music and sleeping. When she's not reading, she's writing. When she's not writing, she's probably talking to her pet fish or doodling with pretty much anything she can get her hands on. Occasionally, she identifies bacteria.

~

352: THE DAY

by Laura Day

Today is the day. We've been anticipating this for quite some time. We've assessed the outcomes of every scenario. Reviewed every detail.

My hands are shaking as I answer the phone. "Hello… Yes, this is she."

My mind starts racing as I try and grasp the news. I know I have questions, but no words come out of my mouth.

How do I tell him? Do I even tell him?

Oh god, he's only five. Will he even understand? Diagnosis sucks.

Laura Day's Biography

My name is Laura Day. I'm a special education teacher, a mum and a self-published author. My debut children's picture book, *My Special Mind*, was written and illustrated with the help of my eight-year-old son.

353: GLASSES

by Helen Merrick

"That's an 'N'."

"Is it?" Squinting at the fuzzy blob, I'm forced to face facts: I can't see.

"Most people need reading glasses eventually," says the optician.

I'm sure they do, but my vision's always been perfect. It's age, isn't it? I'm getting older.

"Try these. They'll suit you."

Actually, they do. The glasses make me look intelligent. Wait a minute... I peer at my reflection. Are those grey hairs?

Swiftly removing the glasses, I take another look. Ah, that's better.

Helen Merrick's Biography

Helen Merrick is a writer from North Wales who aspires to pen the next ground-breaking, awe-inspiring best seller. She's written 81 words so far.

~

354: TAKING CARE OF BUSINESS

by Cameron Crebs

They met at a wooden bench in front of the Wendy's on Manatee Boulevard.

They didn't look at each other as they sat. Nick had gotten there first.

They both had paper bags from the Wendy's. They both placed them in the space that divided them on the bench.

After a few minutes, Nick picked up Michael's bag, full of cash, and walked away.

Five minutes later, Michael picked up Nick's bag, full of dextromethorphan, and left in the opposite direction.

Cameron Crebs' Biography

Cameron Crebs is a freelance writer and journalist making a living by selling short stories, articles and essays to magazines and newspapers.

355: THE KING'S BIRTHDAY

by Lucy Camilla

The king jumped out of bed and ran downstairs. Today was his birthday. He was going to receive his presents sitting on his throne and he needed to polish his crown.

The king opened the crown cupboard, got out the polish, but somebody had moved the crown. The king looked in the bedroom, the throne room, the speech room and... in the kitchen.

There, on the table, was his crown, filled with presents, balloons and birthday cards.

The king was happy.

Lucy Camilla's Biography

I dabble with writing and spend a little more time gardening. I live in the middle part of England, but have also lived to the east, to the north, a little bit west, but not too far south.

~

356: THE COLLECTION

by Lynn Gale

Gas lights flickered, then went out, one by one, as he walked by.

Doors and shutters closed and bolted, as he walked by.

Mothers cuddled their children and prayed, as he walked by.

"Who has he come for?" they cried, after all their suffering lately.

Stopping at the last door on the left, he stepped inside.

"No," cried a voice within, "not now, you promised me immortality."

"You will be remembered," smiled the devil. "Jack the Ripper has a certain ring."

Lynn Gale's Biography

Living in Westcliff on Sea, working in a post office, would love to write fulltime. Love reading, badminton and netball. Influences include Margaret Atwood, Stephen King and Wilbur Smith.

357: SMALL BUT RESILIENT

by Isabella Rae Wharton-McLellan

Hell is not a place where anything could survive, obviously. The tortured souls, hellish demons and the rivers of molten lava make the place extremely inhospitable.

But one day? Eternity? I stumbled across a single seed. It was small, but that didn't matter.

I planted it. There was no sunlight, no water to nourish it. But eventually there was a shoot clawing out of the earth. It was black and ashy, but it was alive.

Maybe Hell was hospitable after all.

Isabella Rae Wharton-McLellan's Biography

I am 19 and currently in my first year with Open University studying English literature with creative writing. I've also been a bookworm and loved writing (so much so I used to bring books to parties).

www.instagram.com/ozzie_eh/

~

358: CATS AND DOGS

by CB McCall

There are cat people and there are dog people. He'd fudged the issue, saying he was an 'animal lover', but he was a dog person through and through.

A cat person would have delighted in her independent nature. But dog people need creatures they can own. Who enthuse at their every homecoming, slobbering devotion. Growl at strangers. Beg for treats.

Disillusioned, she did what any cat would do. She transferred her affections to a neighbour and never thought of him again.

CB McCall's Biography

CB McCall is an obvious pseudonym.

www.facebook.com/CBMcCall1/

359: CHASE ME

by Christine Hursell

Hello, dog. I'm friendly. You have ball. I want ball.
Look, My Person, ball mine now. We have game. Chase me.
No, not that trick, too close, you chase me. Don't run away, you must follow.
I'll go to car, this is good game. Ball mine. Chase me.
Here is car, no, not inside, play my game, chase me. Fields over there, you follow.
Cars. Zooming quickly.
Screech, bang, screaming. My Person lying down. Someone comes.
Ball mine. Someone chase me.

Christine Hursell's Biography

Retired, currently divorcing, started creative writing to meet people and help rebuild my life. This submission is my fourth (ever) short story and the first attempt at being published.

~

360: THE ROBOT

by Wanda Wright

The robot rolls over the jagged planet with ease, created for it. The hot star above beats on its metal body as it scans the terrain for other life. It had been left here, 1,000 years ago, and was certain it had been forgotten, but its duty remains a relentless call.

Flames roaring transform into a spaceship. The robot darts over, hopeful it will be freed from its solitude. Hope of rescue turns to horror when it is scrapped and dies.

Wanda Wright's Biography

Wanda Wright is an author of novels, short stories and flash fiction. She is currently writing 50 stories in 50 days; one published so far and waiting on 36.

361: CALL ME CLEMENTINE

by James Braun

The art of peeling a clementine is a forgotten practice.

You labour away, scraping with your manicured fingernails at the solid exterior only to make slight openings, revealing the juicy insides. You pick away until nothing remains. Until the outer shell has fallen away to reveal its exposed orange self.

And as you sit across from me, biting into your hard-earned reward, I can't help but marvel. Because you are the outer protective shell, and I am just the fragile inside.

James Braun's Biography

James Braun is an undergraduate student at Oakland University, double majoring in creative writing and secondary education English with a minor in biology. He lives in Rochester, Michigan, with his cactus. His name is Cabot.

~

362: MANNERS

by Pamela Pope

The Edwardian ladies had the vapours. Debonair actor Peregrine Blackmore was visiting, frock-coated, his top hat set jauntily over dark curls. Lady Finchcombe had invited him to tea with her Ladies Friendship Group.

"I'll take your hat, Mr Blackmore," fluttered the Honourable Daphne Pratt.

"Thank you, I'll keep it on," said he.

Surprised looks were exchanged, whispered murmurs of, "Manners." Then a forceful wind through an open window sent the hat flying, along with the curls. Peregrine Blackmore was completely bald.

Pamela Pope's Biography

Pamela Pope: novelist, short story writer, playwright, artist. I am a member of the SWWJ.

363: THE DOOR ON THE WALL

by Joe McMullen

The door had not been there before. Its small rectangular frame jutted out from the wall above my bed, covered in crusted crimson paint.

Running my finger along the wood confused me, for it was warm and throbbing against my skin. Fear took me. What if this door was somehow sinister?

Opening the door to find out, I found myself awake and discovered the door was absent. *Stupid dream*, I thought, and with that I rolled back and returned to sleep.

Joe McMullen's Biography

Joe is currently a student of philosophy, although he doesn't really understand it and would rather write. In his spare time he enjoys walks in the mountains and reading.

www.thoughtsofaaspiringwriter.blogspot.co.uk

~

364: THE NOTE

by Maria Noble

The note lay beside the body. The officers were trying not to contaminate the crime scene. It looked like murder, but it wasn't.

The woman, who took her own life, was an actress and going through divorce. The note read: 'If found dead, my husband did it.'

He had recorded all conversations. She decided to end her own life and ruin his.

A chill ran though the room. Her passing thought was of her leaving the stage of her own death.

Maria Noble's Biography

My name is Maria Noble and I haven't been writing short stories for very long. However, I have always been very interested in writing and only plucked up the courage by attending a writing group at my local library.

365: THE PLOT

by Valerie Fish

Sue never bothered telling her husband where she was going. He was constantly ridiculing her, making her feel worthless.

Thursday mornings were a welcome escape. People were actually interested in what she had to say. She was thrilled when it was suggested her latest work was good enough to be published.

Maybe now was the time to tell him what she had been up to. After all, he had been the inspiration for her story, 'How to Commit the Perfect Murder'.

Valerie Fish's Biography

Have had a love of the English language since my school days; the only subject I was any good at. I like to 'write from the heart' and hope that's reflected in my work.

~

366: THE WITCH THAT EXISTS

by Lidia Giusa

"Witches don't exist." My gran's words echoed around my head as the horrific visage grinned at me through my window.

But, I know they do.

She sits outside my window every night, staring right at me. Sometimes she will wave at me. Sometimes she will call me over to the window, encouraging me to open it.

I don't know what she wants, but I do know I'm the only one who can help her, the only one that knows she exists.

Lidia Giusa's Biography

Lidia Giusa. A Year 12 sixth-form student with a passion for horror.

367: PASSIVE RESISTANCE

by Marie McGinn

She sits.
  He stands.
  She speaks.
  He paces.
  She speaks again.
  He stops.
  He rants.
  She weeps.
  He storms.
  She dries her eyes.
  He threatens.
  She turns away.
  He gives a warning.
  She shakes her head.
  He holds her shoulders and turns her towards him.
  She meets his gaze.
  He shrugs.
  She folds her arms.
  He stamps his foot.
  She looks at the floor.
  He turns away.
  She is silent.
  He leaves.
  He slams the door.
  She sighs.
  Relaxes.
  Stretches.
  Smiles.

Marie McGinn's Biography

Retired academic who swapped academic life for a garden, two lurchers and trying to write short stories.

~

368: MY HERO

by Kira Inglis

My hero doesn't fight crime, she isn't a fireman or a police woman. She can't climb walls like a superhero or even run that fast. Most would say she's not a hero, but she is to me.

My hero is my mum, of course. My superwoman who kept me safe from the scary monster under my bed, who made sure I had a full belly and was never, ever late for school. My protector with unconditional love, my one true hero.

Kira Inglis' Biography

Hey, Kira Inglis here. Born and raised in Scotland with a love for story writing. I find it very soothing and relaxing – it's also very fun to delve into the art of story writing.

~

369: DAY

by Victoria Gaylor

Life was not going at all like she had planned. She was failing school, unemployed, had a lack of true friends and been through a difficult break up.

She couldn't see a point to life anymore. Was there a point if you weren't achieving the things you want, or at least somewhat happy?

Then she saw it. Something that gave her hope again in the world. Joy in the things around her. It was the most magnificent day of her life.

Victoria Gaylor's Biography

My name is Victoria Gaylor. Originally from Glasgow, I now live in Aberdeen, studying social work. I've always had a passion for writing but, being a student, I don't get to write as much as I'd like to.

370: 1942

by Ani Martin

"Whatever happened to Charlie?"

"He jumped ship at Liverpool. Said he couldn't do another convoy. Said he'd had a premonition that the ship would get hit."

"Blimey. He never seemed the sort to abandon his mates. What did you say to him?"

"Just wished him luck. I'd never seen his eyes look so wild. Terrified, he was."

"They caught him then?"

"Oh yes, the shore patrol arrested him and threw him into Speke Gaol."

"Court Martial?"

"Prison got bombed. He's dead."

Ani Martin's Biography

I am a member of a U3A writing group and our leader has challenged us all to enter the 81 Words story quest.

~

371: TUNA INDUSTRY

by Jessica Turnbull

Cats are perfect killing machines.

Their sharp claws, long teeth and lean bodies make them the ideal predator. So the world thought, *Why not make a house cat the size of a tiger? Nothing bad can come of that.*

But they were wrong.

Cats had been waiting for an opportunity to strike back, to rule the world with an iron paw. Yes, they liked being fussed over and given treats, but they wanted more. Much more.

They wanted the tuna industry.

Jessica Turnbull's Biography

My favourite genres to write about are fantasy, sci-fi and horror. Although I do try to squeeze an animal, especially cats, into everything I write. I have written since I was five and I'm hoping to become a published author.

@jess_a_turnbull

372: THE ALL-NEW AUTOMATED CUSTOMER SERVICE LINE

by Mairead Robinson

"This is Death," the voice said. "I'm calling to remind you of our appointment on Friday." His voice was eerie, as though he spoke from a cave, or an empty room. "This is an automated message. To speak to me in person, please call 000000."

I called the number. "I haven't made an appointment," I whined. "And I'm busy on Friday."

"Didn't you get my email?" he asked.

"Well, yes, I think there was an email."

"Friday then," he replied. "Goodbye."

Mairead Robinson's Biography

Mairead Robinson is a teacher, fiction writer and poet from Plymouth, UK. She has been published in *Mslexia* and was shortlisted for the Bridport Prize flash fiction competition. This is her shortest ever story.

~

373: GENERATION GAP

by Rachel Smith

With a sip of tepid coffee, I press the home button again. Just wallpaper, a screenshot of a beach, waves gently lapping at the shore. Date and time clearly on display. No message.

"What do you think it was like before mobile phones?" I overhear the boy say. "How do you think they sorted stuff out? Must have been really hard."

Yet I sit, waiting for that text, that call from you. Phone by my side, anxiety rising.

Quiet, I think.

Rachel Smith's Biography

Rachel lives with her son and three dogs near Nottingham and has been a science teacher for 20 years. Wanting to explore her creative side, this is her first attempt at a story.

374: THE NOTHING

by Constance Bourg

The birds have been with me since age 11. I say birds, but they are more of a blindness contained by scraggy bird-like boundaries.

I tried to drive them away by reciting nightly incantations. I had to make the recitations ever longer, until I fell asleep with the light still on.

When I was older, I tried loud music and scoring my body with protective symbols.

Now though, I just leave them be and I look to where they are not.

Constance Bourg's Biography

Constance Bourg lives in the Flemish part of Belgium, where she volunteers at a local social food market. She studied creative writing with the Open University and is known to cross the street to pet strange cats.

www.constancebourg.wordpress.com

~

375: THE ADVENTURES OF AMELIA BORGIOTTI, GHOST – MEETING AMBER

by Patrick ten Brink

"You can see me?" I said, floating in the rose-window light.

"Yes," said the girl in front of the alter.

"Why don't you flee?"

"I'm not afraid of ghosts. And you seem familiar."

"Do I?"

"Aren't you Amelia Borgiotti, who died for the orphans?"

"That is why I grace this church."

"Can't you leave?"

"I'm bound here, unfortunately."

"Unfortunately?"

"Eternity within these walls is not my chosen afterlife."

"Is there a way out?"

"One – if you allow me to possess you."

Patrick ten Brink's Biography

Patrick ten Brink writes fiction and poetry. He is working on *The Guardians of the Tides*, a fantasy trilogy, and *The Adventures of Amelia Borgiotti*, a ghost story. He is the editor of *The Circle*, a Brussels Writers Circle anthology.

@tenBrinkPatrick

376: CLOUDS

by Nam Raj Khatri

Clouds were covering the east, at the point where the sun was expected to rise from. Clouds made a beautiful shape to welcome the sun.

Sun rose from behind the clouds. Clouds became bright at the edges.

A boy just watched from his rooftop. Clouds disappeared and sun continued.

In the evening, he observed, in the west, that clouds again surrounded the sun. Clouds were red while sun was sinking.

The boy was confused. Were the red clouds happy, or sad?

Nam Raj Khatri's Biography

I'm an environmental engineer from Nepal. Interested in art, photography, clouds and story writing.

www.facebook.com/namrajk

~

377: A PUFF OF MAGIC

by Carrie Hewlett

The genie rubbed his hands gleefully.

His millionth wish. Hopefully it would be memorable.

Why don't people think through the actions of their wishes? he wondered.

How he'd laugh as they realised the consequences of their actions.

"What is your final wish?"

"I wish to be president."

Whoosh – it was granted.

The genie vaporised back inside his lamp.

Flicking the kettle for a cup of tea, he peeked out.

Fame could be such a two-edged sword, as Donald Trump would discover.

Carrie Hewlett's Biography

I've been writing for a number of years and been lucky enough to have had quite a few short stories published in both children's and women's magazines. I live in the West Country, love the sea and astrology.

378: THE GATH'RING

by Jamie Welch

Lo, 'pon yore-days there stood many creatures, wand'ring, roaming lands unknown. And yet, as time passed, they passed out of this world.

Hléowlora, and yet hope did come. Gath'ring 'round was thus, the defenders.

And yonder the green lands where Herne roams was the great-men, being whom would stand beside those creatures of yore-times. Fighting off the threat, among all Sidhe and Fae did they stand and become andfeng, bewerigend in ancestor's homes.

And thus they ne'er died, but did gelibban.

Jamie Welch's Biography

I'm an aspiring author. I'm 17, live in London and am currently writing a fantasy novel. I found this world record attempt online, so I put together a story presented as an epic poem, with words of Old English.

~

379: THE EPIPHANY

by Mary Papageorgiou

Sally was returning from work. However, this day seemed different. To her surprise, the grocery shop she was heading to was closed and outside there was a beautiful pink flower with a note:

'I had an epiphany, go find yours.'

She stared at the note with curiosity and then decided to go back home. She opened her closet and pulled out her old violin. She started playing, trying to remember the chords.

And there it was – she had her own epiphany.

Mary Papageorgiou's Biography

My name is Mary Papageorgiou. I was born and raised in Greece. I developed a passion for writing from an early age. Currently, I am doing my PhD in international relations and working on my first novel and poetry collection.

www.facebook.com/sideeffectstrilogy/

380: STARTING AT THE END

by Susi J Smith

"You killed her."

"What makes you say that? Maybe she died of old age."

Alice looked around the small room. Cream-coloured walls were flecked with dark droplets. The once pride-of-place portrait of Sam was smeared scarlet. On the floor, Grace's head lay a foot from her body.

"I don't think this is how a natural death happens."

Rich shrugged. "Shame." He grabbed her, throwing her down onto the body. "Have fun with forensics."

Alice screamed. The door closed. Rich was gone.

Susi J Smith's Biography

Susi J Smith enjoys writing short stories and flash fiction. For more information, please check out her website:

www.mairi187.wixsite.com/susi-j-smith

~

381: A MADNESS

by John Holland

"It's a madness, a sickness, a weakness. What on earth can I do with this so-called love you say you have for me? I can't bake a cake with it. I can't dig it in the garden. I can't take the dog for a walk with it. I'm busy. And it's your problem, not mine."

"But I can't put it back. I can't un-love you. No matter how harshly you treat me."

"Sorry. Was I being overly-negative?"

"Not overly, my love."

John Holland's Biography

John Holland is a prize-winning short fiction author from Gloucestershire in the UK. He also runs the twice-yearly event, Stroud Short Stories.

www.johnhollandwrites.com

382: TAKING FLIGHT

by David McTigue

Kieran's mum greeted him at the door.

"You left your skylight open, there's a pigeon up there. Get it out. NOW."

Kieran ran upstairs, leaving his mother cursing in the hall.

She soon heard him clattering around in pursuit of the terrified bird.

"Vermin. I'll have to change the bedding now," she spat.

Just then, she heard something that froze her. "BAT."

"A bat as well? How?" she shouted.

"I said I chased it out with my baseball bat," answered Kieran.

David McTigue's Biography

From Liverpool, retail manager, crossword setter, sometime poet, short stories published in the mists of time. Errand boy, dogsbody.

~

383: HER

by Olivia-Ann Saxton

She was there again, watching.

I saw her distorted shadow in the doorway. As I cautiously leaned over and flicked the light on, she disappeared. Maybe I imagined it. The nightmares were not as frequent. I told my therapist that I was sure of it.

I could hear the faint noise of unnerving, childish giggles echo throughout the room. I was home alone. Thoughts of her swarmed around my head like a hornet's nest, each idea's sting slowly paralysing my brain.

Olivia-Ann Saxton's Biography

My name is Olivia-Ann Saxton. I am 17 years old and currently studying A levels. This is my first time writing an 81 word story.

384: BRAINLESS

by Heidi Vanlandingham

I awakened lying on brick pavers. What happened? The clammy sheen of perspiration coated my skin as I watched the mesmerising motion of a zombie's bobbing head near my stomach.

Panic welled inside my chest, my recently eaten honeybun helping it along. I'd read the stories growing up. Zombies ate people. I tried to recall details from the childhood fantasies and found... nothing. My brain was empty. Wait a minute... Oh. My. God.

"You ate my brains, didn't you? I'm brainless."

Heidi Vanlandingham's Biography

Whether writing historical western romance, epic fantasy, or paranormal, Heidi Vanlandingham's books are sweet, where characters are inspired to overcome life's hardships and loving families build strong communities. Heidi currently lives in Central Oklahoma with her husband and youngest son.

www.heidivanlandingham.com

~

385: FELINITY

by Peter J. Corbally

The pair of them are at it again, arguing. Over what? It's always trivial.

This time, he's being accused of not washing-up properly. There's a smear still on the gravy boat.

I stir uneasily. She strokes my head and says, "Now look what you've done. Toby's upset." She picks me up and cuddles me.

"That stupid cat," he exclaims. "I'll be in the garage." He storms out.

She croons in a baby voice, "It's just me and you pussy, wussy, pussy."

Peter J. Corbally's Biography

Former teacher and self-employed publisher. Now retired and into writing and amateur archaeology.

386: DEVIL IN THE DETAIL

by David Heaton

The bank robbery went well and no one followed his getaway car. He started to relax, but suddenly his vehicle skidded on ice, flipped through the air and he remembered no more.

When he awoke, the air was hot, the sky orange and the smell of sulphur was everywhere. A smartly-dressed man with dark hair and a neat beard was standing nearby, watching him intently.

"Welcome." He smiled.

The thief stared at him, confused. "Who the devil are you?" he asked.

David Heaton's Biography

David Heaton lives in the north of England and writes speculative and quirky fiction. When he's not doing that, he likes walking the hills. He also likes to attend real ale festivals. Purely for research purposes.

~

387: GOODBYE MR F

by Sarah Everett

The beautiful morning was still and bright. It felt good to be alive.

But then the ground began to shake. The silence was broken by screaming hounds. Thundering hooves. Which way were they going? Closer, definitely getting closer.

Oh, how I ran, with my heart pounding and blood rushing. I RAN.

As exhaustion took hold, I glanced behind me and they were there.

With nowhere to hide, they were on me and, amidst the howling of the hounds, I was done.

Sarah Everett's Biography

Between hot flushes and midlife crisis situations, Sarah enjoys the country life with dogs and ponies. Now that the chooks have flown the nest, she is beginning to get into writing for fun.

388: SECRET REVENGE

by Sarah Stephenson

"It's gorgeous," she squealed, proudly holding it aloft to show the room. They all murmured appreciatively. "See, Jane," she continued, "it *is* possible to buy good vegan leather if you really put your mind to it." Her followers nodded in unison.

"You're so right, Charlotte," I agreed brightly and poured a glass of wine. I drank it quickly and finished with a satisfied sigh.

When I got home, I threw my bag on the sofa. A label dropped out: 100% leather.

Sarah Stephenson's Biography

Sarah Stephenson is a coat-owning Geordie who lives in Manchester.
www.linkedin.com/in/slstephenson

~

389: PLUM JOB

by Olusanya Anjorin

John was a blood donor known throughout the medical centre for his generosity. His blood group was O positive. Blood donation was a plum job for him.

The last time he donated blood, the doctor warned him to take care of himself.

He was answering the call of death when the doctor plucked him out and saved him. When John was revived, the doctor asked what he was doing in the brothel.

"I was donating blood to angels," he said sarcastically.

Olusanya Anjorin's Biography

I am a creative writer and an accountant. My writing has appeared in a wide range of publications in my country. My work has also appeared in various electronic journals and on blogs.

390: THE POCKET UNIVERSE

by Jack Purkis

I was raised in a pocket universe; a green valley shaped like a bowl. My friends and I played amongst its fields, woods and streams. Joy was pure, our lives seemed eternal; we knew nothing of what lay beyond our sphere. We played to the sun and, when it called time, we slowly, reluctantly, withdrew.

At some point, we went out together for the last time. One by one, we left the universe and, when we looked back, it had gone.

Jack Purkis' Biography

Jack is an actor and writer, forever flying between Shropshire and London. He can be found on Twitter (@jpurkis8) and www.jackpurkis.wordpress.com where he regularly posts creative content.

~

391: PIECE PIPE

by Chris Espenshade

Faith-keepers unwrapped the classic 1870s plains pipe. A metre long, it was carved catlinite, embellished with beads and eagle feathers. It had passed among chiefs and US representatives. Its smoke sealed promises of peace and land security.

The archivist swelled with pride of repatriation. "Your heritage." The museum wanted a public ceremony. The tribe declined.

The traditionalists placed the pipe on a basalt slab, lifted cobbles and wordlessly took turns smashing it to dust.

Each fracture, a broken promise. "Our heritage."

Chris Espenshade's Biography

A professional archaeologist, Chris Espenshade branched into creative writing in 2017. He's had flash fiction works accepted by Thrice Fiction, *The Paragon Journal, Agora Journal* and The Dead Mule School of Southern Literature.

392: TO LONGER BAD MOVIES

by Aishwarya Harikumar

It was their first date.

She looked ethereal in a yellow floral sundress, which brought out the golden glow of her sun-kissed curls.

The movie had bored him to tears.

She, however, was in tears for another reason. She'd gasped quite a few times and, clasping his hand in sheer terror, she whimpered as she hid her face in the crook of his welcome neck.

He smiled through two hours of blood and gore, and wished it would go on forever.

Aishwarya Harikumar's Biography

I'm a civil engineer, currently pursuing my MA in urban planning from the National University of Singapore. Writing is a huge passion of mine, as is cartooning and drawing. I'm currently working on my first full-length novel.

~

393: CROSS PURPOSES

by Christine Kingshott

"Do you want ham or cheese in your sandwiches, Dad?"

"Do you mean the play about the witches?"

"Not witches, Dad, sandwiches."

"It was called *The Crucible*. It was on last night, Liz. In England, though, witches were thrown into rivers – innocent if they sank, guilty if they floated – then executed."

"I'll do cheese and pickle then, Dad."

"Yes, I know. There's been just a trickle from that tap all day."

"For pity's sake, Dad. How much were those hearing aids?"

Christine Kingshott's Biography

My name is Chris Kingshott and I live on the North Wales coast in beautiful Gwynedd. I belong to a writing group and became interested in flash fiction when entering the *Reader's Digest* 100-words story a few years ago.

394: UNTITLED

by Misa Hennin

I'm sitting on the doorstep at the back of 13 Woodhill Avenue, experiencing nostalgia for a childhood which wasn't mine. A childhood which differed so greatly from my own, yet created somebody who fits me better than I fit myself.

It's nearing midnight, but rays of sun are still visible on the horizon. The air is fresh after a day of heat, but mild enough to sit outside. The murmur of the freezer is the only sound that entertains my ears.

Misa Hennin's Biography

I'm a 20-year-old university student. I study history, though I am very interested in literature and hope to pursue a career in writing or media. I hope to gain experience and develop by writing short stories.

~

395: PERFECT PIE

by Kathryn J Barrow

I needed an apple for my pie.

Mr Barlow had an apple tree in his garden, next to mine. I'd try to take one every day, but he'd catch me.

"Get off my land," he'd bellow.

Today I knocked on his door and asked, "Sir, could I have an apple for my pie?"

"Wait," he said.

I did. He came back, handed me an apple. "Manners, lad, is all it takes."

"Thank you, sir." I went home and made my pie.

Kathryn J Barrow's Biography

Kathryn grew up in a small village, left home at 16 and built a career in retail. Then, at 29, she found the confidence to study part time, completing an open degree, concentrating on design and creative writing.

396: TOMORROW'S A NEW DAY

by DT Langdale

John gazed at his reflection, poking at his cheeks.

What had he done to himself?

The damage from years of drinking and fast food was obvious. Red blotches. Pale, grey skin.

Sort yourself out, John. Do you want to die early? No more. Salads only from now on. Tomorrow's a new day.

The window slid back, revealing a bemused girl in a shirt, cap and head mic.

"Can I take your order, sir?"

John sighed. "Yes, large Big Mac meal, please."

DT Langdale's Biography

Dave is a professional copywriter – and two-time One Minute Briefs winner – who writes fiction in his spare time. When not writing, he's often found in a pub or near cats. Or writing in a pub that has cats.

www.davelangdale.com

~

397: CRIME OF PASSION

by Andre Othenin-Girard

She's asleep, drooling. Her nose twitches. I used to find it cute. Now, I want to retch. I hold the razor-sharp slicing knife behind my back.

I could regret this. What if excessive nagging was inadmissible as a self-defence plea? I am told prison's grub is yuck. Long term, I could be repentant for the consequences, maybe even the crime.

I think I'll use the knife to make myself a chicken sandwich instead, toasted, with pickles, mustard, salt and pepper. Yum.

Andre Othenin-Girard's Biography

I am French, living in Australia. I have three projects in the endless pipeline: an autobiography for my daughters, a historical/ philosophical novel and a book of French yarns. Procrastination is my enemy. But tomorrow, if it comes, will be different.

398: BE CAREFUL WHAT YOU WISH FOR

by Lucy Morrice

I wished for love, for someone to be with all the time, for all eternity.

But not like this. Not to be controlled and monitored, chastised and quashed.

I obeyed but I did not honour. I nurtured the hate until it was strong enough. I smiled, I kept house, I submitted to his whims.

I sharpened my wits and my kitchen knives. He didn't see it coming.

It didn't kill him. But I will not be in this jail for ever.

Lucy Morrice's Biography

Lucy Morrice, born and bred in Scotland and a lifetime of aspiring to write. I think I may have found my home in flash fiction, which challenges while suiting my short attention span.

~

399: ROTTEN LOVE

by Lauren Raybould

Layla knelt in her garden, re-planting her chrysanthemums. She shovelled the soil around her bright purple flowers, her brow furrowed in concentration.

"Why did you try to leave, sweetheart? You won't be able to find someone who loves you as much as I do." Layla spoke quietly, but her words were coherent despite her early morning chardonnay.

"Will you, Evan, sweetie? No." She giggled, smiling as she intertwined her fingers with the corpse's, its rotting arm protruding out amongst the flowers.

Lauren Raybould's Biography

Having graduated from university, Lauren is working on her second book. She holds the position of deputy editor at *Evade Magazine* and is a self-confessed bookworm. She reads and writes multiple genres in her spare time.

400: INFANT AMBITION

by James Smart

World leaders gathered around a simple laptop, their sole interface with their new AI. Great men and women were reduced to biting nails and sweating brows. They prepared themselves for the demands of a sentient cyberbeing that was holding the world to ransom. It had control of every nuclear warhead on the planet and access to all human knowledge stored on the web. Everyone held their breath as letters forming words appeared on the screen:

I want to be a train.

James Smart's Biography

I live in Yorkshire with my wife and son. I have enjoyed writing from an early age and I am fascinated by other people's take on the world in the stories they tell.

~

401: CURSE YOU GLADYS

by Matthew Galic

Of all the times to upstage me, Gladys, this was the worst. I told you weeks ago that I was making pancakes for the picnic. WEEKS AGO. And yet what do you do? You saunter, all smug-like, up to our table, placing the most beautiful looking blueberry pancakes right in front of us.

This was supposed to be my time to shine.

And no, it doesn't matter that I forgot to bring my pancakes. After all, you're still in the wrong.

Matthew Galic's Biography

Matthew Galic is currently studying creative writing. He has had a passion for writing since his childhood, but has only recently started writing regularly. Although it may take a while, he aims to go all the way to the top.

402: CAT'S EYES

by Neil Phillips

What is my cat looking at?

Staring – no, stronger – glaring into space behind my head, like a harbinger of doom is lurking there.

I glance over my shoulder. Perhaps a fly upon the window? No.

Perhaps a mote of dust in sunlight? No, it is England, there is no sunlight.

I glance around nervously, ears straining for sounds only cats can perceive, but all the while he is staring at the space behind my ear.

My cat is making me paranoid.

Neil Phillips' Biography

Neil tries to write short horror stories but mostly ends up writing computer programs, which is what he does for a living. In between this he enjoys geeky games, kickboxing and working his way through a 1,001 world beers challenge.

~

403: A CIGARETTE

by Sam Freer

I am a cigarette.

My purpose is to make you feel at ease, all the while filling your lungs with countless toxins. Ironic, I know, but I feel I perform my job well regardless of the consequences. Nobody ever questions my abilities, so I persevere as I am. I continue to poison those who consume me, and then come back for more. They see me as a cure, not the blight I am. Foolish.

I am a cigarette, bringer of death.

Sam Freer's Biography

Sam is a college student who sits around writing stories and music instead of doing work. This is one of his first stories and was chosen from a collection written during a stay in Greece.

404: CHANCE ENCOUNTER

by Catherine Cade

I slipped into the wake of a goliath, barrelling through the shoppers. We made good progress until I saw the couple gazing into a jeweller's window and felt a thump inside my chest – not unlike the ones in my stomach now baby was big enough to kick.

I passed her father. Should I break up their happy tête-à-tête? Show them my souvenir? No, mine was a better revenge. He would never know his daughter.

She and I continued on to Mothercare.

Catherine Cade's Biography

Cathy is an ex-librarian whose writing was formerly limited to instruction leaflets and annual reports. Now retired, she produces a different type of fiction, which has, so far, been published in *Scribble* and shortlisted in two competitions.

www.cathy-cade.com

~

405: KRISTOFF WAS LOST

by Oscar Kenway

Kristoff was lost.

He was also alone.

So Kristoff was lost and alone which, as you could imagine, made him quite scared.

So Kristoff was lost, alone, scared and couldn't even remember how he ended up in this mess in the first place.

So Kristoff was lost, alone, scared, forgetful, and was getting rather overwhelmed by everything, so he was becoming rather sleepy.

So Kristoff was lost, alone, scared, forgetful and quite sleepy.

So he decided to sleep.

And he did.

Oscar Kenway's Biography

Oscar Kenway is an average dad, who spends time between his canoe racing tournaments (which he once came sixth in) by creating silly stories for his family who have convinced him, against his better judgement, to submit to this anthology.

406: T.L.C.

by Val Chapman

"Hello, beauty, how are you doing today?"

He had been coming to visit every day, sometimes several times.

Especially in the beginning.

Carefully, he bent down and tenderly brushed away a speck of dirt from her delicate skin.

He was very pleased with the way things had been progressing and, after all these years, he felt he finally stood a chance.

The county show was nearly here, and he was certain that this year he would win the 'biggest onion' prize.

Val Chapman's Biography

Val writes for her own amusement, and started in her 60s. Although brought up in England's north-east, she now lives in Fenland, thoroughly enjoying her life.

~

407: MIND GAMES

by Blerina Kapllani

Get closer... this time I won't step back from you. We're playing out a mysterious plot in our own game.

You provoke me by carving ashes in the fire, lit by the full moon. I feel... my desire is like a beast, trying to escape from a cage and infect its victim with the power of fear. Yes, fear of an empty cage.

Thus, we continue to live out this plot, where the silence is crossing every inexistent boundary of absurdity.

Blerina Kapllani's Biography

Writing is my hobby. It gives me the freedom to create my own reality. I have been writing stories in my first language for more than 10 years now. Lately, I have started to write flash stories in English.

408: SAVED BY ZERO

by Jordis Fasheh

'Through faith we understand that the worlds were framed by the word of God, so that things which are seen were not made of things that do appear.' Heb 11:10.

The tribal leader stands at the water's edge, in front of his starving and subdued people, arms outstretched, hands with palms wide open, praying for help.

When that which is unseen engaged heaven and earth, summoning being, the water rose, providing sustenance to the village.

Zero, the centre of an atom.

Jordis Fasheh's Biography

Jordis Fasheh lives and works in Fallbrook, California, with her small Chihuahua, Luna Gracie. Jordis likes to spend most of her spare time writing poetry and short stories. She has studied and practiced esoteric mysticism since her early teenage years.

~

409: THE GERMANS ARE COMING

by Alyson Faye

Me and Dad are watching a war film, cosy with mugs of tea and chocolate Hobnobs.

"One of them's a double agent. Working for the Germans. Now, which one is it?"

I know, but I stay silent.

The film's two stars, in camouflage whites, shoot guns, steal trucks, and dice with death.

"Bloody Germans." Dad stands up. Pointing. Red faced.

"That's not PC, Dad, now, come on."

I follow his finger.

I see, in his immaculate garden, two German shepherds, fouling.

Alyson Faye's Biography

Alyson writes flash fiction, as well as horror stories, most frequently on the *Horror Tree* site. Her collection, *Badlands*, is out from Chapel Town Books. She loves old movies and chocolate.

410: HIS CURSE

by Chloe Frost

I don't know why I dream of him, but every night, under the cover of darkness, he always seems to find me.

He has found a way to slip under my eyelids and burrow his way into my head.

I try to dig him out, to reach into my skull, pull him off and throw him away.

But try as I might, my grip is not tight enough, my will not strong enough. Thus, I am cursed to love him. Forever.

Chloe Frost's Biography

Chloe Frost is an aspiring author from Leicestershire, England. She loves reading detective novels and fancies herself as a bit of a Miss Marple. Unfortunately, as the crime rate in her village is low, she has taken to writing instead.

~

411: 81 WORDS

by Anne Copeland

How many times had she been hurt?

How many times had she been assaulted?

Bullied?

How many times had people spoken ill of her?

How many times had she run away?

How many times had she tried to end it all?

Today would be different.

Today she stood, her arms slightly back.

She looked up toward the heavens and she knew she was ready.

Her body began to lift from the ground and, as she rose, she realised she could fly.

Anne Copeland's Biography

Anne Copeland, published author (*Artful Alchemy: Physically Challenged Fiber Artists Creating*, and *Pumpkin, Pumpkin: Folklore, History, Planting Care and Good Eating*), professional mixed media and fiber artist, former teacher / paraeducator tutor for special needs children, and youth and criminal justice / archaeology graduate.

412: IT ALL COMES BACK TO BITE YOU

by Francesca Pappadogiannis

"Johnny. Did you tidy up all your toys?"

"Yes, I did, Mummy. They all have a home."

Later…

"Johnny. Why are all your toys in the fridge, washing machine, oven and toilet?"

"Because, Mummy, you told me to tidy them up."

"This is not tidying up. They belong in your bedroom."

"No, they don't. Daddy always says that it's all tidy as long as Mummy can't see or find them."

A lovely note left for Daddy: 'Babe, there will be no…'

Francesca Pappadogiannis' Biography

A writer and a wife and mother to three awesome children. I love poetry, I love to write and I love to feel the words while I express them on paper, literally and physically.

www.linkedin.com/in/francesca-pappadogiannis-1441ab14a

~

413: THE VALUE

by Murodova Marjona

I have a close friend. I was her confidant listener. She had an extended family of nine people. But she always wanted to be alone without her two sisters. She never thought about the disadvantages and menace of extreme loneliness.

It was her only dream. Days turned into months. Months into years. Unfortunately, she did not realise the opportunity God had given her.

As her destiny showed, one of her sisters entered a foreign university and another died of a cancer.

Murodova Marjona's Biography

My name is Marjona. I study at school. I live in Uzbekistan, one of the most exciting lands in the world.

414: THE BIG YAWN

by Alan Barker

I sit in my garden, staring at the fence.
    I stare at the fence because there is nothing else to stare at.
    Unless I stare at the patchy lawn, riddled with weeds.
    Or at the sky, full of unbroken cloud.
    Or at my ramshackle bungalow.
    I yawn.
    I glance at my watch.
    Time has moved on.
    A little.
    I resume staring at the fence.
    I yawn again.
    A wasp flies into my mouth.
    My day is no longer such a yawn.

Alan Barker's Biography

I am a retired tax accountant looking to fulfil a lifetime's ambition of writing stories and having them published. I recently completed a creative writing course. I am married and live in Epsom, Surrey.

~

415: LAST DAYS, FEW WORDS

by J. Rosina Harlow

In the last few days of the Glorious New Regime, the burble of running water was our only music. The slap of feet on concrete, barking dogs, slamming doors, these were our most treasured conversations.
    Language was strictly rationed.
    People crowded around their radios to hear the announcer clear his throat and tell the time. Such precious, sparse jewels of human expression filtered through our memories into radio silence.
    Dead air.
    But somewhere, the birds began reading their poetry out loud.

J. Rosina Harlow's Biography

J. Rosina Harlow graduated from University College Chichester in 2005 as a joint recipient of the Philip LeBrun Prize for Creative Writing. A musician, she lives in Kent with her husband and various other pets and writes dark, surreal fiction.
    www.facebook.com/JRosinaHarlow

416: UNCONDITIONAL LOVE

by Fiona Campbell

Summer evening, when the light lingers and the sun sets late. Hues of lemon, gold and flaming orange paint the sky as the silhouette of the moon rises. Creeping into bedrooms, planting kisses on foreheads and watching chests rise and fall. A heart full of unconditional love. Pondering on how amazing they are. From new-born blank canvases to troublesome tweens and teens. Forming opinions, making choices and following dreams. Sun sets on a summer's day. One step closer to the future.

Fiona Campbell's Biography

I am a single mum of three with MS. I was a music teacher before I was diagnosed. Now, I'm following a different dream. I'm studying for an MA in creative writing.

~

417: THE VOICE

by Robert Wood

Light flashed before my eyes. My surroundings were all blurry and would not stay one size. I tried to get up to see everything more clearly, but I quickly fell back down.

I was in a small clearing, surrounded by trees and it was humid, really humid. As I got up, I heard an eerie voice in my ear.

"It is time," whispered the voice. I felt a chill run down my spine. I never saw the light of life again.

Robert Wood's Biography

I enjoy writing fiction and poetry. I tend to specialise in children's literature, but I will write things from other genres. I enjoy reading World War II books and anything that catches my eye.

418: I LOVE YOU

by Sarah Ann Hall

He challenges her to convey her feelings without words.

She contorts her face a dozen ways: lips purse, cheeks twist, eyes bulge, ears rock up and down. Whatever she does isn't enough.

He shrugs. "I don't understand."

His refusal to comprehend infuriates her. She jumps on his back and slaps his shoulders playfully. "You can be so dense," she laughs into his ear.

Deafened, he pulls her into an embrace and they dance.

"You could have just kissed me," he says.

Sarah Ann Hall's Biography

Sarah Ann Hall left a proper job in 2001 to write fiction. She has written novels, none of which are published, short stories, some of which are published in anthologies, and is continuously looking for agent representation.

~

419: THE JOY OF A CHEERFUL GREETING

by Amisha Bansal

"Help," the poor man shouted.

It was dark inside. Workers had already left and he was locked inside the lab. The musty chemicals made him feel like his end was near. The next day was Sunday, a holiday.

Suddenly, the guard unlocked the door.

"You alright?" he asked.

"How did you know I was in here?"

"I wanted to hear the greeting 'Jai Shri Krishna'. Out of all the people I see daily, only you say this," replied the emotional guard.

Amisha Bansal's Biography

I am Amisha Bansal and I'm pursuing law in India. I've a great passion for writing and flaunting my knowledge. My dream is to serve my nation by joining the Army.

420: MASQUERADE SOCIETY

by Skylar Kim

Everyone is born with a mask that grows with them.
Yours doesn't fit.
The mask bruises your face, but you don't dare take it off.
One day, rushing late for work, you crash into someone and your mask falls off.
You freeze. Terrified. *Exposed.*
Cringing, you wait for the inevitable disgust, every second an agony.
Instead, she wordlessly hands you your mask back, along with a note.
When you arrive home, you open it.
You are not alone. From a 'he'.

Skylar Kim's Biography

Skylar listens to music and takes pictures of every cat they come across – and is an aspiring writer who is currently juggling time between their studies and writing.

~

421: IT'S ALL YOUR FAULT

by Jenny Butler

While staying with me you contacted your crazy, abusive imprisoned ex and ran up a very high phone bill. On seeing that you used a return address, he came here when released and has absolutely destroyed my entire life.

He started stalking me, continuously asking about you. I have lost my job, my home, and my dog who is not allowed refuge in the women's shelter where I now reside, and I want you to know I will never forgive you.

Jenny Butler's Biography

Jenny Butler has had numerous short stories published in a variety of literary journals. You can read more about her on her website www.drjennybutler.com. You can also find her on Twitter (@jenny_butler_) and on Instagram (@spiral_eyed_grrl).

422: SELF-SERVICE

by Patricia Mudge

Tom's heart banged in his chest. He'd expected Toby's usual exuberant welcome, but instead he found him lying flat out on the kitchen floor with laboured breathing and a bloated belly. Tom laid down next to Toby to comfort him.

"What happened here, mate?" he asked as he scanned the room for clues.

The penny dropped when he spotted, screwed up in the corner, the newly opened but completely empty bag of kibble.

"I get it, self-service and self-inflicted," he said.

Patricia Mudge's Biography

A bit of a late starter, I qualified as a primary school teacher as a mature student. Now retired, I enjoy unleashing the stories in my head onto the written page. I'm hoping to be a published author one day.

~

423: LOSING THE GAME

by Neil D Cross

"Which bit of the rules didn't you understand? After you use up a billion words, you're excluded from The Game."

I stared at the avatar sullenly. I knew his sort; trying to trick me into using my word quota.

"I need you to speak to me, sir."

I panicked. "I thought it was only my words that counted."

"I'm afraid not, sir. If you'd read the small print…"

I shushed him. "How many left?"

He held up 2 fingers.

GAME OVER.

Neil D Cross' Biography

Living the simple life in sleepy Suffolk, I've taken up samurai blogging. Gonzo tales of nonsense and nuggets of insight that filter through to my stupid brain. Or just shouting at emptiness. Or just being. Or all of the above.

www.searchingforstillnesszen.wordpress.com

424: FINAL

by Karen McClure

"Do you want the bad news now, or after your shift?"
    "Now."
    "You're on a final."
    "A final, final, or a just a final?"
    "A final, final."
    "Why aren't I fired?"
    "We like you."
    "You can fire me if you want."
    "We don't want to, we like you."
    "But I'm on a final, final. I should be fired."
    "You have to be good for six months."
    "Is that even possible?"
    "You've done it before."
    "Really?"
    "On your final, final, final."
    "Oh."

Karen McClure's Biography

My name is Karen McClure, I am 56 years old and I live in the state of Washington in the United States. I have been writing most of my life. I work for a hardware store.

~

425: RICKY THE BORDER COLLIE AND IRA THE COCKAPOO

by Linda Scogings

"Why did she bring that ugly, smelly puppy home?" asked Ricky.
    "I am not ugly or smelly. I'm your new friend."
    "I hope you don't bark too much. I like to doze in the afternoons."
    "Life is for fun and playing," Ira said, in a squeaky little voice.
    "Just behave. The rules are, don't eat my food or lie on my chair or sit with Mum. She is mine."
    "I just want to be your friend. Let me be your brother."

Linda Scogings' Biography

I enjoy writing and love dogs, they have such great characters.

426: UMBRELLA MANIFESTO

by Brianna Damplo

Have you ever considered the fact that I might hate the rain?

Why do I need to bear, stoically, all the cold, dampness in my wings, when you shiver at the first drop of water?

Coward.

I've talked it over with the others. We're done. Done with being forgotten in restaurants and movie theatres. You think we enjoy being propped up against hard, dirty concrete? Forget it. We're through.

And if you don't like it, then you can just get wet.

Brianna Damplo's Biography

Brianna Damplo is a poet and a writer who enjoys throwing her characters into dangerous situations for their own development. She also appreciates the quiet life of tea and fantasy novels.

~

427: THIS IS THE WAY THE WORLD ENDS

by Charlotte West

Birdsong.

Sweet music speckled through the dust, which settles on broken bricks and shattered glass.

Sobs.

Intertwined with the melody, a baseline of deep sadness, throbbing like a heartbeat.

Rain.

The harmony, dripping from clouds, suffocating the sickly yellow sky and bleeding into the ground; scorched, bruised, aching with the pain of what it had to endure.

But that birdsong keeps playing. Piercing its way through the smog, clean and determined, it tries to bring back light to the dying land.

Charlotte West's Biography

Charlotte is a keen amateur writer, putting her mind to a range of projects including children's stories and recipe books. Her favourite genre to write is dystopian flash fiction, which she hopes to one day amalgamate into one coherent novel.

428: FORGET IT

by Chris Green

Dennis was becoming rather forgetful. He had been on his way to the dentist when he realised he'd left his wallet at home. Now he was rushing back to his house.

Last week, he'd forgotten his twin sister's birthday.

He was going to be late – only ten minutes or so – but he was a stickler for punctuality.

He arrived at the surgery hot and flustered.

"Dennis Crunchfoot," he announced. "Eleven thirty."

The receptionist frowned.

"Ah, Mr Crunchfoot. Your appointment was yesterday."

Chris Green's Biography

Chris Green is a former accountant from the north west of England. He is a reader, an occasional writer and a failed singer. His interests include football, music hall and cheese.

~

429: OPIOID EPIDEMIC

by Matthew Willis

The man sits and drinks wine and waits.

Packages are delivered to cities around the nation. Satellites coordinate and connect to a supercomputer, ready to recognise and process over three hundred million faces. An automated factory continues its work, untouched by human hands since it was built. The design for the mosquito micro-drone hides in his files. Three milligrams of carfentanil rests, divided between each drone. The wine falls to the floor, but does not fall alone.

Tonight, a country dies.

Matthew Willis' Biography

Matthew Willis is a contractor in Appalachia, writing when he's not building kitchens and baths.

430: MUM AND ME FINDING OUR OWN CHURCH

by Sandra 'Chas' Hines

Before Dutch elm disease claimed all the trees, the park whispered with a gazillion branches of conversation. Removing our shoes, we dug our toes into the mud edging the pond, then, dipping them into the water, watched the earth ebb away in grey-green toned ripples.

"Pah," she scoffed, ever the fashionista, "blue and green should never be seen? Nonsense." She swept her arm wide, indicating the colour of the trees against the electric blue sky. "Now, this," she said, "is heaven."

Sandra 'Chas' Hines' Biography

Hi, my name is Chas. As a very creative child, I won lots and lots of competitions. I suppose adult life and adult responsibilities got in the way. So, here I am. First words for years. First competition for years.

~

431: THINGS THAT HELP

by Niamh Burke

"How will we keep her cool?"

"Just shove her in the freezer beside the peas."

A brief silence. My mouth quivered and I made a strange noise. I tried to disguise it as a cough. There's inappropriate and then there's laughing at a joke where your dead niece is the punchline. Stillbirth is hardly side-splitting material, is it?

In the end, we howled with laughter. Screeched the place down. Granny blessed herself, as if by way of an apology to God.

Niamh Burke's Biography

Niamh Burke has an MA in journalism and a professional diploma in digital marketing. She is based in Dublin.

432: EXPECTATION

by Julie Goodswen

I paced the room, glancing every time I passed.

Waiting.

How long had I been here? Patiently waiting.

Seconds turned into minutes; minutes became hours.

Still waiting.

I checked my watch, not remembering the time when I last looked. Pointless.

My heart beat its anticipation into my temples. The clock on the far wall beat its own hypnotic rhythm.

I walked the slow walk of a man who could do nothing. Headed back, finally done.

The message read: 'Windows Update Complete'.

Julie Goodswen's Biography

Nearing the end of my first half century, I have yet to have significant work published but am continuing valiantly on my quest. I write short stories and am working on my first novel.

www.storytellingdancer.com

~

433: IMMORTAL LIFE

by Michaela Mechura

"Madeleine?" Her mind drifted away. "Can't live without you," I sang, hoping memories would flood her brain.

Silence fell, increasing the distance between us.

"I'm so close to discovering a drug. Some of your prions are in the wrong conformation. We just need an enzyme which can change their structure. And then you live on. And I will live on in you."

"You already do." She longed to touch me, but couldn't. For I was only a memory. "You always will."

Michaela Mechura's Biography

Michaela Mechura is studying microbiology and genetics at the University of Vienna. She loves to combine her knowledge with creativity in research and in writing, perceiving that science doesn't suppress her imagination but sparks it.

434: FATHER KNOWS BEST

by Diane de Anda

"You're too young to go to an R movie," her father insisted.

"But Steve's 18, so I can get in with him," the 15-year-old replied.

"You're too young to *see* an R movie. Subject closed." Her father turned and walked away.

She ran into her bedroom and locked the door, yelling, "It's so unfair."

She sat on her bed, pulled the plastic stick out of her sweater pocket and stared at the window in the centre, which was no longer clear.

Diane de Anda's Biography

Diane de Anda has published fiction, poetry and essays in *Rosebud, Straylight, Storyteller, Pacific Review, Bilingual Review, Frogpond, Modern Haiku, Bottle Rockets, Presence* and others, satire in *Humor Times*, eight children's books and a collection of 40 flash fiction stories.

~

435: RHYTHM

by Esosa Kolawole

"Trust me."

I felt his heart beat through the tip of my fingers. Every single pound in his chest sent a shock through my body. I could tell a good or bad person through the rhythm of their heartbeat. It was a gift but, with Ade, I couldn't.

Eye to eye. Another blast tore into the air and my eyes darted everywhere. Tables and chairs were all upside down, legs in the air, amid debris of cement block.

"OK," I whimpered.

Esosa Kolawole's Biography

Esosa Kolawole loves writing paranormal stories and when she isn't writing, she's playing games on her PlayStation or learning graphic designing online.

436: THE CURSE

by Kerry Robinson

The town had been silent since the hanging of old Beatrice Macintyre. She was hung for practicing sorcery. Local legends claimed she'd cursed Beacon Cove and all who resided there. Her body was then buried in an unmarked grave, high along the cliff's edge, near the outskirts of town.

Twenty years later a monsoon hit the coast, causing mudslides on the cliffs. Her remains washed up ashore. The curse returned with a vengeance, delivering evil darkness.

History's bound to repeat itself.

Kerry Robinson's Biography

My name is Kerry Robinson, I'm 49 years old and write on a website called *FanStory*. I write poetry, short stories and am currently working on my first novel. I'm published in *Haiku Anthology – Observations and Insights*.

~

437: HOTSHOT

by Amanda Garzia

Was that Alexandra? Vacuuming?

Nah, her flawlessly groomed daughter was more likely drying her curls.

She raced up, dust cloth and all, to check.

The teenager, hairdryer in hand, was blasting the carpet with heat.

"Look. Gum's almost gone. I'll remove what's left with tweezers."

The girl had potential.

The wall-to-wall still needed hoovering, but that was child's play compared to this.

And with a blow-dryer, no less. It might just be the thing to lift the fluff off those lampshades.

Amanda Garzia's Biography

At age 12, Amanda typed the first edition of her own (now defunct) magazine, posting copies to Canadian friends left behind on coming to Malta. Having written for *The Times of Malta* and *Child* magazine, she's presently concentrating on fiction.

www.facebook.com/mandy.garzia

438: EVERYBODY, SOMEBODY, ANYBODY, NOBODY

by Reed Markham

I teach college. It was a warm September afternoon when I assigned my class a group project on communication. I had one common group with four members named Everybody, Somebody, Anybody and Nobody.

Everybody was excited about the project. Somebody was worried that Everybody would procrastinate working on the project. Nobody thought that this would be a big problem. Everybody, the group leader, asked if Anybody would be willing to work on the assignment.

In the end, Nobody completed the work.

Reed Markham's Biography

I am a college professor who teaches classes in speech communication at a state college in central Florida. I enjoy creative writing and editing.

~

439: A SURPRISE FOR THE WEEKEND WARRIOR

by Rebecca Capel

We are grouped at the start line in the pale light of dawn.
Nervous. Excited. Warmed-up.
The claxon sounds. We charge off. An hour of magical freedom.
Legs pump. Hearts thump. This is what we came for.
The crowd chants, "First the worst, second the best, third the one with the hairy chest."
Months of training. So close. Not close enough.
I look down and see the first downy fur start to sprout.
It itches.
Always read the terms and conditions.

Rebecca Capel's Biography

Rebecca Capel is an academic researching the heart. In her spare time, she is a competitive judo player and an only slightly less competitive D&D bard/dungeon master. She lives with her husband and cat in the countryside near Oxford.

440: OLD SPAIN

by Patricia Tarrant Brown

Women in black sit, work-worn in shawls, casting dark shadows on bright summer walls.

Girls in white dresses are at the church door. Teenagers throw sunflower seeds on the floor.

Mornings yawn into afternoon, chasing the sun, waiting the moon.

Memories surge of a daughter or son, like layers of petticoats, glimpses gone.

Eyes that were wide are almost shut and trembling hands wrestle to make the cut.

Passion departed long ago, but a thin-lipped smile remembers the glow.

Old Spain.

Patricia Tarrant Brown's Biography

Part Spanish, I am a retired educationalist and academic writer who is now enjoying putting words together just for the hell of it. I've recently written a novel of 85,000 words and fancied a change.

~

441: COTTON CANDY, ELEPHANTS AND LADYBUGS

by Mariam Mansuryan

"How many times do I have to tell you that cotton candy isn't made of clouds?"

"Mum…"

"How long will it take you to finally believe that elephants don't fly?"

"I'll never believe that…"

"So why do you listen to him when he says there's something wrong with you?"

"Mum…"

"What, Jim? What? I'm sorry he says that. Don't listen to him, he's an idiot. The stupidest idiot this world has ever seen."

"There is a ladybug on your shoe, Mum."

Mariam Mansuryan's Biography

I am Mariam, a 17-year-old student who wants to be a screenwriter and a film director someday (hopefully soon). I am from Armenia and I currently live in the Czech Republic.

442: A SILENT LEGACY

by Charles K Manila

Here lies the body of Cormac. Alone. Counting the cracks on the ceiling of a dimly lit hotel room. Dust falling from the walls and the sound of thunder nearby. Static from the nearby television and sirens in the distance. Sinking on the bed, grieving a life lost through his silence. An overwhelming regret left in his bones.

He no longer possesses a genuine smile. But carries the crooked smile he leaves on for show.

The scene of his broken heart.

Charles K Manila's Biography

Charles K Manila is a passionate educator of English and social sciences. With a background in anthropology, he is fascinated with cultures and stories. He is also an aspiring novelist and avid photographer.

~

443: FAIREST

by Sue Vincent

"It wasn't me."

The shattered mirror flickered in the candlelight. A thousand shards of beauty looked back at the queen, each image that of raven-haired youth, milk white skin unflawed by time, and rose red lips parted in sweet serenity.

Majesty turned to look at the flasks and flagons, the lotions and potions that surrounded her. A single tear melted the pallid paint on her cheek, tracking her misery. The vain pursuit of vanity came crashing down.

"It was never me…"

Sue Vincent's Biography

Sue Vincent is a Yorkshire-born writer, esoteric teacher and director of The Silent Eye School of Consciousness. She lives in Buckinghamshire and is owned by a small dog who also writes.

www.scvincent.com

444: THE DREAMED INDEPENDENCE

by Cleiton Pinho

One day, a very depressed boy dreamed of leaving home in search of happiness. His sister, knowing that, invited him to live with her. The boy was glad as he knew this would be a great opportunity. He packed his bags and took the first plane on the fifth day of November.

Arriving there, his sister could not support him. She was being manipulated by her husband. Since then, he's left his sister's house and moved to live alone without disturbance.

Cleiton Pinho's Biography

Cleiton Pinho is from Rio de Janeiro, Brazil. He is in a loving family and passionate about them. An optimist, he is always looking forward for great opportunities, loves helping people and making new friends.

~

445: CHILD OF THE NIGHT

by Amberlie Robinson

She had always been different.

She had never fitted in with her family even as a child and, although she had hoped this would change with starting school, the feeling of being an outsider never left her. She didn't know where her home was. She had to find her place in life.

Then one night, in quiet despair, she looked up at the stars and realised that in them her soul was reflected back at her – a child of the night.

Amberlie Robinson's Biography

Amberlie Robinson is an aspiring writer currently living in London but who hopes to travel the world. Often with her head in a book, Amberlie also enjoys painting and long-distance running, both of which are fuelled by her caffeine addiction.

446: A VERY ROUGH DIAMOND

by Chris Black

Life is a bed of roses. These words were drilled into me from a young age.
So it was, I grew up expecting all to be good with the world.
How naive.
It was all about picking your step with caution.
Don't believe all you're told, less of what you see.
This bed of roses turned into a bed of thorns.
The ring was placed on my finger. Suddenly, the monster was released.
Wedding bed turned from white to blood red.

Chris Black's Biography

Chris is a resident of Enniscorthy, Co. Wexford, Ireland. Writing poetry/short stories for the past quarter century or so. Achieved his goal by publishing his book of poetry/short stories titled *Same Train, Different Track* in September 2016.
www.chrisblack2012.wordpress.com

~

447: HISTORY REPORT

by Emma Burnett

It used to be that people died slowly, painfully. Of course, we're not like that anymore. The designers changed that. Death is quick now, and painless. You just, well, turn off.

You never know when it might happen. The information is part of your design, deep programmed, so you can't access it. No one worries anymore about a slow death, or being a burden on others, or being robbed by corporations that sell life to the dying.

I sometimes wonder when—

Emma Burnett's Biography

Emma is a part-time PhD student, part-time athlete and part-time parent. If she ever has free time, she spends it reading.

448: THE CLEANER

by Sarah Mosedale

She enters the room. First person to do so in 10 years. Dim light struggling through grimy windows, shrouded furniture, carpet almost invisible beneath thick dust layers.

She hauls in her cleaning gear, then, hands on hips, surveys the scene. Where to begin? Perhaps that far corner, do a first sweep while retreating to the door. Makes sense.

Tackling the flimsy spider graveyard first, she holds her breath. But what is that shape rising behind her, emerging from beyond the sofa?

Sarah Mosedale's Biography

Sarah Mosedale is a researcher and writer based in Manchester, England. She has recently started to get involved in writing flash fiction and is enjoying learning from some established flash writers and contributing to her local spoken word community.

~

449: NO USE CRYING OVER SPILLED MILK

by Nicole Loh

A lifetime of history, but words were escaping us.

Our gazes were locked. I had forgotten the crow's feet and his tooth digging into his lip whenever he grinned, or the way he played with his collar.

A bus pulled up at the stop, and kids ran out.

He stood, hugged a girl, and spun her. Before he left, he smiled again. I watched as they left, getting smaller with each step.

In another world, she might have had my eyes.

Nicole Loh's Biography

Malaysian. Lover of all things art. Nicole has chosen the written word as her medium to bring her brand of art into the world, despite the harsh realities of unpaid bills. Her favourite subjects include cultural identities, feminism and music.

Twitter: @nicoleloh_

450: CAN'T WAIT 'TIL MORNING

by Frank Havemann

Out of the window,
slide down the extension roof.
Tap, tap, tap, whooosh, thump.

Hop over the fence,
pull the strings of her hood snug,
breathe. Big smile.

She is good at this.
All dark here, too – no barking...
just cats on this street.

Dash across the deck,
jewellery box through the flap,
breathe, smile and scramble.

Fence, tree, window, breathe...
A green dot pulses slowly.
Grab mobile. Smile. Breathe.

Tap, tap, tap, whooosh, thump.
Alignment: good chaotic.
Little ninja smiles.

Frank Havemann's Biography

Frank Havemann is from the '80s and lives in Oxford, UK, with his family and cats, enjoying a varied diet of writing, maths, books, gardening, photography, music and sports.

~

451: TRAVELOGUE

by Peter Loftus

They saw us coming a mile away. "English, English, hallo."

"We're Irish."

"Ah." Their faces turned to us like sunflowers. "Irish. Shamrock Rovers, Bobby Geldof, Jams Joyce, howsitgoin?"

Anna smiled, and I couldn't suppress a chortle. They pounced on these signs of victory with piratical glee.

"Yes, Irish. I come from Coooark."

Another flashed his teeth. "Ballygobackwards."

They flocked to us like sparrows, holding up hookahs, bags of tissue-soft leather, dervish slippers.

"Buy a present for your wife, you stupid eejit."

Peter Loftus' Biography

Peter Loftus is currently reading (and writing) for an MA in creative writing with the Open University. His short stories have appeared in *Focus Magazine*, *Visionary Tongue*, *Midnight Street*, *AlienSkin*, *Jupiter SF* and *Monomyth*, among others.

~

452: NO MORE FOOTPRINTS

by Steven Barrett

He knew he was dead as soon as he stepped in the snow. There were no footprints.

He'd always loved being the one that left their footprints in the fresh snow. Running outside on a winter's morning as a child. Walking to work, rather than taking the early bus. Finally, seconds ago, as an old man, escaping from the care home.

Sadly, there would be no more footprints. But he hoped that he'd left a good impression on the world anyway.

Steven Barrett's Biography

Steven was born and lives in Edinburgh. He tries keeping fit by running and enjoys entering races. He has just started writing short stories, after years of just thinking about doing it.

453: AWKWARD

by Edward Mortenson

12:31PM
Hi Dani, it's Ben. Cath gave me your number, hope you don't mind. How's your hols? Fancy meeting up sometime?
13:00PM
Anyone there LOL?
13:15PM
Hello?
14:00PM
Fine, whatever. Didn't think you'd be like the other girls, but clearly I was wrong.
14:15PM
You weren't even that hot anyway, so don't feel flattered I spoke to you. I was just really bored. Haha.

14:33PM
You've got the wrong number, Ben. Also, we're having a chat when you get home. Dad.

Edward Mortenson's Biography

Edward Mortenson graduated from the University of Dundee with a BA in English literature and has appeared in Ad Hoc Fiction's weekly competition (though he is still yet to win).

~

454: THE BLACKNESS

by Caroline Cowan

The malevolent apparition slowly materialised.

The room grew icy cold. It glided silently to the sleeping girl. The black form sat by her. She rolled over, pulling the duvet round her, not understanding why the cover wouldn't move.

She opened her eyes and shivered. Was this a dream? The dark, menacing mass wavered, then slithered off the bed and disappeared.

Sleep returned.

Morning arrived and the night's horror came flooding back.

She knew the evil blackness was coming to take her.

Caroline Cowan's Biography

I have been retired for about four years. I have joined the U3A group of writers. This is all very new to me, but I'm enjoying it.

455: THE PERFECT ANGLE

by Sue Moos

They didn't have to wait long in casualty. There was too much blood seeping through the towel, running up her arm and dripping from her elbow.

"We see this so often, it's got itself a name – Avocado Hand," said the nurse.

The woman said nothing. The cut was at a deceptively, perfect angle.

"Is it painful?"

"Not as bad as when the knife went in." She looked over at her husband, not daring to say they had no avocados at home.

Sue Moos' Biography

Sue's hobbies of walking and baking provide endless opportunities for cooking up all sorts of ideas for writing.

~

456: CATFISH FOR TEA

by Peter Gregory & David Gough

Patsy: How was detention?

Jezebel: That teacher called Mum. I'm grounded.

Jezebel: I told you to say you did it.

Patsy: I did try, I'll chat after tea.

Jezebel: Hell no, I'm sneaking out.

Patsy: You're not meeting that lad? The one who messaged you?

Jezebel: Yeah. If Mum calls, say I'm with you, OK?

Patsy: S'pose. You're naughty.

Jezebel: I should be back by 10PM. Bye.

Patsy: You there?

Patsy: Jez?

Network provider: Unable to deliver message. Check network provider.

Peter Gregory & David Gough's Biography

We have a passion for writing. Being homeless only spurred us to write more. We joined a homeless food-bank and charity, producing their very first newsletter specially for them. Several short stories later, we're sending our work into writing competitions.

457: BURIED IDEAS

by Justine Quammie

Woman. Submission good. Independence bad.

Vonnegut's Handicapper General is going to get you. Don't you know that thinking freely could be punished by death? Don't you know your luminous beauty needs to be tempered by masks and mole hairs? Don't you know that glowing in the limelight of ambition and recognition is forbidden? Be a sheep and blend in. Follow your leaders. This might sound cruel and impertinent but really it is for your own good.

Woman. Regression good. Individuality bad.

Justine Quammie's Biography

My poetry name is Travelling Roots (and my government name is Justine Q.B.). I live in Washington, D.C., USA, where I teach English language arts as a way of feeding my love of luxury and comfort.

Instagram handle: @forloveofwriting

~

458: PAYBACK

by Andrew Jones

"Do this for me," he says, handing me the gun, "and we're quits. He always has his breakfast there. Here's his picture. Just one shot to the head, then drop the gun and walk out. No one will remember your face. They'll all be too shocked to react. I'll see to it that the cameras are off."

I raise the gun.

"What are you doing?"

My ears ring. Blood spatters the wall. There's more than one way of cancelling a debt.

Andrew Jones' Biography

Andrew Jones is a retired lawyer who took up writing for fun after years of drafting professional reports and legal documents. He finds it very liberating to just make stuff up.

459: TYRANT

by Roger Newton

You use many disguises to submerge your ambitions, but the result is always the same. Your adversaries are never apprised of your intentions, yet they die in their thousands as a consequence of your aggression. You consider them at best trivial, at worst not at all, being an unfortunate obstruction to your plan.

Had you paused on your journey to consider your actions, you may have realised that your ultimate objective was impossible to achieve. The devil himself awaits your soul.

Roger Newton's Biography

I long since retired from engineering management in the steel rolling mill manufacturing industry. I play the flute badly, enjoy watching cricket and rugby union and also spend a lot of time recycling things from discarded wood.

~

460: DANCER

by Mark Johnson

Phyllis loved watching the ballerina on television pirouette on pointe shoes. She could feel the music, but with muscles atrophied to make her a prisoner in her body. Dance was her life, a soft oasis of elegance in her antiseptic reality of a hospital room, and now she could only watch and listen.

"It's OK, Mum. You can let go." Her daughter's voice calmed her spirit. "I love you." Tired and hurting, she smiled and went home on pointe shoes, pirouetting.

Mark Johnson's Biography

Mark Johnson has published four books: *A Twist of Fate* (novel, 2012), *Mississippi State Boards Handbook* (nonfiction, 2016), *Ecruan Tales*, (short story collection, 2017) and *Managing Using the Diamond Principle* (nonfiction, 2018).

461: THERE GOES THE BUS

by Kylan Fedje

There goes the bus. I'm definitely not a runner. Struggling to catch up. Waving. My. Arms. Frantically. Can't get his attention. I'm always invisible to everyone.

Dad's at work. Mum's halfway across the country. It's a 15 minute drive. Better start walking.

I am not in shape at all. I need to start working out. My feet are so sore. I'm gonna be late. I'm a complete failure. Nothing ever works out. Is everything just doomed to fall apart like this?

Kylan Fedje's Biography

Kylan Fedje is a senior at Lawrence North High School in Indianapolis, Indiana. He plans on graduating in the spring of 2019 and hopes to study history in college.

~

462: YOUR THOUGHTS, MY THOUGHTS

by C. H. Connor

"It'll be quick, I promise. Just wait for him to fall asleep."

"I've already told you, no."

"Oh yes you will. I'll make sure of it."

"Listen to me and leave me alone. I'm not interested in hearing what you have to say any more."

Mike edged the bathroom door open. "Hey, babe, who are you talking to?"

Emma's eyes shifted from her reflection in the mirror as she turned around to face him. "Nobody, darling. I'm coming to bed now."

C. H. Connor's Biography

I have been writing stories since I can remember. Those with thrills and an edge of crime are my absolute favourite. In 2019, I will be publishing my debut novel, which also happens to be of the crime thriller genre.

Twitter: @CharlesConnor_

463: RAIN

by W. E. Jones

The rain lashed down so hard I couldn't see through the windshield. There was no choice but to pull over.

When it finally cleared, absolutely everything had washed away. Nothing but water as far as the eye could see. Almost as if I was parked on a world sized mirror.

Cautiously, I stepped out of the car. The water only reached the top of my soles. The ground was still firm underneath.

I got back in the car and drove on.

W. E. Jones' Biography

W. E. Jones is an Australian writer and psychology student. He has an unused education degree and way too much experience in retail. Like many writers, he lives with his wife, child and cat.

~

464: EMPTINESS

by Anna Ferrar

"What's up with you this morning?" he asked.

I propped myself against the headboard and took a deep breath. I've heard it before; it wouldn't matter. He never listened.

"I... I don't know how to tell you..." I let out a sigh.

He reached for my arm and gave me a pat, as if I was his pet dog or cat. I felt nothing.

As he left for work, I picked up the phone. A voice said, "Hi."

"I need you."

Anna Ferrar's Biography

Anna lives in Brisbane, Queensland. She writes horror fictions, draws, sings and is learning to create marbling effect on canvas, but her main interest is writing flash or micro fiction. She spends her free time at home and reading stories online.

465: FLAT MAP

by Sarah Fletcher

"What are we supposed to do now?" wailed Rachel, turning in circles to gaze in panic at the endless expanse of indistinguishable trees.

Mae plonked herself down with her back against a sapling and looked from her dead mobile phone to the woods and back. She looked at the compass, cracked and twisting back and forth uncertainly. She looked at the ground, the craggy trunks, the hidden horizon, the shadows.

She began to gather twigs, eyes suddenly bright.

"Adventure," she answered.

Sarah Fletcher's Biography

Sarah Fletcher is a generalist creative from Australia now living in Southampton, UK. She writes poetry and fiction, illustrates, photographs and sings. Her blog, and links to the various things she does, can be found on:

www.phdancer.wordpress.com

~

466: GRAVE SITUATION

by Lexikon

We were burying Uncle Henry. Again. It had become evident in recent years that people were starting to doubt an 80 year old could run a marathon.

I spotted him instantly. "You shouldn't be here."

"Look how many people will miss me." Henry grinned, flashing a hint of fang. Wig and make up removed, he was 35 again, like the first time he'd died. He waved playfully at the young shop assistant across his own grave.

"Next time, I'll cremate you."

Lexikon's Biography

Tormented by small children by day, Lexikon retreats to the haven of writing by night. She worked as a scientist before teaching and has thus developed a penchant for experimenting and explosions. Her recent work can be found on:

www.lexikon.home.blog

467: HOME-SCHOOLING HENRY

by Wendy Fletcher

"No school, I just want to play," wailed Henry.

"OK." Mother smiled. "Let's play Sock Sorting. Red, blue, black... Now we will make a shopping list. A for apples, asparagus, B for bananas, biscuits..."

She pointed to the clock hands. "Ten past five, teatime. Can you count out the plates and knives and forks?"

"I still don't want to go to school. Learning is boring."

"Don't worry," said Mother, "you won't have time for school. You will be too busy playing."

Wendy Fletcher's Biography

I am the leader of the Whittlesey Wordsmiths, our local U3A creative writing group. I have just finished writing a memoir of my childhood, growing up in two Great Eastern Railway carriages in the fens of Cambridgeshire.

~

468: MY DARLING

by Kitty Litteur

She came home again. It didn't last. It never does. But for a weighted tear-drop of time, I am permitted to play my part and relish my script in earnest.

I run a deep bath. I run to the corner store for overpriced razors and her favourite sweet things. I brew sugary tea and take my offerings to her.

She thanks me in silence from behind blank eyes. She eats. She sleeps. She steals. She goes. But briefly, I am Mum.

Kitty Litteur's Biography

Kitty Litteur resides in the green blue grey of the South Island, New Zealand. She has also lived much elsewhere. She has an MA in fine arts and theatre studies.

469: LOUGHBOROUGH LITE

by Robert Adams

Libby lights her Loughborough Lite.

She inhales, lingering over the flavoursome fag.

She takes another deep draw, savouring the taste. Her Lionel. He's still sitting on the shelf on the sideboard. Or at least, mostly.

Libby glances at the Loughborough Lite. She slits them open and sprinkles in a splattering of Lionel before re-sealing them with a slither of rolling paper.

Libby sucks in a last ardent, intense intake of her fag.

Her throat burns in loving memory of her Lionel.

Robert Adams' Biography

Robert Adams. Author of *DISCover the Power of You*. Winner of writing awards. Most recently, flash-fiction 'Time to Think' accepted for publication in 2018 Autumn/Winter edition of *Reflections* magazine, and winner of the Stanley Wilson Monologue Competition for 'Gavin's Revenge'.

~

470: A WHALE OF A TALE

by Jon Spencer

Forty minutes after the first whale breeched, the boat captain blew the siren to signal the end of the boat tour. No one was disappointed. Except Doug, who was still sleeping.

Sister Emma, who was soaking wet from whale spume, grinning ear to ear, gave him a hug, which, naturally, woke him up. His wails, the siren's wails and the smack of the whales tails, all made for good tales in the pub afterwards.

Emma learned to let sleeping Dougs lie.

Jon Spencer's Biography

Jon Spencer works in non-profits and writes fiction, screenplays and fantasy business plans. He has written and edited for Thomson Reuters and runs a writers group out of the back room of a Toronto tea shop.

471: CHARLESTON, 2081

by Kelsey Gallo

I'm an archaeologist emeritus, equipped with an iPhone 75. While swiping through my career's work, I happen to find a digital time capsule: a poem I wrote while just an undergrad there.

"81 words, 81 years since I was born."

Who'd ever know? It was a homage to times unchanged – to times when word counts spurred creativity. It was a glimpse years into the future... but each year was one off my life.

"81 words, 81 years since I was born."

Kelsey Gallo's Biography

Kelsey Gallo is a freshman at the College of Charleston, majoring in religious studies. She hails from Pittsburgh, Pennsylvania, USA. Writing is her hobby and she thanks Mr Adam Rubenstein and Mr Christopher Fielden for allowing her to develop it.

~

472: TAKEN FOR A RIDE

by Laura Besley

Jeremy needed cash. He set up a fake website and chose a charity that he thought would appeal to people's hearts (and coffers). He posted links on social media informing his friends he was doing a sponsored bike ride.

One person donated. Then another. And another. Each with words of encouragement. The initial elation of money arriving slowly sank and congealed in the legs that weren't out training.

And on the day of the allotted bike ride, he rode fifty miles.

Laura Besley's Biography

Laura Besley writes short fiction in the precious moments that her children are asleep. Her fiction has appeared online (*Spelk, Ellipsis Zine*) as well as in print (*Flash: The International Short Story Magazine*) and in various anthologies (*Adverbially Challenged Vol. 1 & 2*).

473: THE FIRST SOFERET

by Liz Berg

The handwashing, the blessing, the checking, were all completed. The parchment, unrolled and weighted, faint lines scored yesterday in preparation, glistened pristine.

All the arguments, the tears, the blackmail, even the threat of banishment culminated in this momentous occasion.

No time for regrets.

The scribe breathed deeply. Picked up a quill. Sharpened it. Dipped it into the specially made ink. Checked once more. Then began to carefully form the first letter, the angle elegant and exact.

Torah, written by a woman.

Liz Berg's Biography

Liz loves writing and singing in Cornwall. One day she hopes to write everywhere. www.facebook.com/liz.berg.18

~

474: AT FIRST SIGHT

by Ayesha Hassan

My first day and I'm lost, thought young Shelly as she opened the office door.

"Please, don't be a fool," she said to herself, clenching her jaw apprehensively.

Close behind her, she heard a booming voice. "Don't worry, I'm new too."

She turned with a sudden jerk and saw a tall boy looming over her.

"How are you? Please, don't be shy."

She stared at the handsome boy for a while, and then responded, with a smile, "Hi, my name's Shelly."

Ayesha Hassan's Biography

My name is Ayesha Hassan, a 20-year-old girl living in the country of Pakistan. My hobbies are simple; writing, reading and listening in on people's conversations. My favourite genre is literary fiction and fantasy.

475: GOLDFISH

by Lynn White

Her favourite foods were prawns and chocolate biscuits.

I wondered if she would be fooled by torn pieces of plastic, heavily disguised. She ate them eagerly. And then she spat them out, her look of disgust clearly expressing her thoughts. *I'm not one of them braindead sea fish, you know. Oh, and cut out the raspberries, please, I'm not a blackbird either.*

Then she blew a few bubbles, swished her tail and swam off in search of tadpoles and other delights.

Lynn White's Biography

Lynn White lives in North Wales. Her work is influenced by issues of social justice and events, places and people she has known or imagined. She is especially interested in exploring the boundaries of dream, fantasy and reality.

www.lynnwhitepoetry.blogspot.com

~

476: TEARDROPS COULD HAVE CHANGED AUSTRALIA

by Ted Bragg

Teardrops in the desert.

No reconciliation with Australia's Aborigines needed... if only explorers could read the signs.

Burke and Wills, commissioned in 1860 to find a route to the top, were staggering back to base, camels and men, weak and dying.

Recently-discovered teardrops, outlined in stone by the Mithaka tribe, pointed to water.

Bad luck if strange spirit white men died there.

If the explorers saw, understood, survived, Mithaka would have been heroes and black and white Australia would be one.

Ted Bragg's Biography

My trade is journalism. For a decade, I ran a defence-focused newspaper from the largest Army barracks in the country. I am secretary for a group of ex-servicemen and women who provide field support for expeditions in the desert.

477: THE GIRAFFE AND THE WATCH

by Vicki Murray

Picked up my books from the library and decided to have lunch in the park. No one was there except an occasional squirrel and shady oak trees.

A man's voice interrupted the silence. "Do you have the time? A giraffe broke my watch."

Startled, I responded, "A giraffe?"

He explained, "Yes, I work for the circus, taking care of the giraffes, and one stepped on my watch."

"Yes, it's noon."

"Thank you. I have plenty of time to walk to work."

Vicki Murray's Biography

Vicki hikes, kayaks and falls off porches. She lives fulltime in an RV at the beach or in the mountains. Enjoys writing, sketching and reading.

~

478: STONES

by Syreeta Muir

She was angry so she picked up a stone. It was smooth, cold, good for launching. As she held it, tracing its white veins, it began to warm in her hand.

A man passed by with a dog, his face drawn and grey. Without thinking, she stopped him, held out the stone and smiled. He took it. Tears filled his eyes. He nodded once, walked on.

After that, she stopped throwing stones. Instead, she collected them, warmed them, handed them out.

Syreeta Muir's Biography

Syreeta Muir writes poetry, short and flash fiction, with a focus on folklore, nature and trauma.

Find her on Twitter: @hungryghostpoet

479: REMEMBER, REMEMBER...

by A.H. Creed

His infamous temper came from, and was restricted by, his exhaustion. It would rocket up out of nowhere, zenith in a bloom of firecracker rebukes, and fall as a light shower of chagrin straight back down to earth.

Heart attacked, two years before I was born, he saved his pyrotechnic energy for those he loved best. So on broken feet I'd go out all night dancing, if Dad could be there to shout his love at me when I came home.

A.H. Creed's Biography

I am dyslexic, I can't spell. Don't know my commas from my colon, which means I don't write well. But sometimes I write unique, and sometimes I write funny. So I might write *Sixty Shades*, and make loads of money.

~

480: SÉBASTIEN

by Jocelyn Wong

We met in a coffee chain in a foreign country and I let myself set all of my emotional baggage aside and poured myself into adoring him. He made it so easy.

Four days wasn't enough, so I stayed an extra week, yet all the Guinness in the world couldn't drown out thoughts of my imminent departure.

He kissed me at the bus terminal one last time before walking off without a glance back.

Well, at least my conversational French improved.

Jocelyn Wong's Biography

Jocelyn writes candid recollections about chance encounters and failed romantic escapades. She also enjoys dancing salsa and making animal-shaped mugs.

481: ROAD RAGE

by Kelly Van Nelson

Someone is riding my tail. Why can't he allow breathing space like a normal, courteous driver? If he gets any closer, I'll see the hairs up his nostrils.

Horrendous rush hour traffic. I slam on the brakes. My eyes dart to the rear-view mirror to check he's not about to crunch into my car. Catch him muttering something. Maybe he swore. Nah, looks like he's singing. Must be a good tune. Perhaps a bit of Michael Jackson, 'Man in the Mirror'.

Kelly Van Nelson's Biography

Kelly Van Nelson is a fiction author represented by The Newman Agency, with several short stories, poems and magazine articles published in the UK, USA and Australia. Novel shortlisted PenFro, longlisted Exeter Novel Prize, third place Yeovil Literary Prize.

www.kellyvannelson.com

~

482: POISON TONGUE

by Lee Kull

When he laughed at her decision to become a herbalist, she smiled. It hurt, but she smiled.

When he saw that she was serious, he yelled, "What will the neighbours think? You're some kind of incense-breathing new-age nut? Or a witch? Are you out of your mind?"

She argued.

He struck her.

She didn't say another word.

Next morning, she was harvesting herbs, choosing carefully. Hemlock. Belladonna. Wolf's bane.

He didn't even have a chance to complain about his strange-tasting coffee.

Lee Kull's Biography

Lee Kull is an aspiring author with three books in progress: a Christian action/adventure novel, a collection of short stories and an educational children's picture book. Lee's interests vary greatly, but reading, writing and herbalism have always topped the list.

483: PRAYING

by Wright Stone

My knees ache from kneeling on the concrete. I feel the coolness of the gun on the back of my head.

"Please, I don't want to die," I whimper. Tears run down my face. Snot drips over my top lip.

"You don't?"

"No. Do you?"

"Of course not."

"Then why would I?"

"I see your point."

The feeling of metal disappears. I lower my hand, still clutching my wallet.

"Sorry about that," he says. "Slight misunderstanding. Do you need a tissue?"

Wright Stone's Biography

Wright Stone has spent the last four years travelling and teaching English in China and Spain. He now lives in Scotland, where he never takes off his dressing gown and is working on his first children's story.

~

484: LEARNING BY EXPERIENCE

by Khamis Kabeu

I'd been raising chickens for some time and decided to diversify into ducks. One of the ducks laid eggs in a place being wetted by rain. I took the eggs and put them in a dry place.

When the duck came, it dispersed the eggs and refused to sit on them. I tried to force it, to no avail. I enquired about this strange behavior of ducks and was told they don't sit on eggs that have been touched by anybody.

Khamis Kabeu's Biography

I'm a writer from Kenya. I studied writing with the Writers Bureau College of Journalism and once worked as a local correspondent for *Insight on Conflict*, an online publication. I'm now a volunteer with an NGO.

485: THE LAST LAUGH IS ON US

by Patrick Christian

"You ready?" Linda asked.

"Yep," Sara replied.

"Let's go," I said.

We walked quickly toward Michael's Country Bar. We were going to make fun of people.

We walked in. As we walked up the steps, I tripped. I fell and reached up for something to catch. I grabbed onto Sara's shirt and tore it off, exposing her bra. I rolled down the steps clutching her top. Linda burst out laughing. She peed her pants.

We left with everyone laughing at us.

Patrick Christian's Biography

My name is Patrick Christian. I am a 47-year-old author from Wilkes-Barre, PA. I have three books, *Tales of Man, The Tale of Two Hells* and *I Know the Speed of Darkness*.

~

486: IGNORANCE IS BLISS

by Debbie Singh

It was dark, really dark. I walked carefully, eyes squinting, nose wrinkled by the awful stench that grabbed hold of the cold evening air and invaded the anorak that covered my school uniform.

Reaching home, I heard my mother shouting about the government.

"Flaming morons," she screamed. "Pay the proper wages, street lights out, rubbish piled up." Pointing at me, she shrieked, "She has to come home in that. It's like the blitz."

I washed my hands. "Mum, what's for dinner?"

Debbie Singh's Biography

I'm a part-time uni student who writes as a hobby when I have time.

487: BLUE AND PINK

by Liam Rayner

Our first house. The gate squeaked and the path leading to the door was smattered with puddles, even in the summer.

We fought and fumbled. In the winter the wind howled. We huddled underneath the patched blanket we had planned for the dog.

Wood and screws dotted the spare room. One wall pink the other blue. The call came on the way home. I stopped in a layby and prayed for the first time.

I never did finish painting those walls.

Liam Rayner's Biography

Liam spends his time writing novels and shorts, and very occasionally fixes helicopters. A self-published author, dedicated to fantasy and science fiction. If he's not halfway around the world covered in oil and grease, he's at home, deep into his next adventure.

www.amazon.co.uk/-/e/B078JSPWJ9

~

488: THE MAYBE

by T.N.M. Sheppard

It's this moment, harsh fluorescent lights and loud music, tucked into a corner; safe.

I rambled about the sea and, as I glanced up from the greasy burger and fries you had doused in more salt, there was this look on your face. Soft, bright-eyed, a hint of a smile.

Like I was so endearing.

No one had ever looked at me that way.

It stuck in my throat and pulled at my chest like maybe...

But no.

You looked away.

T.N.M. Sheppard's Biography

T.N.M. Sheppard is (mostly) a prose writer with a love for YA literature. She's completed the creative writing MA at Newcastle University and received her BA in psychology from the University of Tennessee in Knoxville.

www.twitter.com/tsheppa3

489: THE DEEP END

by Alison Clary

Harry was not permitted to enter the deep end, per his mother's strict rules.

All summer, she watched him vigilantly as he sat on the pool's edge, poking his toes into the water's surface. The other children splashed and played gleefully, while Harry enviously observed.

One day, he defiantly took a glorious dive into the deep end. His mother, horrified, leaped after him.

As Harry casually and proudly swam to the ladder, he noticed the lifeguard frantically sprinting from his post.

Alison Clary's Biography

Alison Clary is a technical writer from Ocean City, MD. She enjoys participating in fiction competitions, partaking in Netflix binges and pampering her deaf senior rescue dog, Stanley. Her creative work has been accepted by *101 Words, Penultimate Peanut* and *Literary Heist.*

~

490: UPLOAD THIS

by Sean Bain

"I saw you filming it."

"I was trying to help."

"You were laughing?"

"No, I was…"

"Gaining popularity on social media. Do you feel better with your new status?"

"Please, I was trying to help. They caught them, they're imprisoned."

"SHE'S DEAD. Now I have nothing because you're a coward."

"You're blowing this out of proportion."

"No, I'm blowing your brains out."

"Please don't do this, you'll spend the rest of your life in prison."

"I won't. I have two bullets."

Sean Bain's Biography

My name is Sean Bain and this is my first entry to any writing competition of any kind. I am 48 years old, live in Bedfordshire and have no idea what else to put in my 40 word biography.

491: NEVER FALL IN LOVE AT THE END OF AUGUST

by Layla Rogers

We were kids when we met at the end of August, masquerading maturity with lipstick and coffee and crying in the early mornings.

Smokey apprehension foreshadowed classes approaching. It was summer. You should've been outside enjoying the sunshine, but instead you were wherever you were.

The English heat bubbled under her gingerbread skin. I wanted us to be puzzle pieces, but we walked willingly into the honey-trap.

I tried to hide baby fat under my chin, but September found me out.

Layla Rogers' Biography

I'm a student. My submission is a condensed version of a love story I wrote at summer's end while feeling blue about going back to school. My writing is super wordy, so this was a fun challenge for my self-discipline.

~

492: WHAT IS THE SOUND OF ONE HAND?

by Alcuin Edwards

I am the sound of one hand.

I am a singer without a band because I had to leave England in something of a hurry. My band became a trio.

This is not a true koan because, without me, they sound tight, albeit lacking luster.

I, on the other hand, sing only in the shower and covers. Not even my own songs.

What I want is Tinder for bands because I'm lonely on my own.

Is that too much to ask?

Alcuin Edwards' Biography

Performer, promoter, politician, punk, Big C survivor, epileptic. Geschwindischer Schreiber Alcuin Edwards aka Quinn Agathoni aka Emily Zero in Bedford for now.

www.twitter.com/AlcuinHimself

493: THE WALL

by Jackie Hindmarsh

Excited. Today was the day. He clambered out of bed, slipped on his silky, striped trousers, buttoned up his waistcoat and pressed down the lapels on his blue velvet jacket. Dressed regally, he marched stoically towards the wall.

He climbed with ease, the loose stones not giving way until he was at the top. Positioned like a king on a throne, he looked across the landscape.

It was magnificent.

His mistake was to look down at the wall before he fell.

Jackie Hindmarsh's Biography

My name is Jackie Hindmarsh, recently retired and enjoying life with my new puppy Monty, in County Durham. Enjoying giving time to the arts with my art class and the 81 Words challenge.

~

494: DECISIONS, DECISIONS

by Margaret Bell

The group is together, tables set,
the nicest people I've ever met.
Boards at the ready, paper too,
then comes the cry, what can I do?
What we need is a teacher, to help us along,
I think the paper might be wrong.
Is it coffee time yet? I need a break.
With all this thinking, I have a headache.
Oh that is better, now I have an idea,
Christmas time picture is Santa Claus,
together with his sleigh and reindeer.

Margaret Bell's Biography

My name is Margaret Bell, a widow who's 76 years old. I have 4 children, 10 grandchildren and 6 great grandchildren. I lived in Germany for 21 years, then returned to Co. Durham where I started doing art 9 years ago.

495: DEAD SIGNAL

by Diontae Jaegli

They'd done their best to kick the broken glass from their last encounter with a survivor into one corner. Jagged glitter still remained.

In the other corner, Ally huddled. A dirty rabbit plushie pressed to her chest. The tears had dried long ago, but the tracks down her cheeks remained. Her back was pressed to a slab of scratched mahogany; the old, chunky radio that spat static as Danielle twisted knobs.

The signal fizzed as she cranked. They prayed for rescue.

Diontae Jaegli's Biography

Diontae Jaegli is a Canadian mechatronics engineer and fledgling author that takes breaks from building robots to write about them. She's definitely not a time traveller introducing technology early to accelerate history. Who told you that?

~

496: INSIDE

by Alex Blair

He had been placed here by one of the others, sitting on the floor, leaning against the column. His legs were bent up, arms over his knees, his everyday position.

Sometimes he saw the others, sometimes he didn't. Sometimes one would put their face right up to his and make noises. At those times, he'd have to retreat away from the others' world, to his inside world.

All his friends were there and it was beautiful. Nothing bad ever happened there.

Alex Blair's Biography

I'm a retired public servant from Australia. My day job is historical fiction author. Just thought I'd give this a try as a bit of a distraction.

497: FANTASY

by Katie Pepper

His delicate fingers grazed my cheeks as his rich viridian eyes assured my beating heart that the glittering of stars rang true.

He stole the breath from time and reality to tease my heart strings, as the dangerous illusion of twinkling perfection grew from golden moments.

Yet as his lips began their irrevocably consuming descent to seal our esoteric connection, a sharp incessant tug somewhere deep inside me rippled our world.

But I continued holding on, and I almost—

"Wake up."

Katie Pepper's Biography

I am in Year 12, aged 16, and one day I hope to be an author. For now though, I aspire to get through my exams with my sanity intact.

~

498: THE PRIMATE PROJECT

by Tony Thatcher

"Right, let's see what you've done."

A thousand fingers pressed the send command. The invigilator used Bardscript 2231 to scan the day's work and commented, "Not bad, number 387. Could you read it to us please?"

A lightly bearded, stocky man nodded and looked at the antique framed picture on his desk. It showed his rather more hirsute great, great, great, great, great, great, great grandparents working in the same office.

He grunted and whistled the words, "Where are you, Romeo?"

Tony Thatcher's Biography

When I'm not designing stuff for a living, I write short stories, flash fiction and an epic blockbuster novel. Can't complain but would love to tip the balance in favour of the writing.

499: THE SUSPICION OF HERBS

by Jerome Parsons

They had married on Christmas Day and had honeymooned in the lakes. He had sold his flat and moved in on their return. They had been back at work by New Year.

Now it was Easter. Working hard and working late was taking its toll on the two of them as they spent less and less time together.

Then, one night as they tried to talk it out, they kissed. Cumin and mint. From then, he knew it was all over.

Jerome Parsons' Biography

Jerry Jerome worked for years as a teacher in an increasingly politicised environment before moving to the Midlands to concentrate on more mindful things. He has just bought a dog.

~

500: UNSINKABLE

by Abby Shue

The *Titanic* was a fine ship, a cruiser, thought unsinkable. Two passengers – a newlywed couple on their honeymoon – squinted, watching from the deck, and tried to warn the captain.

Then – *CRASH*. Water everywhere, filling the cabins, sweeping away the frantic passengers as the captain steered and the people screamed.

Titanic versus iceberg, who will win? Man against nature, what will happen? Will we survive? That must have been what they were wondering on the ship's deck on that fateful, deadly day.

Abby Shue's Biography

Abby Shue, 13, is a never-before-published writer who heard about 81 Words while looking for writing contests to enter. She hopes you, the reader, will enjoy the book.

501: INTENTIONAL PARENTING

by Aigbonoga Omoh

Fatima and Ken grew as friends and were always together. Just a few people knew that they were neighbours, living in flats opposite one another.

Even as teenagers, their bond was strong and built on intimacy. When intimacy is established, it becomes difficult to separate both parties.

No man can put fire in his heart without being burnt. From the holding of hands, to kissing, then romance and finally... more.

Where were the parents of these youngsters when all this happened?

Aigbonoga Omoh's Biography

I am from Edo State. I am currently studying public administration in Auchi Polytechnic, Auchi Edo State, Nigeria. I am a writer, speaker, advocate and event planner. Making positive impacts and transforming lives is the very essence of my being.

~

502: THE IRONY OF LIFE...

by Madamraj Mrinalini

I was on an exciting mountain trek with my friends. Suddenly, there was ice all around us. I was stranded and shouting for help in vain.

It was midnight. I woke up with a jolt. Beads of perspiration covered my brow. *Whew, it was only a dream*, I thought.

I woke up with renewed vigour the next morning. Life, 'til yesterday, was dull and monotonous to me. When I experienced desolation, although in a dream, life became more precious to me.

Madamraj Mrinalini's Biography

I am Mrinalini. I am passionate about writing in general and flash fiction in particular. This is my first contribution in flash fiction. I hope the readers like it.

503: SWORDS TO PLOUGHSHARES, PLOUGHSHARES TO SWORDS

by Liam Hogan

Metal screams.

Railings and rusted cars tortured into tanks, into terrifying leviathans. Toys mangled by fire into shells, rifles and bayonets.

Metal screams in battle. Screams in tented hospitals and operating theatres. Screams as graves are dug, as coffins are nailed forever shut.

Now metal is needed for peaceful purposes. Melted down, hammered flat, shaped into ploughs and plates and even toys for too silent houses.

Tanks and tin soldiers and model aircraft.

Metal slumbers. Metal remembers. Metal dreams…

Metal waits.

Liam Hogan's Biography

Liam Hogan is a London based short story writer, the host of Liars' League, and a Ministry of Stories mentor. His twisted fantasy collection, *Happy Ending Not Guaranteed*, is published by Arachne Press.

www.happyendingnotguaranteed.blogspot.co.uk

~

504: GREENBACK

by Denis Joseph

Greenback was the name given by the park ranger to a big brown moose.

One day, Greenback decided to migrate to the far side of the forest. He came upon a sign on the road that said 'Duck Crossing', but he didn't qualify because he couldn't quack.

And then he saw another sign: 'Deer Crossing'. Greenback ambled across as cars screeched to a halt.

"You have violated a presidential decree," said a wise old grizzly, "because the buck doesn't stop here."

Denis Joseph's Biography

Denis Joseph finds it very difficult to write serious stuff. He feeds on twisted quotes, impossible scenarios and stories that spring from 'As the Duchess said to the Deacon', to quote Sam Weller from Dickens.

505: ROLLERCOASTER OF HEARTBREAK

by Samantha Gunton

I've been alive for nineteen years, long enough to realise all rollercoasters eventually stop; all 'ups' have their 'downs'. However, this rollercoaster brought me so close to the heavens I almost believed the ride down would be worth it.

Four words stopped our upward progress. "Laura, I've been drafted."

I walked with Chad to his plane. *Down.* Took Chad's love letters as he gave his life. *Down.* Ended the ride without a start. *Down.*

Sometimes, the 'ups' aren't worth the 'downs'.

Samantha Gunton's Biography

Samantha Gunton is an author in 8th grade. She won the Cotsen Critix 350 for 50 Writing Contest. During her free time she enjoys writing, swimming and hanging out with her friends.

~

506: THE BRIDGE

by Rosie Cullen

Business was bad. Too much competition.

But what else did Sami know how to do?

Then the rains came. The streets were flooded and there were no customers at all.

"What the heck?" Sami laid a path across the square with tables and chairs from his restaurant.

His neighbour could now reach the doctor.

The children could get to school.

The baker stayed open.

When the sun returned, Sami opened his door to find a queue stretching right around the block.

Rosie Cullen's Biography

Rosie Cullen is an Irish-born writer living in Manchester. She's written plays, short stories and scripts. Spent a year as a writer-in-prison and (not connected) hopes to get her historical crime novels published one day.

507: SUPERVILLAIN

by Gloria Ames

I ravage every face, mind and body. Fortunes are lost, found, and lost again. I am the grinder of stone, corroder of iron, annihilator of civilisations. Legions of the strongest warriors wither to nothingness in my grasp. Kingdoms are obliterated by my relentless battering; the thickest walls will fall to me. The universe is mine to dispense. Nothing that exists can escape destruction at my merest whim, nor overwhelm my might. My mastery is absolute.

I am… the march of time.

Gloria Ames' Biography

I am newly retired and live in South Florida with my youngest son of three and our two dogs. I am the grandmother of seven wonderful boys and girls, and most recently twin girls who joined the family.

~

508: LURKING

by Rowan Lewis

Never understood all those billionaires going into the superhero business, if I'm honest. It seems a bit… flashy, I s'pose. It's showing off. "Look, I've got so much money that I've decided to help people, and I'm still managing to spend most of it on myself."

I'd rather stay skint and have a good heart, thanks. This isn't a career for show-offs. Like most jobs, I find that you're only doing it well if nobody notices you doing it at all.

Rowan Lewis' Biography

Rowan Lewis is an English literature graduate who dabbles in screenwriting, short works of fiction, and songwriting.

www.rowanlewis.org

509: COLD TEA

by Sheannah Guillemette

I walked into the kitchen and poured myself a cup of tea. I got my book out, had my tea beside me and...

Three hours later, drat. My tea is cold. I walk over to the kitchen to heat it up again in the shady looking pot I've had for many years – it is blackened all over, but I keep using it anyways. Mmm, nice and warm. I see dirty dishes. I get distracted.

Frack. My tea is cold again. *Sigh*

Sheannah Guillemette's Biography

Sheannah grew up in Ontario, Canada. Now living in California, she is a model, actor, singer, photographer and writer. She also writes a blog mainly on the subject of narcissism. The arts have always been what brings her joy.

www.sheannahg.wixsite.com/sheraveh-blog

~

510: REJECTION

by Maria Carvalho

Hugh eyed the unopened email from Sweeney Press with trepidation. His dreams of getting his first book published had faded further with each rejection. If Sweeney rejected it too, he'd probably give up and focus on his accounting career. His parents would be thrilled.

He clicked open the email. 'Unfortunately, your submission does not meet our needs at this time...'

Disappointment jabbed him in the gut.

He sighed, then opened his list of publishers to see which one he'd try next.

Maria Carvalho's Biography

Maria Carvalho is a multi-genre author whose 2013 children's book *Hamster in Space!* remains a current best seller. A number of her short stories have appeared in collections, most recently *Under the Full Moon's Light* published by Owl Hollow Press.

www.amazon.com/Maria-Carvalho/e/B00FI2WLJI/

511: THE CLOG

by Anastasia Bromberg

I sat before the shower drain, pulling on bright white gloves.

Shower clogs were my fault, he insisted, patting his thinning head.

I sat and pried the grate away, reaching to feel the wiry clump. I pulled. It detached, a tangled mess of dark brown, matching mine shade for shade.

I saw the other. I screeched and pushed myself away. Its blue shell skittered across the tile. Six tiny legs rattled and pincers clacked angrily.

It's not my fault. This time.

Anastasia Bromberg's Biography

Avid reader. Sci-fi/fantasy writer with short forays into horror. Professional procrastinator and font of useless knowledge. Self-proclaimed nerd and devout knowledge seeker. Currently working on too many projects, with many more ideas incoming.

~

512: NO ANSWER

by Jane Imrie

The phone rang and rang. She clamped her hands over her ears in a futile attempt to drown out the shrill noise. In frustration, she screwed up her eyes, instantly wincing at the pain across the bridge of her nose. Eventually, the answerphone clicked on.

"Please pick up," the pleading voice whined desperately. She glared sharply at the phone, the red ring around her left eye blooming into a deep purple.

"I'm sorry, I won't ever do it again," he lied.

Jane Imrie's Biography

Jane Imrie is a writer based in the north-east of England. With a background in banking and marketing, she currently works as a fundraising bid writer. As well as writing, she co-hosts research podcast *The Last Tuesday Project*.

www.twitter.com/red__inspired

513: OUTSIDE HER WINDOW

by Gary Couzens

The blizzard made Helen's window rattle, almost as if someone was tapping on it, calling her. *I'm safe and warm*, she thought. She wrapped the duvet about herself, slept.

In the morning, Helen went outside into the garden. She gasped. The thick smooth snow was scarred by prints, two feet cloven like a goat's but walking upright. The track went across the garden towards the garage wall, then along its roof to the back of the house, just under her window.

Gary Couzens' Biography

Gary Couzens has had stories published in *F&SF, Interzone, Black Static, Crimewave* and other magazines and anthologies and two collections: *Second Contact and Other Stories* (Elastic Press, 2003) and *Out Stack and Other Places* (Midnight Street Press, 2015).

www.gjcouzens.weebly.com

~

514: REFLECTIONS

by Jodi Nicholls

"You look well."

I rolled my eyes and huffed a breath.

"You do. You just don't see it."

I zipped my coat to my chin, the worn threads barely resisting the chill.

"Perhaps you'll go outside today?"

I shrugged and gazed through the dusty window, a clutch of weeds grasping at the sill.

"You need to eat. We have no food."

I held up my hands and smiled at my fingers, a single ring too large.

Beside me, the mirror sighed.

Jodi Nicholls' Biography

I'm an EA from London who writes and publishes books on the side.

515: ACCIDENTALLY ON PURPOSE

by Philip Charter

I left a bobby pin on his nightstand so she'd see it.

Last time I did something like this, things got explosive, but honesty means more to me than the idea of 'the one'.

Every relationship forms a chapter in the book of me. This one's been pretty wild.

I'm not crazy. I'm not jealous or possessive. I just need to know how much of what he said is real. Now I'll wait to see how this chapter continues… or ends.

Philip Charter's Biography

Philip Charter is a writer who lives and works in Spain. He is tall, enjoys travel and runs the imaginatively named website *Tall Travels*. *Foreign Voices*, his debut collection, was published in 2018.

www.philipcharter.com

~

516: THE PRIORITIES OF JOAN

by Amelia Brown

Joan stared with intensity at the plant, as she had all day, willing it to disappear. Her mind was clear, ready for the final step – the magic. She cracked her knuckles and closed her eyes.

Raising her hands, Joan said the incantation. She waited, then opened one eye. She sighed; nothing had happened. Walking over, she picked up the plant and tossed it in the compost. After all, in a world of books and chocolate, she had better things to do.

Amelia Brown's Biography

Amelia Brown writes fantasy and science fiction. She won an honourable mention in the Writers of the Future contest for 'A Womb at the Edge of Space', and is the author behind the blog *Fairy Stories & Other Tales*.

www.fairystoriesandothertales.com

517: THE PASSENGER

by Gitanjali Escobar Travieso

Four in the morning, the streets still dark and quiet. He boards the bus and sits down, his feet slightly touching the large brown suitcase that he has carefully stowed close to his seat.

With an almost inaudible sigh, he leans back and relaxes, his eyes, half closed, not really looking anywhere. He does not want to part from his dream. But all too soon a cool breeze softly touches his face and he realises he has passed by his stop.

Gitanjali Escobar Travieso's Biography

Gitanjali Escobar Travieso, born 1961. Quality manager of a construction company. Dedicated grandmother to Dayram, aged two. Loves reading and writing stories for kids and adults.

~

518: SENSELESS WAR

by Ezeh Michael Ogonna

We are running again today, terrified, the same way we ran ten months ago. Later that week, the government, as usual, announced we could go about our normal business without fear of being shot in the back.

Rumour had it that a herdsman's cow was killed ten months ago, and they needed to pay back. Blood for blood.

"Hurry, I think someone killed another cow," Mum cried.

As we raced homeward, past the sirens and chaotic crowd, I heard another gunshot.

Ezeh Michael Ogonna's Biography

Ezeh Michael Ogonna is from Nigeria. He is a mechanical engineer with much love for the beauty of literary works and art.

519: MARMALADE

by Sunshine Tibod

Her eyes bloom in surprise, excited to seize the day. Every day she wakes at six in the morning without setting an alarm. Her mother prepares food and ushers her to the academy. "See you later, Mama," she says and waves goodbye.

Today is her first day at school. Though she is new to the place, she has a very good feeling. Her blue eyes sparkle, as innocent as her smile. She is only seven, as fresh and sweet as marmalade.

Sunshine Tibod's Biography

I am Sunshine Tibod, born a full-blooded Filipina. I've polished my writing as a member of our school publication. One of my interests, besides books, is the internet.

~

520: THE SKELETON

by Tom Bullimore

"You were walking in the woods and found a skeleton?"

"Up a tree."

"Yeah, where else."

"A skeleton of a boy... been up there fifty, maybe fifty-two years."

"So you climbed the tree and carbon dated it?"

"I climbed the tree, but I didn't carbon date it."

"So please explain to this very simple police officer how you worked out the age of the skeleton?"

"It had an inscribed medallion around its neck."

"Saying what?"

"Village hide and seek champion 1968."

Tom Bullimore's Biography

Tom Bullimore was born in 1950 in the village of Thornton, Fife, Scotland. In the 1980s he created a number of cartoons that all enjoyed success in national newspapers. 'Shuggie and Duggie' still runs in the *Scottish Daily Record*.

www.facebook.com/Tom.bullimore.1950

521: A SMILE TO FALL IN LOVE

by Dionne Burton

I see you. Immediately my sensory neurons jump into action and respond to the stimuli I see: you. The neural signals shoot to the sensory cortex of my brain, the part that responds to pain and other sensations. Then they're carried down to my brainstem, the oldest part of our brains if you didn't already know and, knowing you, you probably didn't. The cranial muscle ferries the signals further to my frontal lobe.

And on the outside, I smile at you.

Dionne Burton's Biography

I come from a small town of people who tend to leave school but never leave said town. With my words, I am able to go anywhere I desire. With a bit of luck, they may inspire others to do the same. Happy writing.

~

522: BOY MEETS GIRL

by Pete Armstrong

Boy meets girl.

Moonlit night on the deck of a ship. A ripple of gentle waves, soft breezes, somewhere a band is playing. Stars shine above and all is calm. How could they not fall in love?

All these plans they had; meetings, places. All gets rearranged. Rewritten. Obliterated by the surge of romance.

They will marry, make a fortune, live in a log cabin. Something. Their future years stretch out blissfully before them.

It all starts when the *Titanic* docks.

Pete Armstrong's Biography

Pete lives in a leafy suburb in central Sweden. He mostly looks after children, and he writes stuff and listens to Dvorak when they are not about. He remains unsure about how he landed such a cushy number.

www.armstrong99.com

523: LACK OF A LACK OF COMMUNICATION

by Kathleen E Williams

"You didn't tell her about me?"

"No."

"Why not?"

"I'm done with her. She doesn't need to know."

"But you told me about her."

"Because we're sharing our pasts. Because you're my future."

"But she's contacting you and you didn't tell me."

"Because it has nothing to do with you. I'm ignoring her."

"She must still think there's a chance with you and you still didn't tell her."

"I didn't want to upset you by talking to her."

"It didn't work."

Kathleen E Williams' Biography

Kathleen Williams, recently retired from a 25-year teaching career and 35-year marriage, is beginning to share a lifetime of stories and eccentricities in publication. This lifetime Chicagoan visits her children and grandchildren in warmer climates.

~

524: ANTI-GRAVITY BATHROOM

by KM Arhel

There's no gravity in my bathroom.

It's been that way for two years, ever since I got a dodgy plumber in to unblock the sink. Now nothing stays down: my toothbrush spins slowly, head over handle; the soap bar orbits the mirror. Showering is pretty tricky when you're floating upside down with water bouncing off you in tiny silver globules. Needless to say, I always keep the toilet lid closed.

But on the bright side, the bathroom scales always read zero.

KM Arhel's Biography

KM Arhel is part-time book wrangler at an academic library and part-time child wrangler at home. She writes short fiction on her shopping list while pushing the trolley round the supermarket and frequently gets home only to realise she forgot the milk.

525: THE MEANING

by Lynsey Calvert

I wait.

A woman walks past.

I wait again.

A man walks past.

I have to know. She told me to come alone. She is going to tell me the answer to the only question mankind wants to know.

A lady stops and sits next to me.

This is the moment I have been waiting for my whole life.

I turn to her. "Please tell me, I'm begging you."

She slowly turns towards me and smiles. "The meaning of life is..."

Lynsey Calvert's Biography

I have been writing for years, but I still haven't finished any of my books – I'm working on that. I enjoy doing short stories or writing challenges like this one. I feel writing was what I was born to do.

~

526: FINDING MARJORY

by Mandy Whyman

The kids were screaming again – a fight about cereal.

Marge contemplated getting out of bed and making lunches, packing school bags, cleaning the house.

She thought about what a good mother she was, finishing off the homework, wiping snotty noses and ensuring that dinners were nutritious.

She had worked hard at her super-mum image and was the envy of all in her lashes, tightly toned jeans and efficiency.

"Mum," someone screamed.

"My name is Marjory," she yelled, and locked the door.

Mandy Whyman's Biography

A journalist in a previous life in South Africa, I have always written. Just lately, I have taken the plunge of giving up my job as a full-time English teacher to pursue the writing dream.

527: A GREAT FEAT

by Mark J Towers

"Prepare to be amazed."

Robbie threw some snap-bangers at the ground. With a swish of his cape, he disappeared.

"Yes, I am invisible," he announced to his audience.

Robbie jigged, celebrating his feat.

The four boys gawped, bewildered by this spectacle.

"You do realise…" one boy started, stopping to snigger.

Another lad reached out, pushing Robbie to make the point.

Robbie was confused. He'd seen it work on the telly.

As he started running, Robbie decided magic doesn't work on bullies.

Mark J Towers' Biography

Mark J Towers writes children's books, short stories, flash fiction and poetry whenever he has spare time from 'Dad-taxi' duties.

~

528: WHO WANTS TO BE A MILLENNIUMAIRE

by Carl Palmer

Host: "Hello contestant number one, what is your name and where are you from?"

"Hi, I'm Des from Tavistock, and I'm 124."

(CUE audience applause)

Host: "Number two?"

"I'm Matt from London, and I'm 125."

(Applause)

Host: "And, number three?"

"Hi, Liz, and I'm 127."

(Applause)

Host: "Last, but not least, contestant four."

"Hi, I'm Mark, from Wellingborough, and I'll be 128 – tomorrow."

(Loudest applause)

Host: "OK, big shout out to all our contestants on *All the Time in the World*."

Carl Palmer's Biography

Carl Palmer is a journalist from Manchester. Highlights of career include interviewing Nina Simone; lowlights, a daytrip to Tokyo. His experience as a journalist lends him credibility in storytelling. His favourite writers include James Baldwin and Courttia Newland.

529: THE GUIDE

by Michael Swift

Ghost hunting? What a load of nonsense. She wanted to go so we went.

Even I had to admit that the guide was strange, somewhat other-worldly. He made me feel uncomfortable as we shuffled from room to room.

"The last room is believed to be the most haunted." His voice crackled like dried grass. We followed at a respectful distance.

No one spoke. I shivered at the sudden chill. A windowless room, only the one door in and out. No guide.

Michael Swift's Biography

Retired pharmaceutical chemist and volunteer centre manager. Member of two local writing groups and have had some success in local writing competitions and poems published in several anthologies.

~

530: THE MISCONCEPTIONS O' A YOUNG GLASWEGIAN?

by Grant McKain

Don't believe whit ye hear aboot Glesga folk. The truth is ah'm 15, ah huv a lit cigarette in ma mooth, ah've goat ginger hair, wi' a can o' Irn-Bru in ma pocket. Ah'm the leader o' a gang, wi' a scar across ma cheek, so ah'm staunin' oan a corner ootside the shop.

"Hey mister, kin ye get me a bottle o' Buckie? Gie ye ten quid." So don't believe whit ither people say, that's jist naw the world today.

Grant McKain's Biography

Grant McKain is an aspiring poet and writer, originating from the west coast of Scotland. He is currently residing in Menorca, the little rock in the Balearics where he is concentrating on his next novel, *The Night Watchman 19:07*.

531: LANDERS AND WILSON, INCORPORATED

by Julia T. Spano

"Should we invest in it?" said one businessman to the other.

"Possibly," Landers replied, biting his knuckle. "It will be a very expensive venture, Wilson. There's no guarantee we'll ever see a profit from it, we'll need some loans, the liability rate is…"

"…high. But give it twenty years or so, and it may represent a positive return on our investment."

They stared down at the gurgling new-born baby.

"Very well," Landers sighed. "I just hope our partnership can handle it."

Julia T. Spano's Biography

Julia Spano is a high school student with the sense of humour of a five-year-old. She hopes to be a novelist someday and infect the general public with her idiotic musings. She also likes cats.

~

532: MEMORIAL

by Lynne Arnot

Born in Edinburgh, Alfred went to school in Dublin and graduated from Oxford. He married Doreen, had two children and worked abroad for six years.

Whilst young and fit, he enjoyed skiing holidays in France until a leg injury at age 65 forced him to take things easier.

Latterly, he enjoyed reading to his five grandchildren, tending to his allotment and writing his memoirs for future generations to read. It didn't take him long – his entire life summarised in 81 words.

Lynne Arnot's Biography

Lynne lives in Edinburgh with her family. She enjoyed writing as a child and has resumed it as a hobby in recent years, having the odd piece published. She currently writes a monthly column for a local free magazine.

www.linkedin.com/in/lynne-arnot-56942b148/

533: THE EMPTY CHAIR

by Bruce Millar

The bar was full, and cheerful conversations floated upwards to mingle around the ornate ceiling rose.

He sat opposite the empty chair, nervously watching groups of friends, couples and obvious first dates all basking in the enjoyment of each other's company.

A girl glanced at him, smiled and walked over.

"Is this seat taken?"

"No."

She pulled it out from under the table and dragged it back to where her group of friends were sitting.

He felt more alone than before.

Bruce Millar's Biography

Bruce Millar is a member of The Millhouse Writers. He has a family, a full-time job and a head overflowing with untold stories. He never has the time he needs to write what he wants but enjoys himself regardless.

~

534: THE WALK TO SCHOOL

by K. J. Watson

Each day, he would wait outside number 22 for his friend. Together they would amble across Tooting Bec Common to school.

This morning, he was tired. He had crouched with his parents in the cellar for much of the night. The Blitz had been fierce.

He approached his friend's house and stopped. His right hand trembled. Bricks, tiles and timbers lay jumbled between numbers 20 and 24.

He pushed his trembling hand into his blazer pocket. Then he walked on alone.

K. J. Watson's Biography

I am a copy editor and online content writer. My occasional fiction includes scripts for a comic and annual (some while ago) and stories for young children. I live near Loch Lomond with my wife and two dogs.

535: STREAMS

by Mhairi Bakertzi

It was dark.

It had been dark for a long time.

The light had been shut out, but it fought to slip through the little cracks in the curtains.

At first, she ignored those little streams, those little glimmers of hope.

But one day, she decided to follow one golden shimmer. She traced it with her pale fingers, she felt its warmth.

She reached out and felt the warmth of your hand.

Together you opened the curtains.

The light flooded in.

Mhairi Bakertzi's Biography

Mhairi Bakertzi is a new writer, living on a Greek island, avoiding the rain of her native land of Scotland.

~

536: THE 81ST SHAVE

by Mark Burke

"Please be seated, sir," I said.

He sat and studied himself in the mirror, rolling his head from side to side.

"And what may I do for you today, sir?"

Staring at me in the mirror, he said, "A shave please."

I raised my eyebrows. He had no facial hair... Calmly, but with a hint of inquiry, I said, "A shave, sir?"

"Yes, a shave," he repeated.

I shaved him. He thanked me and left.

It was my 81st shave today.

Mark Burke's Biography

Mark Burke is a writer and artist who lives in Cornwall. His hobby is messing about. Sometimes he plays guitar, sometimes he doesn't.

537: 81 SMELLS IN PSYCHIATRIC NURSING: SMELL NUMBER 81

by Mandy Raywood

Dilys was married to David. They had four sons who were also called David.

Dilys had laid in bed, unwashed, for the last four weeks, wearing the same pyjamas, a woolly hat lined with tin foil and a pair of wellington boots three sizes too small.

My task as a student nurse was to help Dilys to bathe. I carefully cut the boots off her feet with great precision, maintaining her dignity and holding on to the contents of my stomach.

Mandy Raywood's Biography

Mandy lives in Cornwall and has been a mental health nurse for over 30 years. She collects pounds of sea glass in the hopes of doing something with it one day.

~

538: MY PERFECT VALENTINE

by Anu Roy

I stirred rat poison in the coffee. Placed it at her bedside. Damn woman left for work without drinking a sip.

Greased the stairs, but who knew her gymnastic days guaranteed a perfect landing?

Switched ibuprofen for valium. She no longer has headaches.

Got her drunk in the bath. She can hold her breath forever.

Left a loose electrical wire. She wore gloves.

No brake pads, I smiled.

Beep.

Oops, too late to move out of the way of her car.

Anu Roy's Biography

When Anu is not writing flash fiction or about serial killers, she can be found making stories out of numbers in her position as finance director. She lives with her husband and teenage daughter in London.

Twitter: @Anu_Roy

539: STUCK

by Raymond Sloan

"Can't."

"Can."

"81 words?"

"Yep."

"What can you say in 81 words?"

"I could say something."

"Like what? It's not enough time to say anything relevant, really."

"It's plenty."

"Why are you stuck then?"

"I'm pondering. Something happened in '81 and I can't remember what."

"What happened?"

"I don't know. If I knew, I would know, wouldn't I?"

"We got married in '81."

"Oh yeah..."

"And we had Annie, too."

"Oh yeah..."

"And... you came out."

"No, it's something else. Shame."

Raymond Sloan's Biography

Raymond reads and writes when he's not spending time with his wife, daughter and dog, Dolly. He lives in Ireland and holidays there and will mostly likely die there.

~

540: THE FOG

by Renate Schiansky

When he noticed the first wafts of mist, he thought that he could still make it. The cabin was only 80 yards away. Behind him, the trees disappeared. He started to run.

60 yards to go. The grass beneath him blurred, he urged himself on.

40 yards. *Don't look.* The fog absorbed the bushes to his right.

20 yards, almost there.

With one last effort, he stumbled inside and locked the door. The fog halted, marvelling, and then penetrated the keyhole.

Renate Schiansky's Biography

Renate Schiansky, 59, divorced with 2 adult kids, former legal advisor for youths, lives and writes in Vienna, Austria.

541: SIA

by PJ Stephenson

Dozens crowd around her pod. She's sitting up, sipping water. Lights flicker. Generators hum.

"Did I sleep long?"

Everyone exhales. I squeeze Adam's hand.

"Ninety years," says the commander.

"Oh." A long blink. "The war?"

"Sia, Earth lost." He swallows. "We're the only survivors."

Tears splash my tunic.

"The alien firestorm erased our hard drives. Sia, we need you to remember."

"What?"

"Powered flight. Nuclear energy. Antibiotics..." Adam's lip quivers. "You learned engineering, science..."

"Sorry," she says. "What's my name again?"

PJ Stephenson's Biography

PJ is a British writer living in Switzerland. He writes a lot of science and a lot of fiction – and sometimes science fiction. You can find his short stories online and in various print anthologies.

Follow him: @Tweeting_Writer

~

542: THERE ARE NO MONSTERS

by Vicky Garlick

"There are no monsters." I try to soothe my baby girl, but she just sobs into my shoulder.

"They're going to take me," she cries.

"No one's going to take you, I promise."

It takes another half hour to settle her, but she finally falls asleep and only then do I check her room, to prove my promise to her is true.

I open drawers, cupboards and finally check under the bed.

Two bright eyes stare at me from the darkness.

Vicky Garlick's Biography

Vicky was born in North Yorkshire and began writing at primary school where she was encouraged to follow her creativity. Vicky took a creative writing course at university and has continued to write in her spare time, self-publishing two novels.

543: GONE

by Anna Sanderson

I remembered her the best way I knew how.

I went to the bar, ordered her favourite drink.

Each sweet sip erased another painful memory: the sickening sound of Mother's cry when she heard (gone); her coffin, lighter on my shoulder than the guilt (gone); my sister's lifeless body on the concrete, consumed by narcotics. Too young. Too cold. Too still (gone).

I remembered her the best way I knew how. I drank until I forgot she was no longer there.

Anna Sanderson's Biography

Anna Sanderson is a writer from Nottingham, England. Her work can be found online at sites like *101 Words* and *A Quiet Courage*, and in various literary zines and anthologies, including *Razur Cuts* and *Lights Go Out*.

Twitter: @annasanderson86

~

544: MIKE

by Cath Allwood

I find him lying at the bottom of the stairs.

"Gerrup, our kid. Stop messing."

"It's me back, me back…"

"No." I know him of old. I won't be caught again.

He moans loudly.

I hesitate. Perhaps this time… I stand irresolute.

"Get Mum. Honest, it's me back. It's killing me."

Oh no, it's true. He's really hurt this time. Lower lip trembles, a fat tear wells out of my eye.

"Ha, mardy baby." Mission accomplished, he leaps up and away.

Cath Allwood's Biography

I live in Hope Valley. It's in Derbyshire. I'm 65. I came late to writing – 2015. I used to be a librarian in London.

www.cathallwood.wordpress.com

545: THE RAINBOW REVELATION

by Lorna Dougan

Sienna had been obsessed with rainbows ever since THAT morning – 16 years, 41 days, 36 minutes and 23 seconds ago.

That morning when mother solemnly revealed that Sienna's daddy was gone forever.

This life changing news filled their lives with intense darkness but, amidst the gloomy conversation, a magnificent rainbow appeared miraculously like a symbol of hope.

Sienna's mother took comfort in this sign for her daughter, vowing to take her secret to the grave – there was no rainbow that morning.

Lorna Dougan's Biography

I'm a mother of two boys, Alex and Aaron. I work as an orthotist for NHS Lanarkshire and have recently started following in my grandmother's footsteps by embracing my passion for writing after I won a poetry competition at work.

~

546: MY SOUL, THE SEA

by Stephie Simpson

My body felt so heavy against the ground as I listened to the waves that crashed against the rocks; it was almost deafening.

Cold spray kissed my feet as they dangled over the edge of the sand coated cliff. Dark – almost sparkling – water swelled below. It felt like hours had passed beneath my feet.

Slowly, the turmoil that filled my soul mimicked the calming sea. As the chilly air filled my lungs, I noticed the bristly grass beneath me once more.

Stephie Simpson's Biography

I have always enjoyed writing fiction but ended up writing an ostomy/mental health blog *Colitis to Ostomy*. I love crime and fantasy genres but find myself reading about unicorns and cars to my two small children.

547: ON THE SPIT OF A MILLIPEDE

by Elizabeth Lamb

"Inchbel, how many is it this time?"

"Ten. No, twelve." Sobs relentlessly.

Pollymill looks at her sister's trapped legs. "I'm going for Packham."

"No, he'll spit on me."

"What's the choice? Leave you to scorch?" Pollymill climbs to the tip of Chris's nose, rears up and waves her front milli-legs.

"Pollymill, is she trapped again?"

She nods.

Packham's head shadows Inchbel's sun-drenched form and spits liberally over her. The cooled wood expands.

Inchbel slips free, lifts her dripping head. "Thanks, Chris."

Elizabeth Lamb's Biography

I work as a carer for people wishing to stay in their own home. I love nature, eating, exercising and am blessed with a warped sense of humour.

~

548: THE SNUB

by Kathleen Hearnshaw

What were you doing? You even involved your children.

We were from the same village so we thought, *Let's go and say hello.*

We regretted it as soon as you turned your backs and turned your children away from us.

Do you think you are a cut above us? If so, you are wrong. Poor manners show poor breeding.

Class is not about where you come from, more about how much you achieve with the opportunities you have.

Shame on you.

Kathleen Hearnshaw's Biography

I am a 65-year-old retired nurse living in the Peak District. I have always enjoyed writing but only did it seriously after retiring and joining a creative writing group in the village where I live.

549: THE OPEN SECRET

by Alan Dale

"We can order any fence panels, if your choice isn't in stock. Please, take a look round."
    Tom nodded and began pacing, examining the various designs.
    "You want something solid," said Sheila, "to keep Tracy's dog out."
    Tom shrugged. "True." Suddenly, he stopped in front of a panel. "*That's* what I need."
    "It's got loads of knots, it's rotten quality. Those two have fallen out, look at the holes."
    "Doesn't matter. This'll be fine."
    "She'll catch you one day, you know."

Alan Dale's Biography

I belong to the Woking Writers Circle and the Association of Freelance Writers. I have had stories, articles and features published online and in print for various magazines and sites. My first novel is due for publication in 2019.

~

550: THEY WERE THERE

by Jacky Ellis

A perfect August afternoon.
    The shimmering sands stretched far into the distance, the sea meeting them with a misty kiss.
    The children wriggled, frenetic with excitement, barely yet squeezed into their costumes.
    "Mummy," said the eldest, "we have to go now."
    Screams of laughter, chubby feet slapping the ground as they ran, ran, ran.
    This part of the coast had been carefully chosen not only for its natural, unadulterated beauty, but its calm.
    They were there, but now they have gone.

Jacky Ellis' Biography

My name is Jacky Ellis and I am 46 years old. I live in St Leonards on Sea in East Sussex and this is my first foray into the world of the short story.

551: TIES THAT BIND

by Bernard Hicks

"I'll give you 400."

Patience. Pregnant.

"But it's 24 carat..." One more line.

"Sorry, lady, it's closer to 8 carat."

Dead Balian memories.

"Look, I'm not trying to fleece you. Feel free to walk away, but that is what it's worth, and I can't pay a cent more."

Deeeeeeeep breath. Focus on the sensation of the air filling my lungs. In. And. Out.

Accept the things to which fate binds you.

"I'm going elsewhere. This ring is worth $10k, minimum."

Delay.

Bernard Hicks' Biography

Early 30s, used to be a physicist but decided that it wasn't for me. Still figuring out what path I'm going to take next, but I've started writing as a hobby while I figure it out.

~

552: THE GHOST OF TEAM ROOM 13A

by Johannah Lipscher Simon

Lorna sat quietly at the back of the room, her eyes purposely positioned down to focus on the nondescript pad of paper in her lap. A corporate chameleon. Angling her chair behind the boisterous gaggle of interns, she ensured she would not be seen or noticed at today's project kick-off.

Over her 20 year tenure, she'd mastered the art of blending in. Her track record was perfect, 1,000+ meetings and not a single action item assigned. 13 more months to retirement.

Johannah Lipscher Simon's Biography

Johannah Lipscher Simon is a professional ideator, who writes and speaks on the power of living a creative life. You can find her at:

www.thewritingtype.com

553: THE DOCTOR IN THE FAMILY

by Haley M. Hwang

"How much this time?"

"Can't a mamma call her daughter just to talk?"

Jackie didn't have time for this. But if she hadn't answered, her phone would have persistently buzzed during the five-hour surgery. The unwelcome calls came without fail toward the end of the month when her mother needed money for rent, cigarettes, or booze. She demanded reverence and repayment for her promiscuity and prolific womb.

Distance had been Jackie's escape. But cell towers kept her shackled to her family.

Haley M. Hwang's Biography

Haley M. Hwang is a writer living in the Chicago area. Her career spanned working as a newspaper reporter, medical writer and entertainment editor. When she isn't writing, she is drinking coffee, eating pastries and thinking about her next meal.

~

554: INFATUATION

by Natasha Ali

She didn't need him. Wanted him, sure, but it wasn't a life requirement.

Nothing about him wasn't interesting. Every detail was a spark of knowledge. Electricity. Lust?

He didn't feel the same way. She didn't think he felt the same way. Or if he did, he was going to figure it out too late.

How badly could you want someone before igniting?

He was definitely a specimen.

Maybe he was interesting purely because she was interested.

He might matter too much.

Natasha Ali's Biography

Just a biology student who loves writing. And reading. And anything to do with words. There's not much you need to know after that.

www.facebook.com/natasha.ali.5623

555: THE FEAST

by Yelena Kart

Another cup of pudding,
another slice of pie,
one more piece of turkey,
I feel like I'm gonna die.

I shouldn't have eaten,
that chunk of casserole,
and those garlic mashed potatoes
have really taken their toll.

The last spoonful of salad
sits in my stomach with the rice,
and the chocolate-raisin cookies,
and the very berry ice.

Now I lay here on the carpet,
clutching at my pain-filled tum.
I'm sure I'll explode soon,
saints or devils, here I come.

Yelena Kart's Biography

Yelena is a freelance writer based in the Chicago area. When she's not writing or reading, or thinking about writing or reading, she enjoys spending time with her pupper and taking Zumba classes.

~

556: ANTICIPATION

by Colette Kriel

Pinky Bottom huffed as she sat down. She had been waiting for what seemed like eternity. Oh wait, in Frothom Forrest there was only eternity, fairies never died.

Jemima Witch lazed languidly, after a hard day conducting Pinky's final lesson in working fairy dust.

"Jemima, do you think the children will notice?"

"Well, if I hadn't thought so, I wouldn't have allowed you to cast the magic. I don't waste fairy dust on pointlessness."

Pinky could hardly contain her enormous grin.

Colette Kriel's Biography

Since young, I've enjoyed the craft of creative writing. I've penned many stories which ended up in the bin. Now, I'm taking it seriously. It's my goal to publish a novel. In the meantime, I'm have fun writing short stories.

~

557: CALLING IN SICK

by Noel Alcoba

"Hi, this is Nate. I won't be coming in to work today because..."

Why did I pause? It always sounds like a lie when I pause.

"Hi, Boss, my alarm didn't go off..."

No, that's a lie.

"Hey, craziest thing happened..."

That sounds stupid.

Fine, I'll just tell him the truth.

"Hey, it's me, Nate. I can't come to work because I followed my cat through a portal and I'm stuck 100 years in the future."

Funny. My phone still works.

Noel Alcoba's Biography

By day I work in the evidence unit of the county sheriff's office, by night I make ice cream and tap dance. I live in the Pacific Northwest with my lovely wife Alison and a Maine coon named Gritty Kitty.

558: NO LONGER MISSING

by Holly Garcia

Claire's mother had been missing for seven years when she saw her on the crowded beach. She was applying sunscreen to a child's back, white streaks across dark brown skin. The boy ran into the waves, then her mother leaned back onto a towel beneath a large umbrella. Her eyes were still closed when Claire walked up, catching wafts of peach that had always been her mother's favourite shampoo.

Her mother turned around, startled, but saw only footprints in the sand.

Holly Garcia's Biography

Holly Rae Garcia is a professional photographer on the Texas Coast. Her short story, 'Flap', will be published in 2019 for *The Bookends Review* online journal. She is currently working on her first novel.

www.twitter.com/HollyRaeGarcia

~

559: SLEEPING WITH STARS

by Melody Bowers

I ask him to come to bed.

"I'm studying shards of Mars so I can visit it in my dreams," he says.

I sigh. He had spent thousands on tiny pieces of Mars that fell to Earth in the 1800s.

"Dear, I'd love to give you the Moon." He laughs.

"You could be rolling in Moon rocks now that your sister lives there."

He sings, "I only have eyes for Mars."

I roll over and count galaxies until I fall asleep.

Melody Bowers' Biography

A writer in training going on 50 years, Melody is a member of the Just Write group at the Creative Light Factory in Spring City, Pennsylvania. She loves writing to prompts because they lead the mind on unexpected journeys.

560: SURPRISE

by Nikki Butcher

I can't stand Crown Casino, but you like going there because it means connecting with your unsophisticated heritage, so I planned a surprise there for your 30th birthday.

Your friends were a glittering posse awaiting our arrival on the marble stairs. We downed cocktails, played your favourite tables and then ended up bowling in our sequins and bowties at 1AM.

As we stumbled to our hotel, you glowed like the house strung with the brightest Christmas lights on a suburban street.

Nikki Butcher's Biography

Nikki J composes poetry, prose and music, seeking the horizon between the quotidian and the sublime. In her spare time, she is a teacher of German and English. Her new obsessions are acrobatics and clawhammer banjo.

~

561: DRIVING THE SLOPES

by Dan McConnell

The icy drive home was a guarantee someone was going into a country ditch. Sure enough, he crested the hill and down the dip to the side, on the opposite side, lights and flashers on: a car off the road.

Driving SUV number three (the first two totalled on roads much like these), he slid gracefully towards the guardrail, then back towards that car. Deftly drift-cranking the wheel, he skated by, barely missing the opportunity to total two cars at once.

Dan McConnell's Biography

Elementary teacher, shaper of minds, bender of wills, father to three beautifully dangerous daughters... or is it dangerously beau... ahh, never mind.

www.realedreform.com

562: THE LOCUM

by Fiona Aitken

The locum doctor was greeted at the reception by the centre manager. "You're aware of our work?"

He frowned, unsure.

Reaching the patients' lounge, he was greeted with sights beyond imagination: young women sawn in half, torsos hanging by a thread of skin; elderly men levitating, hands replaced by streams of coloured handkerchiefs; white rabbits and fluttering doves everywhere.

"At H. Houdini's clinic, we manage a variety of magical illusionist accidents. Understand now?"

The doctor nodded slowly, in amazement and wonder.

Fiona Aitken's Biography

Fiona is a mother of two and works for a charity in her spare time. She loves to read, and sometimes finishes books. She is trying to rediscover her love of writing, theatre and literature.

@Scotland_Fi

~

563: SOMEWHERE UNDER A TEXAS RANGE, 1869

by James Louis Peel

Billy put the glass down. "Johnson, this business is a-gettin' old."

"It's noon. Sherriff's outside," Johnson the barkeep said, and poured another.

"Already?"

"Whisky again?"

"Yeah, I know. It's just that sign."

Johnson grinned, eyes red. "Outlaw's curse. As many times as sands number."

Billy felt his navy colts holstered and stepped out.

Ka-baaang.

Falling face up, before his sight faded, he saw the sign 'Hell's Saloon ~Outlaws Welcome~' hanging over the door.

Billy put the glass down. "Again?"

Johnson grinned.

James Louis Peel's Biography

I was born in Kentucky on a day I don't remember. But fortunately, Mother did. Since then, I grew, got bored and left. Now I reside in Japan. Writing is the backbone of therapeutic mind massages when the spirit requires.

564: WIND

by Josephine Queen

We listened to the wind howling all day. It sounded like ghosts tormenting wolves, or the other way around.

"Stop howling," said Sarah. "I'm trying to eat my soup."

Dad ran all the way to High Street to rescue the bins. Next door's cat flew off and was found three streets away, dishevelled and annoyed.

The wind carried on into the night, upsetting cats and soup eaters all over town. It evaporated with the sunrise, fading into a sweet, morning breeze.

Josephine Queen's Biography

I moved to the northeast corner of the US from England. I live here with my husband, daughter and crazy cat, who have all been subjected to my stories at one point or another.

~

565: INSOMNIA

by Laurie Hicks

My mind is blank. A thought creeps in, then another. Before I can stop it, there's a cacophony of thoughts clamouring for attention, creating an ebb and flow of invisible sound.

I imagine a blackboard and eraser, but chalk is held by an invisible hand, scribbling faster than I can eradicate. Imagining a whiteboard has the same result. I throw up my hands in despair and allow myself to be overrun. My mind overflows.

Suddenly, it's blank once again.

I sleep.

Laurie Hicks' Biography

I am a computer technician who would rather write. Two cats own me and grudgingly share me with my husband. Though I now reside in Kentuckiana, my heart will always be in Cleveland. Yes, I am strange. Why do you ask?

566: THE VETERAN WANTS A LETTER

by Laila Miller

The veteran wants a letter. He likes mail: a rough envelope between his fingers, bulkiness within, contents he can guess at.

He thinks of dreaded telegrams to mothers, sisters, lovers. Welcome wedding invitations, thick, embossed. Christmas cards with family photos. Terse, thin bank statements. Funeral notices, folded, pocketed.

He will be 95 soon. Fingers, once crack-sharp, tremble. His crew are gone.

Grandchildren plan: emailed invitations, recycled banners, square cake, wrapped gifts of black liquorice.

But all he wants is a letter.

Laila Miller's Biography

Laila Miller grew up in rural Western Canada and has worked for many years as an environmental consultant. She wrote this story from her home in Perth, Australia, after seeing a social media appeal on behalf of veteran Recil Troxel.

~

567: BEST SERVED COLD

by Darren Hackett

All those times in your life when someone does you wrong, from when you're a small child to adulthood. Taking your lunch money, stealing someone away from your heart, ruining your life in either a small or seismic way.

And you may think that you've got away with it, leaving me to deal with your vengeance whilst you scoot along, thinking that I'll never gain my revenge.

Wrong on every count, amigo. It's your Uncle Bingo. Time to pay the cheque.

Darren Hackett's Biography

I'm a 50-something who wants to spend all his days as a writer, looking for his own Harry Potter to create and write about. Self-published and seller of 10 copies. One day…

568: NEVER KNOWING WHAT CAME NEXT

by Barnaby Page

They met at 9: adjacent desks, glances, then giggles.

At 18, each wondered if the other was the one, or if this was merely, concerningly, inertia.

At 27, he wondered again, and took a woman's number in a bar.

At 36, he rediscovered the scrap of paper and couldn't remember whose the number was.

At 45, they rediscovered each other.

At 54, they were young, they thought; likewise at 63.

At 72, she felt him drifting, faintly, but still there, always.

Barnaby Page's Biography

Barnaby Page lives in England and works as a journalist. For the last year he's been concentrating on 100-word stories, so he had to rein in his verbosity for this challenge. Barnaby also writes on film.

~

569: RECIPE FOR A FAST BUCK

by Doug Forrest

His words are drowned by the passing train. I'm glad. I've heard enough of his money-making ideas.

"Tomorrow, OK."

"What?"

"Tomorrow." There's conviction in his voice.

"What about tomorrow?" I ask.

"Told you. This time tomorrow." And he's gone.

One sleepless night later and I'm there.

He's capable of anything. I shudder.

He arrives carrying a box. I look round. It's just us.

He lifts the lid and hands me a cake. "Made them this morning to sell at the market."

Doug Forrest's Biography

I am a 69-year-old retired teacher living on the Shetland Islands. I try to write something every day I can. I have self-published a book about a WWII Royal Signals dispatch rider, *Jimmy Wilds: The Soldier Who Elected A Government.*

570: DANIEL

by Sidonie Baylis

He punched me. My nose cracked. I doubled over. He brought his elbow down on my back, forcing me to the floor. There was a thud as I hit it. He kicked my back. I curled up into a ball, covered my face, covered my stomach. He forced me open. I screamed. He covered my mouth with his hand, pushing my head back and the knock as it hit wood vibrated through my teeth. I spat at him. He kissed me.

Sidonie Baylis' Biography

Sidonie Baylis is a creative writing student at Falmouth University. She is currently trying to publish everything she's ever written in order to fulfil coursework requirements.

~

571: A MIXED DOZEN

by Kim Hart

He told them lies.
"You're so beautiful. I love you."
And they lied back.
"I love you too."
His mother had warned him about women.
"They're all the same, under the skin. Lying, cheating witches. Don't trust 'em."
And he hadn't.
He labeled each one:
- White, age 22, "You're the only one."
- Black, age 29, "I'll love you forever."
He sipped his wine as he refilled the bottle with the ashes of the last liar.
He'd order another mixed dozen tomorrow.

Kim Hart's Biography

I live in the Snowy Mountains of Australia. When I'm not writing (or procrastinating), I work in a kiosk at the base of a ski run. I have one husband, two daughters, one grandson and a dog named Kody.

572: SKIN DEEP

by Catherine Harkness

She watched her baby intently. The doctor spoke reassuringly. "I know it looks scary, but he's responding well."

He grew stronger daily, losing his premature redness, his hair turning dark and curly. At last the doctor could say, "Good news. Now he's off the ventilator he'll be home soon." There was something bothering her. "Is there anything you want to ask me?"

Her blue eyes brimmed with tears. "Just tell me, I have to know. Is my baby black or white?"

Catherine Harkness' Biography

I am a retired GP enjoying my new-found freedom to write.

~

573: GET OFF MY FOOT

by W. G. Miller

"Excuse me."

"Huh? What do you want, little fella?"

"You're on my foot."

"You sure? I can't feel anything."

"I can feel it. Can you move?"

"Nah. Don't think so."

"Typical."

"Whaddaya mean by that crack?"

"Typical of your type. I used to be like you. I know. You all think there's gold in your left ear. By the way, you have a crack in your head."

Along the highway, uncomfortable silence settled over the igneous rock and the sand grain.

W. G. Miller's Biography

W. G. Miller grew up in Western Canada but now lives in Western Australia. He is inspired to write to make children laugh and adults grin (even a little).

574: JUST SAYING

by Lydia Collins

Slithering. Sliding between saliva and sound. I don't make my presence known. The host is not ready yet. A little more seasoning, plus a feverish heat, is necessary to tenderise my meal. Just one more moment of rage. Just one more seething, screaming word and the psychic barrier will crumble. That is when I will strike, conquer and snake my way towards the brain stem, happy to feast.

My host should be grateful. His own poison certainly tasted worse than mine.

Lydia Collins' Biography

Lydia Collins is a freelance writer who is always simultaneously chasing a toddler and a hot cup of coffee around the house (sadly, the coffee is usually abandoned). In-between naps, a dystopian novel is being shaped into reality.

www.lydiacollins.blogspot.com

~

575: MY CLASSMATE

by Andrew McGill

A man I went to school with died last week, aged 35.

As I haven't seen him for 19 years, in my mind he will live on as he was at school.

Frozen in time.

The problem is that 19 years is a long time. And I struggle to remember what I did last week.

So, in my mind, in perpetuity, he is shouting, "Sod off," at Mr Hill, the geography teacher, then wetting himself in the classroom and crying.

RIP.

Andrew McGill's Biography

Andrew is aged in his 30s and lives in the West Midlands in the UK. He enjoys making sarcastic comments about current affairs and eating Haribo.

@AndrewRMcGill

576: TINGLE

by Heidi Lobecker

"Can't you just look at what the mannequins have on and wear that?" Joe asked, pulling at Shelly's thick sweater.

"I hate shopping, it's so—"

"Your body is a pear shape," he said, cutting her off. "You need to accent your top. Draw the eye away from the bottom."

Shelly's cold sore was back, a telling tingle on her lip. Her body's warning system: *This guy is no good.*

He moved in for a kiss. Mouth to mouth, she pressed hard.

Heidi Lobecker's Biography

Heidi Lobecker writes about how the body holds feelings and emotion and how movement can transform pain. She puts her pants on and hopes they fit, just like everybody else.

www.sailinginchester.wordpress.com

~

577: CASSOWARY CHICKS AND OTHER FOWL

by Huguette Van Akkeren

"Everyone, please be aware that many cassowaries were displaced by Cyclone Yasi and they're roaming freely between Mission Beach and Tully."

With this morning's briefing echoing in their ears, the two urbanites coaxed the young bird – wandering aimlessly along the highway – into the backseat of the dual cab, using an apple from their lunch packs. Not knowing what else to do with it, they took it to the local vet.

"This is a fine example of a healthy chicken," he chuckled.

Huguette Van Akkeren's Biography

I was a retiree. Now I'm an aspiring writer and student who loves challenges and useful feedback to help further my dreams of one day publishing a novel.

578: THE PROOF

by Tim Gomersall

Syen-Tiss was very hungry and her feet hurt, but her vindication was worth all that.

To prove to her friend Thlatt-Uffa that their world was round, she had walked its dusty red plains in a straight line for four years, holding course until the day she returned to her starting position.

Now she stepped upon her own first footprints, elated.

"See, my friend." Syen laughed. "Our planet is a ball."

"You fool," replied Thlatt. "You've just walked in a giant circle."

Tim Gomersall's Biography

Tim lives in London with his wife, two kids and an unfinished novel. He writes primarily for recreation, but when necessary for a living. He is, despite everything, fundamentally an optimist.

~

579: SECRETS

by Madeline Green

The night of the circus, the moon took up the whole horizon and it scared me. Being only eight years old, I had never seen anything so vast in my life.

Inside the hot, sweaty tent, fire breathers and acrobats swirled and smiled inhumanly wide.

But the highlight, in my young eyes, was my dad buying me some candyfloss. He told me not to tell my mum. I wasn't supposed to have it. Mum wouldn't be impressed, so I stayed quiet.

Madeline Green's Biography

I'm Madeline Green and I am a 20-year-old student, born in Liverpool, UK. I discovered the art of flash fiction late last year through my creative writing work at university and I really enjoy writing and reading it.

580: A CAT OWNER'S QUESTION

by Kim Witbeck

Cat litter. Splashed across the laundry room with excitement, as one imagines a child frolicking in a snowfield. Yet in actual snow the cat tiptoes daintily, leaving just the oval trace of her finicky paws.

Why the cat litter, cat? The large tray of glorified sand is a wonderland, and the basket of colourful, fuzzy toys is a no-cat's-land. In one room we trip over turds, the other forgotten catnip-sodden fake mice.

I love you yet can never hate you, cat.

Kim Witbeck's Biography

Kim Witbeck is a communications analyst who lives in Oregon and practises fictionalising various annoyances, life questions and media obsessions in her spare time. She is currently working on her first historical fiction novel.

~

581: THE WITNESS

by Arthur KC Chan

Tim was perturbed to see the pickpocket pushing his way out of the train.

A minute ago, the man's hand was creeping into the woman's handbag for the purse. Tim was stunned to witness the crime, which nobody else seemed to heed. When the man's eyes met his, the boy trembled and turned away.

Suddenly, a voice shrilled, "Thief, stop him."

Amid the chaos, Tim noticed a little girl sneering at him. Crawling up his face was a blush of shame.

Arthur KC Chan's Biography

A Hong Kong citizen, Arthur has written plenty of short stories in Chinese. He finds writing flash stories in English can help improve both his language and storytelling skills. He is having fun with it.

582: PURSUIT

by Evie Nicol

I think I might die soon.

I'm being chased. I was ahead for so long. But I'm too tired. I've had to stop.

I'm writing this in the hope that someone will find it. Give it a read. Tell my story. But, even in this crucial moment, I cannot think of anything remotely profound or interesting to say.

I'm so sorry. Hopefully my end, if it comes, will be profound enough.

I would explain, but they're here. It's time to fight.

Evie Nicol's Biography

I'm a 19-year-old English literature and creative writing student. I have loved reading and writing for as long as I can remember and have a great interest in flash fiction, so this project was perfect for me.

~

583: SELF-CHECKOUT

by RJS Cantwell

I could see my reflection in his eyes, and that was all it took. The stare of a woman who had fallen in love at the most unappealing time. Yet love does not discriminate, no matter the depth of sacrifice.

We arranged our flights; my bags were packed and I kissed my children goodbye.

As I was leaving, my husband asked me to bring him back some cigarettes. I said I wouldn't be long; there was self-checkout at the Tesco now.

RJS Cantwell's Biography

I work at a LGBQT-focused art gallery in King's Cross, where I publish essays for contemporary artists. My work has been published in *After Nyne, Artnet* and *Blouin.* I was also part of the 2017/18 writer's group at the National Theatre.

584: ONCE UPON A TIME

by Neil Davie

George slowly got to his feet, brushing himself off as he stood up. In the distance, he could just see his horse galloping off into the woods. He turned to look at the creature that had thrown him from his mount.

Before him stood a huge dragon, covered in glistening, green scales. It must have been at least thirty feet tall. Smoke billowed out of its nostrils. Its mouth of sabre-sharp teeth opened gradually and it roared out, "Tag, you're it."

Neil Davie's Biography

Neil rediscovered creative writing in 2019 thanks to Chris's website and competitions. When he is not writing, he is trying to teach engineers English — whether they want to learn or not.

~

585: A GUARDSMAN'S DUTY

by Kim Steindel

Boring.

"Be proud, son, you are doing God's work," Ma always said.

Nonsense.

There's a righteous war in a faraway land. God doesn't want me sitting on my arse watching peasants and fields. It has no meaning.

Enough.

I'm destined for greatness, Father Joshua told me so. I will see him in the morning and join the crusade.

Satisfied, I stretch my legs and close my eyes. Soon I'll be a hero.

I wake to the smell of wood burning.

Eek.

Kim Steindel's Biography

Kim lives in Ireland (because New Zealand is too far away) with his wife and when he's not seeking shelter from the rain, he's probably eating, writing or petting his German shepherd. You can read more about him on:

www.kimsteindel.com

586: SENSORY REINNERVATION

by Matthew J Morine

Lab coats swarm around you. One holds a mask to your face as you feel a pinch in your arm. Slowly, the bright room fades to darkness.

As you lay motionless, the lab coats open up your flesh. Then, a flurry of nerve grafts and rearranged tissues.

Weeks later. You are awake in your room. You can't help but smile to yourself as your polyethylene hand caresses your blankets. For the first time since your amputation, you can feel your hand.

Matthew J Morine's Biography

Matthew is a high school student who builds combat robots, runs long distances, uses HAM radio and manages some high altitude ballooning on the side. He is currently pursuing college and a career in neuroengineering.

~

587: ROSE IN THE WIND

by Ty Hall

Rose wakes up every morning and sweeps the floor like she's in the second ring of Hell because the gap at the bottom of the door lets the dirt in. It's so gusty in Amarillo.

She'll buy a hat. A hat will improve her situation. That's the thing about hats and shoes: they'll almost always fit, no matter what. And Rose already has a pair of shoes.

She's happy wearing it out of the store, but it's so gusty in Amarillo.

Ty Hall's Biography

Ty Hall Lives in Texas, makes up stories, and tries to be good.

588: BAD FRIENDS

by Caleb Jansen

"You know, I have no regrets. Even though I have made mistakes in my life, I feel reconciled for them."

"You're 100 percent sure you don't have any regrets? Any major ones?"

"Nope. I feel OK with how my life went."

"Really? Here's one you might regret. GETTING US PUT ON DEATH ROW."

"That's just something minor. Plus, this is the time we should forgive each other."

"Oh my god, you are the worst human being ever."

"Was. Was the worst."

Caleb Jansen's Biography

I am a high school senior at Lawrence North. When I was writing my story, I had trouble determining where the story was going to go. Eventually, I settled on having it be a singular scene in a larger story.

~

589: RETURN TO KNOWLEDGE

by Jayanta Bhaumik

It was late afternoon when he started trudging up the hill. He had a hazy memory that the village was on the other side. He must cross the peak before it was dark.

Soon he began huffing and proceeded haltingly. On and on, but the snaky uphill track reached no peak, mingling into dense jungle.

He paused and thought about the distance between imagination and acquiescence.

This was dangerous. It was pitch-dark. Turn back...

He quickly retraced his steps to safety.

Jayanta Bhaumik's Biography

I'm based in India. A commerce graduate and a diploma-holder in software applications, I am now an astrologer and therapeutic counsellor. I am a research member of the American Federation of Astrologers. I regularly travel the entire south-east of Asia.

www.facebook.com/jayanta.bhowmick.9

590: MISSING

by Bekk Escott

In a matter of minutes, Jane's flat had turned from a place of calm into a whirlwind of chaos.

All of the cupboards and drawers were flung open, the contents strewn around on the floor.

"It has to be here somewhere," Jane shrieked out loud to no one but herself.

But alas, as Jane sat, head in her hands, surrounded by the entire contents of her life, it all meant nothing. The only photograph of her late father was still missing.

Bekk Escott's Biography

Bekk is an aspiring writer, hoping to embark on a creative writing degree in the near future. She lives in Chester with her girlfriend and their baby – a fluffy black cat called Meadow.

~

591: THERE IS NO PUNCHLINE

by Jace Henderson

A man walks into a bar. Many men walk into a bar.

They keep walking – the bar does not impede them.

There they go, through the bar's wall. A roaming stampede of men keep walking. The bar is no longer their concern, world domination is what they lust for.

The men keep coming single file behind them, the bar now tattered ruins.

The world forces try to stop them. All weapons fail.

The men walk past the bar, into the cosmos.

Jace Henderson's Biography

Jace Henderson is a high school senior from Indiana. If you were to describe him in one word, it'd probably be 'charcuterie' because he's fancy, yet palatable, with a meaty physique and a cheesy personality.

592: IT'S THE END OF THE WORLD AS WE KNOW IT

by Rachael Hinshaw

I squirmed in my seat, my ears popping from pressure. My mum looked at me. She looked sad.

"What's wrong, Mum?"

"They warned us. We didn't listen. I didn't know today would actually come."

"Who warned us?"

"The scientists, protesters... so many people."

"At least we did what we could. We tried to recycle."

"It wasn't enough," she said, disappointment clear in her voice.

I sighed and looked out the window as I watched the grey Earth disappear behind the ship.

Rachael Hinshaw's Biography

Rachael Hinshaw is a senior at Lawrence North High School in Indianapolis, IN. She enjoys bunny rabbits and romantic comedies.

~

593: THE KISS

by Fiona Flower

I saw her fall on the rocks at the edge of the beach.

I raced over, all thoughts of splashing in the boiling surf forgotten, the rain stinging my face and soaking my coat.

I dropped the stick. Her eyes were closed. Rain drops sprinkled across her face. I nudged her gently. Her eyes flickered open. I kissed the salty water from her face. She smiled and ruffled my head.

"Throw the stick again. I rescued you. More sticks," I panted.

Fiona Flower's Biography

Fiona loves cinema and is just starting out on her writing journey. Raising four foster children with husband Ian. Two birth children have flown the nest. Grandmother to two granddaughters. Life is a little hectic but very fulfilling.

594: THE DUCK'S KING

by Natasha Nagle

Today was a nightmare. A disaster.

The king asked for a duck. Mistake number one.

It was angry and hated everyone with a vengeance. Bandages covered arms and several men's prides needed to be stitched back together.

That it was to eat, mistake two.

Why might this have been so calamitous, you ask? Surely innumerable mistakes have been made, this doesn't seem so bad.

Well... here's the thing. We don't have one of those, a duck nor a king.

Mistake three.

Natasha Nagle's Biography

Natasha Nagle is an archaeology graduate student who enjoys writing in the bits of spare time she can glean. Her forms of choice typically include poetry and creative prose, with the aim of connecting people through talks of her travels.

www.nagleadventuresofthepath.weebly.com

~

595: ICE BLAST PINK

by Linda Jones

James puts on the red dress.

Aged 10, his hair falling to the kitchen floor as Mum saved a fortune at the barbers.

Aged 13, standing miserable in the rain as the other boys found sport kicking the football at him.

Aged 21, tried kissing girls, tried kissing boys. A stranger to himself.

Aged 30, high flying career, wedding bells, fatherhood. Empty.

Aged 40, puts on kitten heels, paints on a smile in ice blast pink, time to face the world.

Linda Jones' Biography

Linda Jones lives in Wales. Her dog ignores her and her cat is senile. She is part of a local writing group and her short stories have been prize winners in competitions and have been read out on local digital radio.

596: A CUT TOO FAR

by John Rivers

The metal blade pressed hard against Mike's face, sharp against his dry skin.
There was no time to waste. He had to focus on what to do next.
The day before he had avoided a similar encounter.
Concentrate. Stay calm.
Mike felt the grip on the handle move slightly, and the blade change angle.
A quick movement. Two drops of blood appeared as hundreds of bristles were cut.
Damn. He had cut himself shaving again and would be late for work.

John Rivers' Biography

John Rivers works as a classical musician and teacher, maintaining a freelance career. As a home husband, he has gained an unexpected interest in growing vegetables – acquired from his wife – and constantly reads all manner of books.

~

597: THE RECOVERING PERFECTIONIST

by Laura Foakes

An open driveway.
Two adventurous dogs.
A fence was needed.
He sawed and sanded, shaped the laths, dreaming of gleaming white pickets.
A gate for ease of access? No problem. Heavy hinges for a satisfying clunk when the gate swung shut. Two coats of paint, no drips or brush marks, the Leonardo da Vinci of fences. His work done, he stood back and admired. Then:
Sheepishly.
Furtively.
He took it all down because he'd built it *in front* of his car.

Laura Foakes' Biography

I am the founding member of a writing group (The Incorrigible Rogues). We meet for murder, mayhem, and madness – but only on paper. Our next undercover mission is to decorate our town with poetry and fiction. Quills not balaclavas.

598: WHEN THE WORLD ENDED

by Beth Kander

I was in the bathroom when the world ended. It's not where anyone intends to be at a time like that but there I was, on the pot.

When you think about it, at any given moment, millions of people are relieving themselves. I found some comfort in that, in those last moments. A sense of community.

After years of loneliness, I felt kinship with every other soul who was literally caught with their pants down when it all went dark.

Beth Kander's Biography

Beth Kander has an MFA in creative writing from Mississippi University for Women and an MSW from the University of Michigan. After writing a dystopian trilogy (*Original Syn*), she's decided her new literary goals are 'concise' and 'contemporary'.

www.bethkander.com

~

599: THE WAIT

by Oghogho Odiase

My husband and I sat across the mahogany table, looking at Dr Adams as we waited to hear the words that could change our lives forever.

Ben gently squeezed my hand to reassure me. He had promised to always be by my side no matter what. I could feel the beads of sweat dripping down the middle of my back as we watched him open the investigation result.

"Congratulations, you are pregnant," he said with a broad smile on his face.

Oghogho Odiase's Biography

Oghogho Odiase is a medical doctor with a passion for writing short stories and poems. She finds inspiration from the lives of people around her, and lives in Lagos, Nigeria.

600: UTERO

by Judi Edwards

The fierce breeze lifts Monia's hair from the back of her hot neck as the queue shuffles forwards. The friends wait, ready to raise the child as decreed by the matriarchs. Thoughts of the unknown donor fill her mind. Does he think of her? Of her baby? Of the many children he's fathered?

Feeling the life move inside her, she strokes her stomach whispering, "Soon. Be ready." Her fifth and final baby for the population. She feels proud. She feels alone.

Judi Edwards' Biography

Reflected in all she does is Judi Edwards' working class upbringing and her acquired middle class status. This familiar mix of common and snob means that frequenting casinos and playing poker sits alongside knitting socks and flower arranging.

~

601: THE RIGHT INGREDIENT

by Kent Raddatz

"Life isn't all pop tarts and gravy, ya know."

As he imagined that horrible combination of flavours in his mouth, she went on.

"Sometimes you need some spice to make the magic."

"I just wanted to know if I should ask her out."

"I know what you wanted."

"Well then, is she the pop tart or the gravy? Please don't say both."

"She's the spice."

"So I'm like gravy – boring?"

"Call her."

He shrugged. He called. And nothing was tasteless again.

Kent Raddatz's Biography

Kent Raddatz is an eclectic writer who works in a variety of genres, including mid-grade, memoirs, picture books and short stories. He received the Fox Ridge Award from the Novel in Progress Book Camp.

602: IMPOSSIBLE ESCAPE?

by Annika Franke

He awoke and had neither an idea how he had ended up in this cage nor a functioning plan how he could get out of it. People ignored his calls. Bending the bars in front of him worked just as little as picking the lock. The ground was far too solid to dig. No way out…

If he had turned around, he would have seen the thin curtain that was the only thing separating him from the rest of the world.

Annika Franke's Biography

Annika Franke enjoys travelling with floating islands, talking to dragons and using magical hourglasses. No, she isn't crazy (and she should know it because she studies psychology), she just loves writing.

~

603: BAD DAY

by Andy Langdale

Nobody wakes up thinking they are going to die today.

At least, I didn't that morning. But there I lay, flat on my back, staring at the ceiling after being stabbed in the back.

The wound was throbbing with pain but it seemed distant compared to the panic I felt. I tried to look around, eyes darting back and forth. I couldn't move my neck, but just as things faded to black, I saw them.

Oh, it was you… I thought.

Andy Langdale's Biography

Andy is a director of a software support company and an avid gamer. He takes writing inspiration from Lee Child, Robert Crais and Michael Connelly.

604: WHAT'S WORSE, A SLIP OF THE HAND OR A SLIP OF THE TONGUE?

by Reha Tanör

I shooed the bee out the window, only to knock my wife's laptop out as well. Down below, it grazed a woman's head and smashed into pieces.

The woman froze, as did I. If it'd fallen a second earlier, I'd be looking at time in the big house.

"Here's Apple's latest model, courtesy of Steve on high," I almost said, following the shock.

I can't help a slip of the hand but I can a slip of the tongue, at least.

Reha Tanör's Biography

Born in Istanbul in 1947. Former entrepreneur, retired law professor, chairman and CEO of Garanti İnvestment Trust. Author of law books and numerous academic papers. Author of a book describing his days as an entrepreneur. Author of *Restaurants and Tales*.

~

605: THE INEVITABLE

by Lynn Morcombe

The shop was crowded.

My heart raced. What had I done?

"Excuse me, miss."

I turned, nervously. "Yes?" I hadn't thought it through. I was caught.

"This way." The security guard ushered me along.

I could make a break for it, it wasn't too late... yet. Get lost in the throng of shoppers.

He opened the door at the back. I walked through, jelly legged, resigned.

They had me and I was swallowed up... as he handed me my new uniform.

Lynn Morcombe's Biography

My name is Lynn Morcombe and I love to write when I can find the time. I have not written very much but want to dedicate more time to writing in the future.

606: SHOO FLY

by Judy Reeves

Dad's behaviour had been rather odd since Mum's death.

No wonder, he was the one that found her on the floor.

One day, about six months after she'd died, I saw him kneeling.

"Are you OK, Dad? Have you dropped something?" I asked.

I heard him mutter something. He seemed distressed.

"What did you say, Dad?"

"She wouldn't shut up, nag, nag, nag. I silenced her, but she's still buzzzzz, buzzzzing in my blooming head."

Then I saw the crushed fly.

Judy Reeves' Biography

I retired early from working in social care to concentrate on writing. I enjoy writing short stories and memoirs, and recently discovered a talent for poetry too. I have completed a creative writing course with the Open University.

~

607: THE NINE DAY QUEEN

by Maggie Elliott

10th July.

I, Lady Jane Grey, succeed Edward VI to the throne.

His will prevents half-sisters, Mary and Elizabeth, from succession on account of their illegitimacy.

Awaiting coronation in the Tower of London, word has reached me Mary is gathering support to oust me.

19th July.

The Privy Council of England denounce me, proclaiming Mary as queen.

Viewed as a threat to the Crown, my husband and I are to be executed.

Hereafter, I'll be remembered as the Nine Day Queen.

Maggie Elliott's Biography

Maggie is retired and writes purely for pleasure. Her poem 'Picture Me Calm' won third prize in the *Writing Magazine* poetry competition. She has three stories published in anthologies – 'Sweet Treats', 'Safe Passage' and 'An Unwelcome Guest' – and two more pending.

608: DESIRE

by Lorna Stewart

His hands run over the sleek body, wet with soap suds.

Gently, with a soft towel, he begins to dry her off.

His pupils dilate with longing. He takes in her curves, her smell.

He wishes she was his. That he could afford her for his own.

Sighing, he turns to the guy in the suit who is impatiently counting out cash in his hands.

"That's 15 pounds for the car wash," he says, handing the guy back his car keys.

Lorna Stewart's Biography

Lorna likes to daydream, a lot. She finds that writing these little stories up is far more fun and rewarding than doing the housework. Otherwise you can find her wandering the canal network in a state of mindfulness.

~

609: A SILENT CRIME

by Katherine Kogoy

A little boy ran through the streets, his hands in his pockets. A man was chasing him, screaming words that the boy couldn't hear.

Eventually, the boy rounded a corner and the man cornered him. The only way out was a 10 foot jump into the air, so the man had won. However, before the man could apprehend the boy, the boy looked up, smirked and pulled something out of his pocket.

They say the man died with no physical injuries.

Katherine Kogoy's Biography

Katherine enjoys writing, playing the flute and piano, and playing rhythm games on her tablet.

610: MONSTERS

by Ava Groth

She came into my room tonight, declaring monsters in her closet. She crawled in next to me, promising sleep. Later, I was awoken by her tiny hands shaking me awake.

"Mummy? Can you hear it breathing?"

I stiffen. Not now. It hasn't been long enough.

"Please," I whisper. "I'm not ready."

"Now," says the voice, sending chills down my back.

Reluctantly, I take my pillow into both shaking hands. I place it over the little girl's head, press down, and wait.

Ava Groth's Biography

I am a ninth grade student who enjoys reading fiction books and writing short stories.

~

611: WORDS UNSAID

by Alan Ridley

He woke before dawn. After a breakfast of porridge and a mug of tea laced with rum, he quietly smoked a cigarette. He considered writing home, telling his mother how much he missed her cooking and that he loved her; something he had never done before. He decided to do it later that day. When the order came to go over the top, he was the first of many to fall.

His final thought: *When will I write that letter now?*

Alan Ridley's Biography

Now retired, I went to sea at 16, swallowed the anchor at 23, chopped down trees, emptied bins, spent time as a lifeguard and ended up teaching. I was once told that I have had a chequered career. Right on.

612: TRAVEL GUIDE TO THE NETHERLANDS: DUTCH POP UPS

by Marilyn Rucker

The Dutch love 'pop-up' stores. Everywhere you go, you'll see little shops spring up in once empty plazas. At Christmas, ice-skating rinks and oliebollen stands appear in every square. In spring it's ice cream stores and bike parking lots. Some businesses only last a few hours, then disappear overnight.

Today, two Dutch birds took down the nest they'd built outside my window last spring. They dismantled it in two hours. I assume they rebuilt it in a more centrally located tree.

Marilyn Rucker's Biography

Marilyn Rucker has written hundreds of ridiculous and occasionally popular songs, as well as two novels. Rucker currently lives in Holland with her family, including a cat who enjoys bird watching. Her music and other books can be found at:

www.marilynrucker.com

~

613: SLEEP

by Claire Gee

"Why is it hard to sleep?"

"What?"

"Why can I never sleep without waking up and feeling a pit in my stomach, certain someone is there in the shadows, watching me?"

"Well. I am. I am always there, waiting for your sleep to be deep enough to finally win and have a body of my own instead of lurking in dark corners."

"Great. Now I am talking to the voice in my head. Please stop so I can finally rest."

"Never."

Claire Gee's Biography

Claire Gee is a 17-year-old student from Archway School who enjoys reading and writing.

614: MR TRUE-BLUE

by Sagar Jadhav

I run towards the door. Keys jingle, the door flies open and in comes my favourite person. Seems like she is making sure no one, other than me, is at home.

I sniff some unfamiliar scent on her. Definitely not Derek's. I must alert him, though, for it seems his companion has been fooling around behind his back. Not just cocaine, I can sniff out infidelity, too.

How, you ask? Well, they don't call me 'the best sniffer dog' for nothing.

Sagar Jadhav's Biography

Sagar is an engineering graduate and a mathematics aficionado. A die-hard mystery and thriller fan, his favourite author is Dan Wells. He hopes to finish reading 1,000 books by 2050.

~

615: AISLE MEET AGAIN

by Peter Stanton

She shouldn't have felt nervous. For goodness sake, she was a grown woman. People were staring at her. Perhaps if she avoided eye-contact… Now she could feel herself growing red, her cheeks burning hot, and a thin bead of perspiration was forming on her top lip.

She looked down at the console. The button with the red light was right in front of her hand. She pressed it and the silence was broken.

"Dear customer, we are opening till number five."

Peter Stanton's Biography

Retired after a career in sales and training, I have spent a lot of time studying people's behaviour and analysing their reactions. I spotted a young girl in a supermarket and this triggered my 81 words.

616: 1,000 WORDS

by Cathi Radner

One thousand authors wrote one word apiece and dropped them all in a jar in the form of a computer. Biting their nails, they waited for the artificial intelligence to magically transform their clever nouns and adjectives into a literary masterpiece. It would be a ground breaking, first of its kind, feat.

The computer smoked and churned. After a few moments the words were revealed. They had created a nonsensical word omelette. No one had added the a and or if.

Cathi Radner's Biography

Cathi Radner Castrio lives and writes in upstate New York surrounded by chaos, beagles and excellent beer. Her novels, which generally include dogs, death and humour, can be found at:

www.amazon.com/author/castrio

~

617: WHEN TOMATOES KILL

by Natalie Wu

When Tomatoes Kill, announces the TV guide. Sounds exciting... alarming even.

I wonder how. Allergies? Colliding grocery vans? Freak accidents involving dislodged eyes? Drownings in tomato juice? Extreme lachanophobia?

"Put the darts on, will ya?"

I ignore the fat fart in the armchair. Wish he'd choke on one of their spidery stalks. Now that *would* be worth watching.

I click 'view'.

Oklahoma: rural towns, rampaging whirlwinds, total carnage... no sign of any tomatoes though.

I click 'guide'.

Oh, *When Tornadoes Kill*.

Natalie Wu's Biography

Natalie enjoys writing children's picture books, short stories and flash fiction. Several of her pieces feature in the recent self-published collection by the Penistone Writers' Group. She also won the short story competition at Sheffield's 'Off the Shelf' literary festival.

618: GAP-TOOTHED TREASURE

by R.A. Krueger

His heart sank as he pulled an empty beer can from the ground. He knew treasure maps weren't real but he'd gotten his hopes up anyway.

"Darn it."

He tipped it over. At first only dirt poured from the opening, but slowly, almost begrudgingly, a stream of thick smoke oozed out. A woman wearing cut-off shorts appeared in the smoke before him.

"A genie."

"Jenny." She smacked her gum and examined her nails. "You want Jeanie, you got the wrong can."

R.A. Krueger's Biography

R.A. Krueger lives in Florida with her husband, son and fur babies. She writes MG and YA with a dose of humour. Before writing took over her life, she was a pastry chef and still suffers from an insatiable sweet tooth.

Twitter: @RAKrueger1

~

619: EVERYTHING COMES FULL CIRCLE IF YOU WAIT LONG ENOUGH

by Gail Everett

Susan came out of her garden shed, wheeling her rusty bicycle onto the path. The nearside pedal flew off onto the lawn as she mounted the ancient vehicle and, on looking for it, she discovered something glinting in the grass – her wedding ring, which she'd hurled at her husband the day he left her.

After throwing it into the pond, she saw it being swallowed by a toad and thought, *That's appropriate – given by one opportunistic toad and taken by another.*

Gail Everett's Biography

Apart from what I told my mother when I was a teenager, my interest in fiction began at the tender age of 63, by which time I had exhausted most other possibilities for pastimes in which to engage whilst sitting down.

620: A TOTALLY TOGETHER PERSON

by Kenneth Cahall

I don't mind being remotely controlled. Could be Woody Allen, Joe Pesci or Bjork controlling me, I don't care if I don't have to think.

Some folks complain about it; not me. I don't mind getting a paycheque for just meditating in my mind all day while my body goes to work and I don't even sweat. I'm a totally together person; relaxed, calm. Trouble is, I play clarinet and Woody Allen keeps trying to keep the royalties to my songs.

Kenneth Cahall's Biography

Kenneth Cahall writes poetry and short stories. For fun, he has recently begun submitting his work to a few highly distinguished editors. He runs, eats and occasionally teaches English as a second language at a university in beautiful South Korea.

~

621: AU REVOIR

by Vivienne O'Boyle

Abraham Riley's mother was both proud and anxious as he stood to attention before her and his seven siblings. Barely nineteen, kitted out in his Khaki uniform, bearing the Sherwood Foresters' emblem.

Like his father before, Abraham was about to embark on an unpredictable journey to the Somme.

"Be sure to write," said his fearful mother as he bade farewell from the small mining town of Eastwood, where he'd lived forever. A courageous young man departed.

They never saw him again.

Vivienne O'Boyle's Biography

Walking a 45 kilo Bullweiler five miles a day is no mean feat for a 66-year-old female. That aside, my other passion in life is writing, and I've only just started after 40 years of being too busy.

622: FORGIVEN

by Linda Foy

Sebastian took his motorbike along to the park exit. He had promised to wait for her there. She had to go by a longer route because of the double buggy.

With nobody in sight at the exit, Sebastian decided to move on to search the nearby precinct.

"Sebastian, Sebastian." She called out his name loudly, repeatedly. Surely he was nearby. Somewhere?

Face tearstained, dragging a stick by his side, in the distance a small boy appeared. Sebastian's mother embraced him thankfully.

Linda Foy's Biography

I took up creative writing with WEA (Workers Educational Association) in Newcastle-upon-Tyne at the same time as studying visual art. In Bristol, I continued with the practice, using a mix of media, on issues of identity and the environment.

~

623: LOVE LETTERS

by Tiffany Williams

They wrote their first letters like elementary language students. I am well, my mother is well, my brother is well. Then, sickened with loneliness, Anna told Fritz, 'Your letters make life worth living.'

Maybe it was just their isolation, or maybe it was the irresistible luxury of having the 'you' of their most private imagination finally take on a name.

By the fourth round of letters, though, they were afraid to use the word itself. They knew they were in love.

Tiffany Williams' Biography

Tiffany has been writing since she was twelve, when she wrote plays to act out with her friends. Now she prefers the more introverted form of the short story. When not writing, she enjoys reading, volunteering and learning foreign languages.

624: GRANDMA'S FRIEND

by Lynn Zeleski

"Grandma." I grabbed her hand and ran to the playroom. "Wait, what's that? No, no. Run, Grandma, run. No go there."

"What is it, sweetie?"

"A moke dedekdor."

"It's OK, Luka."

"No, Grandma, scary."

"Oh, sweetie, my friend's not scary. You just need to be properly introduced.

"Luka, meet my friend, smoke detector. Smoke detector, this is my grandson, Luka. Will you promise to only yell to keep us safe?

"He promises, Luka, except for when Grandpa cooks. He has to."

Lynn Zeleski's Biography

I'm Lynn Zeleski, grandmother of four. Children are unique and my eldest grandson is on the autism spectrum. I enjoy telling stories. My professional training is in psychology. I've worked in museum education and with special education students.

~

625: SHE SMILED

by Heather Stuart Primbs

She opened her eyes and looked around the room. She'd never seen it before, but knew she'd been here for a long time. Now it was silent. No beeps or voices – she was glad.

Her mind clear; an unfamiliar sensation. She wondered where her family were, but found she was grateful for solitude. They didn't know she could hear everything during it all.

She knew they would be sad, but not her. She looked down at her body and smiled.

Free.

Heather Stuart Primbs' Biography

Heather lives in BC, Canada, with her amazing husband, two astounding loin nuggets, three affectionate dogs, and a dragon that is also a princess. She loves nature, animals, writing and cuddling. She plans to build a massive garden very soon.

626: ROMAN

by Rafe Bellers

Roman dashed along the dark trail. Just as he looked over his shoulder, a root reached up and tripped him. He fell off the trail and down a hill. His body slammed into ageless trees as his momentum carried him down the slope, through heavy brush, and over a cliff.

I deserve this. A thief deserves this.

Roman splashed into chilling water. His hope faded as his broken body helplessly sank.

Suddenly, the man he'd robbed pulled him from his death.

Rafe Bellers' Biography

My name is Rafe Emerson Bellers. I am an aspiring Christian author that dreams of climbing the best seller list. However, I'm happy where God has me now. He has blessed me with life, a wife and His brilliant book.

~

627: A LOVE LIKE CHERRY BLOSSOMS

by Jessica Bowden

A gentle breeze rustled the cherry blossoms. Sakura stood in front of the tree, her heart-shaped face the same colour as the flowers. She was cuter than usual, with her black hair down, her hazel eyes shining with emotion behind her rectangular glasses.

"I like you, Haruki."

A flower floated down onto the ground before him. Haruki bent over to pick it up and closed the distance between them, blushing as he handed it to her.

"I like you too, Sakura."

Jessica Bowden's Biography

Jessica is a hopeless romantic who loves to write stories that have deep, romantic relationships. She's a huge fan of anime and manga, both of which she draws most of her inspiration from.

628: EXTRAORDINARY EVENT

by David John Griffin

The moon cast a ghostly light over the snow on the plain. The woods stood hushed in the chill air.

A tiger, its stripes pulsing as if made of neon, padded slowly across the whiteness towards the shack in the middle of the field. Condensation emitted from its snorting nostrils.

Inside the shack, Angus looked through binoculars to track the progress of the animal. He turned hurriedly, shook his wife by the shoulder and said, "Wake up, Joan, you're dreaming again."

David John Griffin's Biography

David John Griffin lives in Gravesend, Kent, with his wife, Susan, and two dogs called Bullseye and Jimbo. He has four novels and a book of short stories published. He also has stories published in three anthologies.

www.davidjohngriffin.com

~

629: HER

by Brinkinfield

"Look," Janine says, "I'm sure it's her."

Maria glances across the café, over the heads of the seated and towards those seeking free tables, trays balanced in their hands.

"I wonder what she's doing in here."

"Who? Where are you looking?" Inconspicuously, Maria scans each female face. "Who am I supposed to recognise?"

"Over there – she's got her back to us now."

"All I see are people getting breakfast and coffee."

"Wait, you'll see who I mean when she turns around."

Brinkinfield's Biography

Brinkinfield writes short form fiction, moving between unconventional, personal observation and humour. Much of the experimental work can be enjoyed on his website, progressively more can be purchased on Amazon.

www.brinkinfield.com

630: CHEQUERED FLAG FREEDOM

by Micky Rowe

Three hours driving with Doris the Dragon, man-hater and mother-in-law.

Current route + four hours. Reroute?

"Ignore," roars Godzilla in her 40 a day, dulcet tones. Her tongue clicks, lifting false teeth out of her mouth. I gag, click 'yes'. Tuts echo, nostrils flare and swell.

A sweet… toffees?

"If y' skee, ee's not ood en'gh for 'er." Spittle flies. Flinching, I will the chequered flag to appear.

With any luck, she'll be too hungover to speak on the return journey.

Micky Rowe's Biography

I am a blogger, actor and palm reader whose motto for life is: Assume Nothing.
www.morethanamotherandwife.com

~

631: HOLDING OUT AGAINST THE ZOMBIE APOCALYPSE

by Stephen P. Thompson

"Sir, the zombie apocalypse shows no sign of abating. I'm not sure how much longer we'll be able to hold out here. We're surrounded."

"Is there a problem with the electric fence?"

"No, it's working fine, nothing's got through."

"Are we low on fuel for the generator?"

"No, plenty of fuel."

"Food, we're running out of food?"

"No, there's loads of food. Several years' worth in fact."

"Water?"

"Bucketfuls."

"Then what, exactly, is the problem?"

"We forgot to get loo roll."

Stephen P. Thompson's Biography

Scientist, musician, songwriter and author exploring the origins of primitive matter in science, the meaning of life in fiction and its pointless banality in music. My contribution to the 81 Words challenge addresses none of these.

632: 48 DAYS

by Raymond E. Strawn III

My soul chained inside their cage. My innocence locked away. Hope consumed by lies. Rights stripped away. Embarrassment and dread entangled my guts. Trapped in a prism. Forgotten to the world. Death lurked the halls. Threatened, my life erased. Until those words shattered glass.

After 48 days, freedom. Escaped the tainted system. Inhaled winter air. Tasted homemade food. Lay on my bed. I escaped the corrupted cage's nightmare. Yet my soul remained. Lost forever. Replaced with terrors. The nightmare never sleeps.

Raymond E. Strawn III's Biography

Raymond E. Strawn III began writing poetry and short stories in 1999. In 2001-2002, he spent 48 days wrongfully incarcerated for writing and sharing his poetry and short stories at his high school.

~

633: JUMP

by Ashley Vohrer

Eyes close. Breath in. Breath out. Wind swirls my body. Rush of blood thunders in my ears. Ground far below. My eyes shut. Voices scream, "Jump."

On edge. Calm before the final step. I want this to be over without pain. Jump. Time slows the closer I reach my destination. Slide show plays short clips; my life. Head crashes the surface. Slide show ends. Water swallows me without a ripple. Reach the bottom. Kick towards air.

Perfect scores from the judges.

Ashley Vohrer's Biography

My name is Ashley. I'm a novice writer looking to expand my writer's palate.

634: FIREFLIES

by Kaitlin Ellis

I tossed and turned in my bed, struggling to sleep. I knew that only one thing could calm me down: my garden.

Discreetly, I crept downstairs and slipped out of the back door. I sat on the garden swing and waited.

Brightness appeared from nowhere by my side. Fireflies flitted around me, enchanting me, performing a dance, advising me, calming me.

I relaxed, went back indoors, climbed up the stairs and slept like a baby, knowing that I had my fireflies.

Kaitlin Ellis' Biography

I am currently at secondary school in the West of Scotland. I spend much of my free time reading and writing. I get a lot of my inspiration from the nature around me.

~

635: IT'S COMING HOME

by Dinesh Shihantha De Silva

"It's coming home," the queen said.

Her husband was fed up, hearing that famous phrase everywhere. "Definitely not. It's in France now."

The queen gasped. "But Kane phoned and assured me."

"Is he captain of lies now, instead of footie?"

The queen was perplexed.

Later, the doorbell rang. The queen answered and was overjoyed when her neighbour, Mr Kane, handed it over and left. "It's come home."

Her husband was astonished. "The Soccer World Cup Trophy?"

"No, silly. My missing dog."

Dinesh Shihantha De Silva's Biography

I am a published author from Sri Lanka of novels such as *The Big Grudge Volume 1*. Love injecting subtle humour into my stories. A fan of football and chess.
www.facebook.com/DineshShihanthaDeSilva

636: BECOMING AN UNBELIEVER

by Adele Evershed

I try homespun stardust to ease his suffering, summoning the crookback witch with her story, charms and potions. She varnishes his brow with an uncool hand. I spy a sooty spot in the valley of her thumb. Fear like acid burbles up gently, burning my throat.

I noisily pray, "Please let him live," but there is no clemency for my porous soul. He will not wake from his midnight sleep. So prayer is a tinker's dam I will no longer build.

Adele Evershed's Biography

Adele Evershed is originally from the UK. She now lives in the USA where she has had to stop listening to the news, and so has started to write instead.

~

637: THE ORACLE

by Parzival Sattva

Diaphanous silks swirl as her dancing body undulates in ecstatic trance. The petitioner, crowned, refuses to prostrate himself. Attending priests mutter but don't intervene.

Strange sounds erupt from the oracle. Scribes take notes. They translate:

- A board
- Aboard
- Abort

Rage flashes across his face. "Tell that bitch her brother commands victory."

She collapses and whispers, "Pride will be his ruin. He cannot command the future. His disregard of me has been noted by the gods. He shall reap what's been sown."

Parzival Sattva's Biography

Parzival Sattva writes 100-word stories daily and is writing his first novel. A Canadian who calls Thailand home, his favourite meal is grilled meat on a stick and Thai coffee. He's on Twitter (@PSattva) – swing by, say, "Hi."

638: ONLY MEMORIES

by Sarthak Das

Tonight, a moonless night. I look around. There's no one except me. I open the door and enter.

Like always, she is asleep. I kiss her forehead softly. She stumbles awake. For a moment, our eyes meet. Like always, she screams in horror and faints. Like always, I sigh and return to the world of the dead.

With the arrival of dawn, the sun rises. I remember. There was a time I was alive. A time she used to love me.

Sarthak Das' Biography

Sarthak Das is a 19-year-old Indian undergrad pursuing chemistry. He loves writing, watching films and playing the harmonica.

~

639: RECIPE FOR A FAMILY

by Richard Freeman

Flour, water and eggs, well mixed and rolled into little balls. From grandmother to mother and from daughter to granddaughter, this family recipe binds the generations together.

Add mashed potato and enough grated Parmesan cheese so I can feel where I come from and where I belong. Spoon the mixture into little hand formed pastry shells. It's a work of love that takes ages.

They are all gone in minutes – delicious bourekas, baked today and also already hundreds of years old.

Richard Freeman's Biography

I lived in the Lake District for many years before moving to Brazil. Four children, six grandchildren. Currently proofreading a series of books and creating a website.

640: PRODIGAL'S REGRET

by Ginger Marcinkowski

Anguished fingers stroked birch skins, scraping fog from lessons learned. Feet away, grandfather's ghost mines trees in dwindling light. He tears branches, clipping limbs, readying pines for death, scent of forest thick.

"Respect nature," whispers ghost. "Take only what sustains."

Bows head. Motions me to stillness. Puts ear to craggy bark. Listens. Mark is tall. Straight. Strong. Axe hammers. Rhythmic strokes echo lessons.

Trees fall, graceful dancers, slamming forest floor, rising again, settling softly amidst needle swirls. In haste, I'd forgotten.

Ginger Marcinkowski's Biography

Ginger Marcinkowski, MFA, is the author of two award-winning novels. She has been steadily honing her skills in flash fiction and short story writing, a genre she loves. She lives in Panama City Beach, Florida.

~

641: LOST IN TRANSMISSION

by Charles Bonkowsky

Timestamp: 0.81.66.15

It's funny. I saw this radio tower on the hill and dragged myself here, thinking if I was going to die I might as well tell the world, and now I don't have anything to say. No pithy last words to redeem me.

Maybe that's what I deserve. 'Cause if anybody's listening, you might remember why you hated me in the first place. Better you forget. Better I die here abandoned and let you rebuild the world.

[end broadcast]

Charles Bonkowsky's Biography

I'm a 16-year-old writer from Utah, USA – been writing for a little less than two years and I love every part (well, most parts) about it.

642: SCREAM

by Sarah Jae Walsh

A girl knelt by a well. She stared at her reflection in the murky water. In silence, she examined it. Something wasn't right. Then she realised they were completely identical in every way except one: the other girl was crying.

She saw something like a shadow move in the background. Her mirror image's tears turned to screams and, even though she couldn't hear them, she trembled.

A cold shiver ran down her spine as the words, "Don't cry," whispered behind her.

Sarah Jae Walsh's Biography

Sarah Jae Walsh is a BA student at the University of Witwatersrand in South Africa. She enjoys writing stories, reading the classics and playing the violin. She works to break stigmas about mental health disorders such as anxiety and depression.

~

643: DOUBT

by Natalia Wojcik-Smith

"You can't seriously tell me you know what everyone's doing right this second. That's ridiculous."

Neil raised an eyebrow. "You want me to prove it?" He covered his eyes with one hand, facing away from his other three friends.

"Mike, put your phone down before you spill your coffee on yourself. Keith, stop chewing on your hoodie sleeves. Tom, you can't carry that many pens at once."

The doubter blinked in surprise and sighed. "Remind me not to challenge you again."

Natalia Wojcik-Smith's Biography

Young writer based in Oxfordshire, hoping to publish a full book in the future.

644: BLUEBELLS

by Susan Wickham

The police car stopped. She stumbled out into the vast blueness. It overwhelmed her and the tears fell. It wasn't the cruelness that she had suffered all these months that finally broke her down, it was the compassion.

They had found him and then her. She had been in his flat all this time. She just wanted to wallow in the fragrance, the wonder of the bluebells. The colour reminded her of her mother's eyes. She was free. She could smell.

Susan Wickham's Biography

I live in Romney Marsh, a hop away from France and over the road from the sea. I think a lot when I am walking my dog, Meg, who would far rather be in bed.

~

645: INNER DEMONS

by Sai Muthukumar

Broken, alone, shaken.

On the river Styx, the ferryman waits. A shattered soul dances with the devil, as Tchaikovsky plays. Hollow heart, weightless, left in the corpse. Demons toil, fuel the torment, words echo in the cave.

A figure stands at the gate, greetings unnecessary. The quiet goes uninterrupted.

On his own, in the darkness, a boy turns his back on the gatekeeper. The wings eclipse the black. The fallen angel shall rise once more. The flames don't accept the undefeated.

Sai Muthukumar's Biography

A student and aspiring writer who loves to write prose fiction.

646: THE ENFORCER

by S.E. Taylor

"Just give him up," the man shouted, yanking Mikey's head out of the bathtub.

"I haven't seen him. I swear."

"If I find out you're lying..."

The man felt a drop of moisture land on his head. Taking a step backwards, he glanced at Mikey who was unable to disguise the look of horror on his face.

As they both looked up, a second drop of sweat fell through a gap in the floorboards, past the man's face, onto the floor.

S.E. Taylor's Biography

S.E. Taylor resides in Oxfordshire. He enjoys reading and writing crime fiction in his spare time and, if he can get his backside into gear, hopes to complete (or at least start) writing a novel before he dies.

~

647: DID YOU EAT MY FATHER?

by Barbara Eustace

The crocodile watched the boy come down the path. The sweetest of meats, young, juicy, moist.

"Did you eat my father?"

"Maybe."

"He went missing last night."

"Ah yes, I ate him."

"Why?"

"Because he was drunk, it was dark, he fell in and I was hungry."

The boy paused. "What did he taste like?"

"He tasted of anger, violence, hatred. But he was fresh, not old and rotten."

"Will you eat me?"

"Not today. But learn from your father's mistakes."

Barbara Eustace's Biography

Retired computer programmer, who's gone from writing code to writing fiction.

648: THE ELEPHANT IN THE ROOM

by Joyce Bingham

Once upon a time there was an elephant in the room. He was not sure how he got there, but all eyes were on him. He picked up a paper cup of water with his trunk and flicked it expertly into his mouth.

The humans in the room pretended to see through the elephant. He was most perturbed. He was, after all, rather large. He picked up his trunk and trumpeted.

The chairperson sighed wearily. "We need to discuss the elephant."

Joyce Bingham's Biography

Joyce has been writing scientific English for too many years. She has rekindled her original love of fiction writing. In the planning stages of a novel, she has embraced flash fiction to sharpen the mind on plotting and editing.

@joycebingham10

~

649: CHOOSE YOUR REWARD

by Michelle Compton

As Liam McCarthy stoked the fire with his bellows, his mind wandered. Although he toiled endless hours in his smithy, he was still unable to earn enough coins to provide for his large family.

"Down here, on your boot."

Liam glanced toward his boots and saw a leprechaun.

"You're an honest man, so I'm here to offer you two rewards. You will either prosper but you'll die within a year, or live a century but continue living in poverty. Choose now."

Michelle Compton's Biography

Michelle Compton is a historical fiction novelist. When not writing, she enjoys spending time with her pets and travelling the world. She has many fond memories of her time spent in Ireland.

www.facebook.com/Cave-Leonem-1106603249361789/

650: PROMISES, PROMISES

by Christine Tapper

Santa dusted ash from his red outfit. "Thanks, elves, for pulling me from that chimney. So scary being stuck."

And hard work dragging you out, thought Elfin.

At home, Santa had devoured turkeys, vegetables, plum pudding and custard. While delivering toys, he'd scoffed every cake and chocolate left out for him.

Santa loosened his belt and burped. He nudged Elfin. "Next year, tell everyone I'm dieting. I can't handle all this food."

Elfin rolled his eyes. He heard this every year.

Christine Tapper's Biography

Christine writes stories, poems and articles; fact, fiction and fairy tales. ABC Radio have broadcast her short stories and Oxford University Press published one. Her writings have appeared in anthologies and are online at:

www.enchantedconversationmag.blogspot.com

~

651: COLOURS

by Hajra Saeed

I have been told that the prettiest sight in the sky is a rainbow.

That the trees inhabiting the woods come in all hues of green.

That the lake is the same sparkling aquamarine as my eyes.

Yet I can only take their word for it because, since I was born, my world's been black, white and shades of grey. I am day blind, for I can't tolerate natural light. You see I have achromatopsia – the rarest form of colour blindness.

Hajra Saeed's Biography

Hajra Saeed is a freelance writer in Pakistan, where she has been writing for more than two decades.

652: INFINITE

by Alice Hale

Some lights are meant to go out.

It is sad but true.

Still, always remember that no matter how many stars leave, there will always be new ones. As long as the sun burns, and even beyond that, there will be stars.

People will always dream of what is out there. Humans will always look up and be filled with wonder and curiosity for the untouchable.

There will always be lights.

There will always be wishes.

There will always be hope.

Alice Hale's Biography

Alice is a 17-year-old hobbyist writer from the Netherlands. She only started writing a couple of months ago. Her hobbies include reading, writing, listening to music and making bad jokes.

~

653: BEING GINGER BAKER

by Linda Lewis

The drum kit was the present to end all presents. I was overawed, scared in case I broke something.

My first attempt was timid – tap, tap, tap – but slowly, I gained confidence.

One two three four.

A clash of cymbals. A thud of bass.

I was smoking.

Then my cousin grabbed the sticks and began to play. He made those drums sing until the whole room resonated with the sound.

The next day I swapped the drum kit for a bike.

Linda Lewis' Biography

Linda Lewis makes her living from writing. She has sold around a thousand stories to magazines in the UK, Scandinavia and Australia, many of them romantic. Single since getting divorced in 2005, she has stopped looking for love.

www.twitter.com/writingiseasy

654: ACCIDENT

by Scott Parent

BANG.

The airbag exploded into my face. All I could smell and taste was the nitrogen gas it left behind. I couldn't see through all the smoke. The side of my face stung from the scratches and burns it caused. My ears were ringing. I wasn't sure whether I hit her or she hit me. The muscles of my shoulders and back felt sore from being thrown back against the seat.

Everything was moving in slow motion until the police arrived.

Scott Parent's Biography

Born in Massachusetts, Scott Parent earned his graduate and undergraduate degrees from Worcester State University. In 1992, he moved to North Carolina to take a teaching position. He's been writing on and off most of his life, though never professionally.

~

655: KEY, KEY RING AND FREEDOM

by Roshna Rusiniya

The bedroom door opened with a squeak, much to Lyla's chagrin. Her husband's snores were still loud, resembling the growling of a predatory animal. She lifted the suitcase with her uninjured hand and glanced around the room, brightly smiling at the sight of overflowing laundry and dirty plates.

She stepped out into the warm night and pulled the hoodie of the jacket up, so her bruised cheeks were hidden. The key in her hand glowed, free from the key ring, finally.

Roshna Rusiniya's Biography

Roshna Rusiniya is a homemaker and an aspiring writer who currently resides in Qatar with her small family. Her dream book, which is also her first, is a big work in progress.

656: ROY'S DRIVE-THRU FUNERAL HOME

by Paulette Pierre

Pick your casket: oak, dark maple, or silver overlay.
    Interior: silk, satin, or cotton.
    Budget items: pine box or plain hardwood.
    Flowers: dollar extra.
    Sides: wreath with name or blank banner.
    Headstones: marble or slate.
    Engraving: 15 characters. One dollar extra per character over 15.
    Services offered: prayer, non-denominational, or atheist (no charge).
    Forms of payment: In God We Trust. All others pay cash.
    Please proceed through the tunnel to begin your journey.
    Have a nice afterlife. Please don't come again.

Paulette Pierre's Biography

Paulette is an aspiring writer embarking on her third career. She relishes rejection letters because they push her to be better as a writer. She lives in Indiana with her wife, three dogs and two cats.
    Twitter: @padpi52

~

657: TEENAGE PROTECTION

by Toni Peers

"You just want to lock me away," she shrieked, stomping her studded boots out of the room.
    It's true. Given the dangers out there that's exactly what I wanted to do, but apparently it's illegal.
    So I collected up the teenager trash, which prompted our current row: hoodie, chocolate wrappers, phone charger. Then I thought, *bleurgh*. So I sat down, switched on the telly and there was the advert.
    "Virtual cages, the PC way to protect your teenager. Order now?"
    Click.

Toni Peers' Biography

My name is Toni Peers. I have been a frustrated writer all my life, but this year I am actively writing. I teach crafts and write for a history magazine. I've had a couple of short stories published in anthologies.

658: THE VISIT

by John Lane

After I finished my weekly visit with Aunt Shelby at Christchurch Nursing Home, I signed out at the front desk.

A scrawny, wheelchair-bound woman rolled towards me, with an icy stare that froze me.

"Billy, don't you believe in visiting your momma?"

My hands trembled. "Um. Sorry. Momma."

She darted her finger at me. "Next time, see me, son." The resident scooted away.

Sobbing, I knew the truth but left, speechless.

Billy's mother, Sylvia, spoke at his funeral six months ago.

John Lane's Biography

John has published work in *50 Word Stories, Friday Flash Fiction* and *Ad Hoc Fiction*. John is also a slush reader for *Freeze Frame Fiction*.

~

659: UNLIKE FATHER, UNLIKE SON

by Susan Howarth

"Has this guy ever held a bat before?" Dad is yelling at the TV. Again.

He's anchored to his La-Z-Boy with a beer in his hand and a trail of nacho chip crumbs down the front of his shirt. For Mum's sake, I hope the Red Sox come back to win.

"Son, grab me another beer before you go."

I head out the door with a wave, my ballet shoes hidden at the bottom of my backpack. He would never understand.

Susan Howarth's Biography

Susan lives with her husband and two children in Prince Edward Island, Canada. She is a public servant, plays poker, and has degrees in psychology and law. You can find her at:
www.twitter.com/SusanMHowarth

660: A HYENA'S HAPPINESS

by Yabo Anderson

The bee stings again, and I accept my fate. I cannot justify the frown that hangs on my snout.

I clip and cut, stitch and sew, until I am whole once again – an entire hyena. When unsightly lumps appear, I push them back and pretend it doesn't hurt. I adhere to the hyena's words, "Smile and act like us."

Do you hear the hyena in the darkness? It is me, teeth bared to the world, laughing at the choice I made.

Yabo Anderson's Biography

Indentured to her cat, Goomba, Yabo Anderson is virtually chained to her computer writing stuff that will earn the daily cat treats. All the while, Goomba purrs threats and encouragement. But mostly encouragement.

~

661: A MODERN-DAY MONA LISA

by Toni G.

It was Mona Lisa transferred into a thin, fragile frame. That undefined look of hers, now found on this face. Her simple beauty mysteriously transported to the present day.

I looked on from inside my parked car, with the curiosity of someone amazed by a newfound treasure. It had taken me a full seven minutes to realise the object of my surveillance was a feminine 'he' and not a plain 'she'. Somehow that made him even more beautiful in my eyes.

Toni G.'s Biography

Toni G. writes poetry, flash fiction and micro fiction. More of her work can be found at *Elephants Never* and *The Drabble*.

662: MY BACK YARD

by NT Franklin

My back yard is special to me. It merges into a field of the farm my grandparents started many years ago. As the only surviving heir, it is my back yard now. A really big back yard and my private space.

Aunt Gertrude died and was cremated. I was surprised how little ash comes from a cremated body. I sprinkled her ashes on top of the ground in my back yard today. She joins the many others there under the ground.

NT Franklin's Biography

NT Franklin writes cosy mystery short stories, nostalgia short stories and flash fiction, and has been published in *Page & Spine, Scarlet Leaf Review, Fiction on the Web, Mad Swirl, FreedomFiction, Entropy, 50-Word Stories* and *Dime Show Review*, among others.

~

663: AWAKENING

by Adam Down

A hitching rasp, like an air conditioner on its last legs. Breathing.

Light came next – not the one at the end of the tunnel, but something gloomier.

More sensations followed. The feeling of her best dress against her skin. Of being trapped.

She opened her eyes. Pine boards surrounded, hemmed her in. Her hands were clasped across her chest. Somewhere close, a eulogy ceased.

The coffin moved. Unseen flames crackled. A knot in the wood popped.

She'd asked to be cremated.

Adam Down's Biography

Adam lives in the Midlands of the United Kingdom, which is nothing like Middle Earth, much to his chagrin. He works in a university, but would much rather be writing.

664: DECLUTTERING

by Bec Lewis

Ryan tripped over a pile of hardbacks. "Hoarder."

"Books are company when you're away."

"And thousands of ornaments?"

"They were gifts from friends."

He grabbed his keys. "Declutter by the time I get back or I'll bin the lot."

In the post-slam silence, Deb opened the wardrobe. Clothes first, she decided.

She found the letter in Ryan's old denim jacket.

Later, he'd find his possessions outside with a note: *I've decluttered. Your mistress can put you up – if her husband agrees.*

Bec Lewis' Biography

Bec Lewis' short stories have appeared in places including *MicroHorror, WeirdYear, Escape Velocity* and the horror anthology *M is for Monster*.

www.facebook.com/Bec-Lewis-Fiction-103040521381274/

~

665: AN AVERAGE MORNING

by Anastasia Mosher

William kisses his wife's cheek before sitting at the table. "Good morning." He looks perfect today; not a wrinkle on his black suit or a stray hair on his gel-caked head.

"Ready for the big meeting?" Margo sits beside him, sipping orange juice.

"Of course. This is gonna be huge for us, Margy."

It would. Too bad he'd never make it. Margo had cut his brakes lines. He'd been cheating.

"Love you." William smiles.

Love has no place here. Not anymore.

Anastasia Mosher's Biography

Anastasia Mosher resides in Barrie, Ontario and is the referee of three children that she calls her own (along with a loving and supportive fiancé). When she's not cooking, cleaning and trying to keep everyone alive, she spends her time writing.

666: THE DONATION

by Charlotte Farrell-Banks

"I thought you were only meant to take a pint? The bag looks fuller than that."

The nurse gives me a reproachful look. "A pint wouldn't go very far now, would it? It was a catastrophic accident. They need a lot of blood." She taps the clipboard with her pen. "You did tick the box saying we could take as much as we need."

"I didn't..." I begin. The words stick in my throat. My vision glazes, then fades to black.

Charlotte Farrell-Banks' Biography

Charlotte Farrell-Banks is a 30-year-old medical translator from the north-east of England. She is currently working on her first novel.

~

667: THE PRICE OF FREEDOM (INSPIRED BY JENNA RUSSWURM'S BUNNY RESCUE)

by Mary Daurio

I'm raising baby bunnies because my dog killed their wild mother and broke Floppy's back. He can't move. Wilderness Hub recommends, "Keep him as Thumper's comfort-companion."

I caress Floppy's soft fur as he sucks warm milk from a dropper. This martyr won't taste liberty.

The rabbits represent the duality of our being, the wounded and the whole. Must we sacrifice our maimed soul to acquire freedom? Can't we have both?

Floppy accompanies me for Thumper's release. He deserves that much, surely.

Mary Daurio's Biography

Mary Daurio is a Canadian grandmother who likes to write. She has poems in *Grey Borders Magazine*, a couple of short stories in *Fonthill Voice* and some flash fiction in *Friday Flash Fiction*.

668: TWENTY-FIVE MINUTES

by Evelyn Hawke

Twenty-five minutes.

You can do a lot in such a short time. Watch an episode of your favourite sitcom. Change over the laundry. Two ten minute workouts with two breaks. A nice walk with your dog around the block.

For me, I had half a drink and straightened two lengths of my long hair.

Twenty-five minutes is all it took to change "Mum's sick" to "Mum's dead".

I wish I had stayed; wish I had listened to my gut. "Don't go…"

Evelyn Hawke's Biography

Evelyn Hawke – night security and writer. She grew up in a small southern Ontario town that glorified a rock star that had no clue the town existed. In her free time, she'll be in a bubble bath, with wine, brainstorming.

~

669: WINNER = STEAK DINNER

by Karen Walker

Brian was always best in our souvenir contest. With his eye for bad, he found San Fran fog in a can and a chip-dip dish with the bugs of Oz.

Then I spied a pink shell in a Cypriot shop – ancient, sharp little horns on top. But oh the indignity done: red plastic berries, green sprigs, a loop of lace glued on. Snatched from the sea, doomed to hang on a Christmas tree.

Winner, winner, Brian bought me a steak dinner.

Karen Walker's Biography

After listening to long, long tales of woe all day at work, Karen comes home and writes short fiction. She lives in Ontario, Canada.

670: GROWING UP

by Valerie J Shay

Diane's life was never the same after she pulled the trigger. For three years she tried to forget that night; tried to bury it in the recesses of her memory. She refused to talk about it. She forced herself to pretend it never happened. Diane loved Jeffrey, but she loved her freedom, her sanity and her friends even more.

Jeffrey needed to go. She'd outgrown him. He no longer served his purpose. Mother was right, imaginary friends are not real. Mostly.

Valerie J Shay's Biography

Valerie Shay is a short story writer and a novelist who resides in Southern California. She finds characters in everyday people.

www.facebook.com/val.shay2

~

671: FERTILITY

by Austrian Spencer

The seat is leather, my back is damp, my T-shirt sticks to my skin. I'm shaking. I see through blurred eyes, as Phil holds me to his chest and does not let go. The doctor is mumbling but I do not hear. Phil will tell me later that, for him, it is a relief. That he will always have me to himself. That he wouldn't want to share me with anyone else.

All I hear is that I am to blame.

Austrian Spencer's Biography

I write horror. I write about death and dying, and the process of redemption. Horror can be defined in many ways. I'm trying something new, come and check it out. Face your horror, then face mine.

www.facebook.com/Faceyourhorror

672: THE COCKROACH QUEEN

by Denise Senecal

I hated cockroaches; absolutely, positively, without a doubt, despised, could not stand, threw up, ran down the hall buck-naked screaming, hated cockroaches. I was terrified of them, too.

I'm a geneticist now, with a license to do radioactive testing. Do you know that cockroaches are older than the dinosaurs? Or that cockroaches don't get cancers? Or that cockroaches withstand irradiation? Lots of irradiation. Lots and lots of irradiation. Do you know that in the lab I'm sometimes called the Cockroach Queen?

Denise Senecal's Biography

I'm a retired engineer, living in Vermont with two cats. I have a daughter in Colorado. I'm a wordsmith, artist, musician, woodsperson, gardener, cook, traveller, sometime philosopher and snowball thrower.

www.facebook.com/denise.senecal.927

~

673: RED ROCKET

by L.E. Daurio

Struck by an invading gaze, hypnotic and alluring, I stumble backward. Allowing first, then inviting this penetration, I reciprocate. Together, fixed and distant, we navigate, seeking depths of our humanity previously uncharted.

My body responds silently to this insensible touch. With the ferocity of discharged electricity our love materialises and generations of our combined DNA burst forth into existence. An entire lifetime dispensed in one fleeting exchange.

The familiar chime summons the doors shut, severing the connection. The train rolls on.

L.E. Daurio's Biography

I'm an aspiring writer from rural Ontario, Canada.

674: PUPPY MORNING

by CJ Wigg

The clap of thunder startled April, who groaned, pulling the covers over her head. The puppy burrowed in, slobbering his kisses on her face.

She laughed while cuddling him. "Forget dreary mornings."

April gathered the bundle of fur and danced into the next bedroom. She plopped the dog on the bed. He squirreled in, nuzzling another victim. Giggles erupted and off they went.

Sunshine rained inside as laughter expanded. They clapped with the thunder as raindrops tapped music on the roof.

CJ Wigg's Biography

I am an avid reader and a writer with many stories brewing. Nothing is quite as magical as the written word.

~

675: THE GROUNDLING

by Wayne B. Chorney

Harry's whiskers trembled. Never before had he gone to the stone dwellers' realm. He heard them stomp, run and dig, right above his head. The very roots of his home shook when the 'horses', whatever they were, pounded their 'hooves' on the earth above his head.

Father told him of the horses and their hooves, but he never did describe them. Harry was most certain they were horrendous creatures with hundreds of legs to make as much noise as they did.

Wayne B. Chorney's Biography

Wayne B. Chorney is retired and enjoys his retirement by writing books. He has a novel that he is in the process of completing called *Moments of Clarity*. He hopes you enjoy this collection of short stories, including 'The Groundling'.

676: PHONES, VEGETABLES AND MASHED POTATOES

by Em Daurio

Mum sang a huge sigh of disappointment at the dinner table, after observing buried faces in our phones.

"Can you not have one meal without?" she said softly in defeat.

No one replied; we were too involved to hear. Our eyes lit up, screen induced.

I looked up when I had a second to, between videos and messages.

She was a memory. The blink of an eye – history.

Technology doesn't age like we do.

Can you not have one meal without?

Em Daurio's Biography

Em Daurio is a big-city-living small-town-raised mechanical designer trying their take at writing. Coffee addict. Sports and healthy living enthusiast. Life's too short not to double dip.

~

677: THE LIFT

by Umme Ammarah

She was waiting for the lift, files that she had to submit to the upper floor in her hands. She peered down, her head resting on the glass of the lift's door.

Suddenly, there was a sound and the glass broke. She fell forward, papers flying. Grasping for something, the steel wire of the lift came into her hand. She wound her body around the wire and held on, her blood dripping everywhere.

Someone called the lift to the third floor...

Umme Ammarah's Biography

I'm from Karachi, Pakistan. I love reading and reading and reading. I also love painting and sipping coffee. As you already know how much I love to read, I thought maybe I should give writing a whirl too...

678: FOR THE LOVE OF A GHOST

by Veena Rah

"You did this to me," she whispers, fidgeting.

I knew this, of course. I was selfish and weak. *I* left.

I trace the path of her tear with my finger. Almost imperceptibly, she shudders.

She'll be angry with me forever, but it won't matter, she'll be with me again.

"Don't worry, dear. It won't hurt," I lie as she tilts her head back and throws a handful of those little pills down her throat. "Trust me."

She'll be with me again.

Veena Rah's Biography

Just a British/Asian millennial, trying to shed an unflattering image of her generation. Desperately looking for chunks of time to do the one thing I genuinely enjoy: writing.

~

679: DARK TRUTHS

by Francisca Staines

A week ago, Daddy fell off the roof of a very tall building.

Mummy was so sad, she cried and cried.

Today, we went to the cemetery. My aunt was there. So was my grandpa.

Coming home, Mummy told me we were moving.

I didn't like the news. "But all my friends are here. Besides, if we leave, Daddy won't know where to find us."

"Sweetie…" Mummy hugged me. "Daddy's with the angels now."

"Mummy, why you lie? He's behind you."

Francisca Staines' Biography

Occasional fossil hunter, Francisca was raised on bedtime stories and folktales, and enjoys writing for children and adults. In her world, imagination and creativity are as important as water and food.

680: THE PROUD MAN

by Kavitha Yarlagadda

Jenna comes running inside.

"Mama, there's a mad man at the gate."

Kate hurries out on hearing her daughter and sees an old man with shabby clothes and a dishevelled appearance standing at the gate. His eyes look intelligent and he has a proud stature, which shows that he once had a good life.

Kate takes Jenna aside and explains that he's a good person and maybe he is hungry.

Jenna takes the man's hand and leads him into their home.

Kavitha Yarlagadda's Biography

Kavitha is a civil engineer who assists her architect husband in managing their architectural and interior design firm. She is an avid reader and a passionate writer who finds solace in writing poetry, fiction and non-fiction. She's a published author.

www.facebook.com/kavitha.yarlagadda.7

~

681: THE ICE BOX

by Frank Daurio

It was a good day for a hockey game. My buddies and I jumped in my dad's old van.

Dad said, "Welcome to the refrigerator, boys."

Neither of them knew the van would be colder than the ice, and a dram of whisky kept the old man warm. He wasted no money on the heater. It was snowing through the sunroof and our teeth chattered behind blue lips. We called it the icebox, but it got us on to the ice.

Frank Daurio's Biography

Frank Daurio is a welder from Welland who likes to write in his spare time. He has performed at Poetry Takes the Night in Welland and likes to make artistic creations with his welding.

682: AFLOAT

by Michelle Cook

31st May 2050.

Eva. My daughter. Born today to the salty air. Destined never to smell the earth, or sleep in a bed that doesn't rock.

When I was a child, we were islanders. Then came The Last Flood; every scrap of land submerged. From the flotsam of our wrecked homes, we built a tottering city. Cold nights brought lurching shadows. The smallest of us wept years for soft toys, warm baths.

Dear Eva, I survived. Now with you, living begins.

Michelle Cook's Biography

Michelle is an averagely harried UK mum of two young children. By day, she works for the National Health Service. She writes to stay sane, though is never sure if it's working. Michelle's debut novel, *Tipping Point*, was released in September 2020.

~

683: THE BIRTHDAY PRESENT

by Jayne Morgan

A new mini for her 18th birthday. Susie smiled to herself as she raced across town, darting in and out of traffic, ignoring the angry chorus of blasting horns around her.

Pulling out from behind a bus, she manoeuvred the mini into a space in front, quickly swerving out of the way of a speeding motorbike.

"Idiot."

Susie's car mounted the pavement. She didn't see the small child she hit. Not then. But she would forever see him in her dreams.

Jayne Morgan's Biography

My book *Haunted School* was published in 2005 as part of Hodder's 'Livewire' series. Since then I have written two unpublished children's books and am currently working on my third.

684: CLICK AND BANG

by Jaycee Durand

She closed the chamber. Spun it.

"Stop."

Such a shiny little revolver. Look. Her reflection… ha, crazy eyes. Same as her mother's when she ate a bullet?

"Debbie—"

Click.

"God, I'm sorry, OK?"

She cocked the hammer back. That's what she should've done. Used a blunt instrument to bash his cheating head in. No. Give him a life sentence of guilt and she'd get to see Mum again.

Candy pink lips closed over cold metal.

"Debbie, please. I really do love—"

Jaycee Durand's Biography

Jaycee Durand has published shorts on *Medium* including 'Twisted Valentine in The Mad River' and 'Chiller in the Mirror' in *Midnight Mosaic Fiction*, which won second place in their A Season of Strange contest. Jaycee lives in London, England.

~

685: JUST 81 WORDS

by Thomas O'Mara

So good to be accurate, neat and precise,
　　my writing a passioned, explicit device.
Apt comments found where there are phrases to spare,
　　hurtling and flowing with dashes of flare.
Take care with the counting; take care not to fail,
　　just 81 words must my story entail.
A word hurtle train, all engine and coaches,
　　my work gallops on as the ending approaches.
Some final adjustments, some last minute changes,
　　I'm just about there by the seat of my breaches.
The—

Thomas O'Mara's Biography

I'm 60, Irish. A retired accountant living in London. I've written two novels: one self-published, the other seeking a publisher. (*HRH Prince Philip: Escape from the Palace* and *A Teeny Weeny Miracle*.) I've also written quite a few short stories.

686: FATHERHOOD

by Bernard Muslin

I can always hear him. Why am I so afraid? This is not how it was meant to be – I have no control, he has that. Does he hear me? His footsteps echo through my head, louder and louder. His voice is my fear. Occasionally, I get a glimpse of what might have been, and I start to grieve all over again.

I can always hear him. Why am I so afraid? This is not how it was meant to be.

Bernard Muslin's Biography

Bernard Muslin is a marketing manager by day and aspiring writer by night. Father of two children and thoroughly exhausted.

~

687: NEVER GIVE YOUR HEART AWAY

by Frances Tate

"What have you done?" the young vampire's sire demands.

"He gave me his heart." She holds up the evidence.

"You know that's a figure of speech."

"You told me you loved me. It's why I let you turn me…" She blinks ruby eyes. "Was that also a figure of speech?"

"You were a simpering girl. Now you're a goddess."

"I was a girl in love…" She punches through his ribcage. Withdraws a clenched, blooded fist. "I accept *everything* you promised me."

Frances Tate's Biography

Frances writes about vampires in full-length novels and about anything that sits still long enough to be sketched in drabbles. She is self-published in both word quantities and lives in the north west of England.

688: THE FUTURE IS UNCERTAIN

by Lauren J. Phillips

Naomi stared at the horizon, watching the final thruster fall away.

She and Mattias stood at the window, each holding a hand of their daughter, Skal.

"This is it," he said.

The president of The United Globe nodded, tears finally flowing.

The last shuttle from Earth, where they'd left everything behind. The weight of the decisions they'd made to arrive here. Forward was their only destination; the ships sent forward, in all directions, as Mother Nature's fires and melee closed in.

Lauren J. Phillips' Biography

Lauren J. Phillips is a marketing and communications consultant who lives in Bellingham, WA. She loves creative writing, reading and travelling. She is currently editing her first novel and hopes to be published soon.

~

689: DINNER AND A MOVIE...

by Lumen Ros

"Would you like dinner out tonight, dear?"

"Let's eat in."

"Sure. Italian?"

"We've had that three times this week. How about Moroccan?"

"Excellent suggestion. I'll pick it up. Let's catch a movie after."

As I finished getting dressed, the front door opened.

"I'm back, love."

I was so hungry, I flew down the steps.

There he stood, dinner in hand. After 500 years, the gleam in his fangs still sent a jolt of lust to my carotid.

"Darling, this is Nadia."

Lumen Ros' Biography

Lumen Ros is an author/poet with a penchant for writing fantasy and the paranormal. Most evenings she can be found at her laptop weaving magical and fantastical worlds. Lumen lives at home with her awesome family and three pet rescues.

690: FLIGHT

by N.B. Craven

Today was the day he would fly. He'd prepared for months, testing his wings, strengthening his skills. Nothing could stop him from achieving his goal.

The crisp air blew against his cheeks. Leaning over the edge, he peered into oblivion. Anxiety seized him. He paused. The ground spun beneath him.

A gentle push from his mother moved him closer to the edge. Heart pounding in his chest, he swallowed his fear and leaped into the nothingness.

Spreading his wings, he soared.

N.B. Craven's Biography

N.B. Craven is the father of four wonderful children and has been married to the most wonderful woman for twelve years. He is a southern boy at heart but has lived all over the USA. He currently resides in Tri-cities, Washington.

~

691: HOME

by Taylor Elliott

I close the truck door with my back. The original farm house I grew up in is all that remains. I travelled 800 miles to retrieve my youth. I wipe tears away.

Three of the dozen walnut trees that cast moonlit shadows into my second-storey window lord over everything. A golden leaf floats down and catches in my hair. I pluck it free. Its carcass crackles as I crush it. Inhaling citrus, I smile. Childhood adventures flood my mind.

I'm home.

Taylor Elliott's Biography

Having more jobs over his life than you can shake a stick at, Taylor was a journeyman until an accident robbed him of his mobility. He plays cards for a living and is trying to make it as a writer.

692: RUNNING AWAY

by Elliot Cambrey

Dear Mum,

Molly stepped on my Lego castle and broke it. It's your fault, Mum. I always tell you she's NOT allowed in my room but you just won't listen, so I'm running away. I packed everything I need: baseball cards, Nintendo Switch and all of my Lego. Ha. Please DO NOT come looking for me.

Liam

PS If you go to McDonald's, order pizza or get something yummy for dinner, will you come get me? I'm hiding in Molly's playhouse.

Elliot Cambrey's Biography

Elliot Cambrey has been writing stories on scraps of paper as long as she's been literate. When she's not out and about observing the odd behavior of her fellow Phoenicians or shopping, she's writing her next story.

~

693: THE OFFICE OF SANTA CLAUSE

by Jason Barbo

Dear Timmy,

We regret to inform you that we are unable to comply with your requested Christmas gifts, because:

1. Flamethrowers are not considered toys under article 6B
2. Game consoles have been labelled as 'not educational' by the Parental Advisory Committee
3. With 385 counts of fussing, terrorising the dog, fighting with sister and not listening to Mum on your record, this year you are only eligible for coal

We wish you a Merry Christmas,
The Office of Santa Clause

Jason Barbo's Biography

Jason Barbo teaches English by day and at night dreams of bigger, more literary things. He lives in Chattanooga, Tennessee.

www.instagram.com/bornnomd/

694: GOAL HANGER

by Tony Mooney

I admired my friend when we played together in the big games. Time after time, he was the hero – hooking or heading or blocking – clearing the ball off the line. It was very noticeable, and I wondered where his instinct came from.

It took me years, decades, to realise that it didn't just happen. If you want to clear the ball off the line, you have to put yourself on the line. If you want to lead, you have to lead.

Tony Mooney's Biography

Greying middle-aged novelist-in-the-trying, print media background. Starting to have good and bad days, starting to understand the good times, past and present. Fear used to keep me in bed, now it gets me up; freestyle writing from here on out.

~

695: BIRTHDAY PARTY

by Mark Stocker

I want to go home.

"Mummy will collect you later."

I want to go now. I'm bored of running about. And I'm sick of sandwiches with crusts, and jam with bits in.

"Come and play."

Fighting for chairs when the music stops? No thanks. I want to go home to my room and my things.

"There'll be cake soon."

Hold on.

Why didn't you say?

Perhaps I'll stay a while, have some cake.

And go home to my things after that.

Mark Stocker's Biography

Mark Stocker is an advertising creative from Suffolk who loves to write but never has enough time, which is why he thinks 81 Words is just perfect. He is occasionally online at:

@MarkStocker72

696: THE STING OF THE WIND

by Margaret Davis

The sharp November wind stung Elner's already bruised face. Her escape needed to be quiet; her tormentor waited.

Gently, she slid from the window, her heartbeat rapid. Where would she go? No idea. Fear gripped her.

Which way? Left? Right? Move quickly. Noises – he's coming.

Stay in control, the price of panic is death. He promised that the last time she tried escaping.

Running, stumbling, crying. *Is he behind me?* Faster. RUN.

Arms grab her, freedom failed, try again if alive.

Margaret Davis' Biography

Margaret is a retired social worker writing her way across the United States selling Vermont maple syrup. She loves to write and enjoys writing fiction, humour and memoir.

~

697: HOW TO FIGHT A CLOSET MONSTER AND WIN

by Ashley Scott

She crouched in the dark, waiting. Finally, the beast emerged. It sniffed. Drool coated its lips. It saw the offering. Crumbled cookies. It opened its jaws to feast.

She sprung, triggering her trap. The laundry basket fell upon the beast.

It growled. The girl snatched one pink slipper and banged on the basket.

"Quiet," she shouted. "It's not time to be awake. You have to sleep."

It whimpered.

She opened a book and began to read.

The beast curled, yawned, slept.

Ashley Scott's Biography

Ashley Scott lives with her family in the Pacific Northwest. She loves writing that packs a lot into a little. You can find her short stories and flash fiction in online literary publications, including *On the Premises*.

698: JUST A KID WITH A THESAURUS

by Emma Wilson

The old man opened his thesaurus to its one dog-eared page and the words he'd circled in crayon when he was just a kid.

Continue. Synonyms: make last, pursue, linger, elongate, draw out...

Back then, he didn't know what most of the words in the thesaurus meant, much less the word 'synonym', but he knew how to draw.

He'd kept the box filled with drawings – each one of a memory he'd wanted to last forever – even after he realised his mistake.

Emma Wilson's Biography

Emma Wilson is a neuroscientist who likes to write very tiny stories in her spare time. Her stories have previously appeared in *Nanoism* and *Friday Flash Fiction*.

~

699: LOST

by Mary Dharsi

"You always try so hard when the whispers come back," he said gently.

She kept her head bowed but said nothing.

He tenderly brushed back her oily hair and brought his lips to her ear.

"Why do you keep thinking I'll be gone someday?" he murmured.

She squeezed her hands into fists and lifted her weary gaze. Suddenly, she hit the mirror and screamed.

"I'm never going away... unless you want to stop fighting me," he whispered from the red shards.

Mary Dharsi's Biography

Mary Dharsi homeschools her children by day and writes various nonsense in the pale glow of night. In her spare time, she volunteers for Operation Gratitude and provides book reviews. She can be found on www.scribophile.com as Autumn Runningmare.

700: THE BOOK

by Don Bartlome

I stood beside the desk, looking down at an ancient book I'd been seeing for fifty years, with gold lettering no one could translate.

Even with the threat of punishment, the book was comfortable in my withered hands, like a long lost lover. I opened the book, feeling its warmth on my palm.

"Billy," Mother shrieked. "Leave it. You're only ten years old." I looked into the mirror behind the desk and saw myself: a young boy with small soft hands.

Don Bartlome's Biography

Born in Idaho, I always had a way of finding new stories and reading books growing up. Always wanted to show myself I could write, when a teacher said I was no good. Been writing for five years.

~

701: MY MUSE MY MOTIVATION

by Violet James

The blank page stares back at me.
Taunting me.
It's milky white surface pristine, yet vulnerable.
Dare I mar it with unwarranted superlatives?
Shall I scroll along the edges with flowery prose?
Or simply state the facts without frivolity.
In the depths of sadness a swirl of light beckons.
Tactile and pure.
My muse is nearest in the dark.
He holds my hand.
Nudges me forward.
A kind word.
He comforts me.
He is the inspiration for all that I do.

Violet James' Biography

My name is Violet James. I have published flash fiction and poetry on *Medium, Lit Up* and *Mad River*. I have just completed my first contemporary romance novel and am presently querying agents.
www.twitter.com/VioletJames21

702: THOSE WE LOVE

by Rex Charger

"Daddy, is Mum up there?" Lying on the soft grass beside her father, Lily stared at the night sky.

"Yes, baby."

"I miss her."

He sighed. "What happened?"

"My concert..."

"I'll be there."

"But, I wish Mum..."

"Baby, she's with us, always. Wait." Holding the phone up, he turned on the front camera. "See your eyes?"

"Yes."

"They're hers, and this mole on your chin."

She giggled. "Mum had that."

"See, I told you she's with us. You'll make her proud."

Rex Charger's Biography

My name is Rex Charger. I am a writer with several of my prose and poetry pieces published in *Medium* and *Lit Up*. I'm presently working on a time travel romance novel based in the Edwardian era.

www.twitter.com/rex_charger

~

703: THE STOP-START JOURNEY

by Beth Greenwood

Stop. Start. Stop. Start. Thoughts of motorways cross my mind, back when travelling was easier.

Stop. Start. I guess being environmentally friendly isn't that bad.

Stop. The thing about electromagnetic travel is that if there is no electricity – something rarely used nowadays – you don't go.

Start. Hydropower is the only source and it is drying up.

Stop. Demand for water is too high. That and the politicians take a percentage.

Start. They introduced the tax on water in 2026.

Final stop.

Beth Greenwood's Biography

Beth Greenwood is an aspiring writer, bookworm and generally an all rounded literary geek.

704: CAR SHOPPING

by T. W. Garland

Lined up like beauty contestants at a pageant with large numbers painted on windscreens, the cars slope and curve in even waves. A variety of colours offer shades of luxury.

Jordan ponders before the selection box of vehicles. Sprayed on new car smell and the shine of turtle wax drives desire towards decision, hesitation towards hastiness.

A salesperson steps out, the tip of snakeskin boots peeking out from under his flared trousers. Behind him, costly repairs and invalidated warranties approach silently.

T. W. Garland's Biography

T.W. Garland has stacks of Victorian novels that taunt him with unbroken spines. He buys more books than he could hope to read and is glad not to have been born in the nineteenth century or in a Dickens novel.

www.twgarland.wordpress.com

~

705: AN OPEN LETTER

by T. Luxton

At our breakfast tables, we see headlines in the newspaper. In our cars, we hear the flat voices of experts on the radio. We are told you are vital. Without you, our flowers, our beautiful flowers, would crumble to dust.

In our minds, your honey reshapes itself into the golden, untouchable ambrosia of a new, healthy world. We are not so different. We breathe and eat and make more of ourselves, just as you do.

When will you save us? When?

T. Luxton's Biography

T. Luxton lives, writes, edits, edits, deletes, writes, submits and writes in the Bay Area.

706: DIAMONDS IN THE FAUCET

by Danny Macks

A diamond fell out of the faucet and made a solid *tck, tck* noise as it bounced off the metal sink and fell down the drain.

"Honey, guess—"

Nevermind. She was gone.

I spent too much time away and wasn't really home when my body was in the house. I argued that we needed the money, that the house depended on my pay cheque, that we couldn't get by without it.

Then I heard the lonely *tink* of another diamond falling.

Danny Macks' Biography

Danny Macks lives in southern Indiana surrounded by kids, cats and dogs. Danny loves puzzles, big libraries, medieval history and asking questions which don't have easy answers.

www.dannymacks.com

~

707: WHO ARE YOU?

by Carla Vlad

I heard a noise but I didn't bother checking. It was still light outside.

"Sorry, can I hide in here?"

"What are you doing?"

"I'm hiding, hopefully."

I heard a knock on the door. We looked at each other for a long second and then I stood up to answer the door.

"Food delivery for Bianca."

"Oh, yeah. I forgot about that. Thank you." I closed the door and turned to face the man as soon as possible.

"Who are you?"

Carla Vlad's Biography

Carla is a creative writing student with a huge passion for people and art. She is always looking for the next opportunity to learn. Someone told her she could win a Pulitzer and that is all she can think about.

708: CHRYSALIS

by Felix Castrillon

She dreaded staring at the deep darkness underneath her. She had been hanging from a tree for ages now. She wanted this moment to be over; she wanted to become something else, that ancient promise told from one generation to the next one.

She had heard all the stories, all the greatness and all the beauty. She loved all of them. However, all she could yearn for was her final destination.

Once free, that abyss would lead her to the stars.

Felix Castrillon's Biography

A Colombian-born mathematics teacher, I've been living in the UK for over 11 years. I don't regard myself as a writer, rather a storyteller that uses his spare time to leave some evidence of the ideas flying around his head.

~

709: THREE DOORS

by Tessa Elliott

Three doors led off from the dark, dank hall and its small rag rug of flimsy warmth.

One led into the parlour, with its upright piano and corner shrine – photograph, crucifix, gold rimmed black vase of plastic flowers.

One revealed the pantry, with its tin stacked shelves, marble slab and smell of stale, rancid fat, seeping from its walls.

The other led on towards the front garden, but was never opened, except once, for the entrance and exit of the coffin.

Tessa Elliott's Biography

Tessa Elliott took to writing fiction two years ago, after a chronic illness made her housebound, feeling empty and redundant. The worlds she now enters in her imagination, take her beyond the white brick walls that physically bind her.

710: THE VISITOR

by Shelly Teems

The woman was in her early twenties. Her brown hair shone and blonde highlights glittered in the sun. She carried a light red and white striped parasol. Her dress had a petticoat, was tea length and a buttery yellow. A matching Chanel shoulder bag with chain was slung over a shoulder.

She glided through the crowd, confident, smiling, nodding to people she passed, stopping briefly to chat with a man or woman, but always with momentous purpose.

Finally, there he was.

Shelly Teems' Biography

Shelly Teems is a poet and fiction writer. She is an avid reader who blogs about books and mental health.

~

711: WAY OUT IN THE WATER, SEE IT SWIMMING?

by Blake Holcomb

Today, I uploaded my prefrontal cortex to Eta Ursae Majoris via an infinite TB tachyon through a network of wormholes. Relatively speaking, my thoughts travelled 80 light years, arriving 32 seconds before I sent them, allowing me to generate an immeasurable cognitive reverberation that pierced the space / time barrier, escaping the mainframe housing our universe. Once free of that vacuum, it proliferated the 26 dimensions of Kaku's conceptualisation and simultaneously strummed all the strings of totality.

Where is my mind?

Blake Holcomb's Biography

A bit manic philosophically, but learning to find peace in the middle ground. My limited attention span hinders my ability to write the novel in my head. 81 Words is perfect.

712: THE DEAD WIFE

by Christine Bukania

I give the landlord notice to vacate my flat.

His bulldog face creases in concern.

"Is it the leaking pipes?" he asks me.

"No, my carpet got soaked yesterday but I hung it out to dry."

"Is it the smell of sewage outside your kitchen window?"

"No, the smell of excrement chased my appetite away. I'm now six kilos lighter for it."

"What is it then?"

I know he won't believe me when I tell him his dead wife is here.

Christine Bukania's Biography

Christine Bukania is a knowledge management expert, who writes in her free time. As a freelance journalist, she has contributed articles to various local newspapers. She enjoys writing short stories and flash fiction.

~

713: PRACTISE

by MF Mika

"You're overthinking this."

"No, I'm not."

"I don't know what else to say. Do as you wish."

And so I did.

I couldn't help but to meta. I just have this intuition that, if I keep peeling the meta, something will turn up.

Two months later, I take the final steps: review, replace this word by that word, then count again: 80.

I will add another word.

Let's read it one last time.

Good enough.

Copy, paste, send – am I published?

MF Mika's Biography

Mika is a vagabond adventurer born and raised in Brazil, educated in the US, awakened in Denmark, re-educated on the road, and currently based in Ukraine. He runs a weekly newsletter sharing his chronicles and lessons.

www.notmadyet.com

714: THE LAMENT OF ALL OUR TOMORROWS

by Bart Elbey

One afternoon, while walking in the forest, a prince heard a woodsy whimpering from the shady tangle of tall trunks.

"Who sheds such tears forlorn?" the prince enquired.

The soft tremble of leaf and branch was stilled then and the trees fell fast to sombre silence, which dared to endure as long as the proud prince's patience.

Finally, a twiglet voice conveyed a whispered portent.

"Let not the eternal echo of my legions' slaughtering be the lament of all your tomorrows."

Bart Elbey's Biography

Bart is an occasional dabbler in word fabrication and lily gilding, who hails from the Once Emerald Isle. He is destined to complete a novel in time's future vector. He likes numbers 75% as much as he likes letters.

www.medium.com/@bart.elbey

~

715: PAUSE A MOMENT

by Kennedy Meechan

"With all due respect, sir, please reconsider the consequences of what you are about to do."

Surveying the room, he looked at his ashen-faced colleagues one by one. The enormity of what he was about to set in motion engulfed him.

"I don't have a choice, Tom. May God forgive me, and may God have mercy on our souls."

As he pushed the button, the door flew open with a crash.

"Mr President, it's a computer virus. There is no attack."

Kennedy Meechan's Biography

Kennedy started writing at college. This fell away because of family commitments and a lack of encouragement. His family has grown up. He now has all the encouragement in the world. Hold on tight, it could be a bumpy ride.

716: SCRUM TIME

by Mason Bell

"Come on, lads. Remember our chat in the changing room before the game. I want a nice solid scrum that we can actually complete."

"I want never gets, sir."

Unusually witty for a prop, this one. It's normally the sort of lip one expects from their team's number nine.

"Crouch, bind." One second pause. "Set." Down it goes again. "Up, here's the mark, let's go again. Any questions?" Big mistake, the mouthy loose-head's hand shoots up.

"What's for tea?"

Abandon scrum.

Mason Bell's Biography

I have been writing on and off for years and have had a few projects published. This is the first time I have undertaken a flash fiction challenge. I am a retired rugby referee and work in a call centre.

~

717: THE MIRROR

by Roberta Scafidi

The shiny mirror stood tall before the fools.

"Who's this persons staring at we?"

Illiterate fools.

"I've no clue. But that one look like you, friend."

"Your grammar bad. And also, the other one look like you."

"Do you think they will rob we?"

"They seem to be talking."

"They're close enough to hear we."

One of them stepped ahead menacingly.

"Hey. If you hear we, leave we alone."

"He shouts at you, but I don't hear."

"I scared, let's leave."

Roberta Scafidi's Biography

Roberta Scafidi is an Italian author born in Patti (Sicily) in October 1999. She's attended the Classical Lyceum in her hometown and is currently studying foreign languages and literature in the University of Messina.

718: STOCKMAN

by Kathryn Joyce

Jed stands tall in his Stockman coat. William sees him arrive, cross the bar, his mouth twitching as women notice him. There's a flick of finger against lapel, the hook of thumb in pocket, the drawl of, "Cold beer," as his polished boot rests on the brass foot rail.

William folds over his table, his fists curling. William is a stockman; he works their late father's farm, north of Auckland. William has a Stockman coat too. His has seen the rain.

Kathryn Joyce's Biography

Kathryn Joyce's debut novel, *Thicker Than Soup*, was published in 2015. Short stories have appeared in anthologies including *Stories in Colour*, *Borderline Stories* and *To Hull And Back*. Kathryn says she enjoys writing about the vagaries of life.

~

719: LIFE FINDS A WAY

by Matthew Bines

Emptiness. Space's abyss loomed over the planet's arid surface. Not a mutter, a whisper or a signal could reach it. Life was unlikely.

No. It was impossible.

An endless grey surface, the taste of space, the smell of nothing. The desolate wasteland of wastelands trapped in a spiral headed out of the universe.

Nothing could live here.

Yet when I left my ship, beaten and bruised by cosmic storms, I was greeted by a feeble green plant growing in the vacuum.

Matthew Bines' Biography

I am an 18-year-old aspiring writer who has had a passion for creative writing since I first picked up a book. Sci-fi is my usual genre, but I like to write anything.

720: THIS PAGE LEFT INTENTIONALLY BLANK

by Andrew Ball

But it wasn't, was it? Instead of being actually blank, it had this message – this barefaced lie – printed right across the middle. And on an official government document, too.

He'd always suspected you couldn't trust the government. Didn't this just prove it? And what else were they lying to him about? UFOs? Social Security? The flu vaccine? National security? The list went on and on.

Suddenly, all those conspiracy theorists ranting on the internet didn't seem quite so nutty after all.

Andrew Ball's Biography

After a career doing something else, Andy Ball now raises Black Angus cattle on the banks of the Rappahannock River in Virginia – an occupation that leaves his mind free to wander. Occasionally, those wanderings turn themselves into stories.

~

721: THE RED CRAYON

by Yvonne Clarke

"Who's got my red crayon?"

"Not me," – a collective chorus of five-year-olds.

It was essential, this red crayon. How else could he depict the kaleidoscope of colours in the circus ring: the horses' finery, the fiery lions' manes and the crazily contorted crimson lips of the clowns?

Dusk started to cast its gloomy grey cloak and the ring of the school bell was conclusive.

Too late to finish it now, he thought disconsolately, tossing his masterpiece into the waste paper bin.

Yvonne Clarke's Biography

I've just started writing flash fiction, having previously been a copyeditor, content editor and Head of English as a Second Language in a college. I live in Chichester, West Sussex, and love writing, music, cycling and travelling.

722: KNIFE'S EDGE

by Olivia Ackers

Prey.

That's all she was to her.

Alice's slender finger traced the edge of the knife, slicing her skin. The curtains allowed a slither of light to seep in as she held the instrument above her head, the blade shimmering in the pale moonlight.

It plunged into her sister's body beneath, which limply convulsed as Alice ripped the knife away.

Blood stained her victim's clothes and bed.

Tears slid down her pale cheeks as her crimson covered hand stroked her sister.

Olivia Ackers' Biography

My name is Olivia Ackers, I'm 17 years old and I'm a literature fanatic. I aspire to become a writer and, hopefully, this will be a stepping stone towards my life dream.

~

723: FINE ART

by Hilary Taylor

I spent hours carefully composing the structure of it, ensuring there was enough depth and movement, and I had achieved the correct mood: modern art, not classical.

I stood back, pleased with my efforts.

"Bad dog," my human exclaimed. "Now I'm going to have to clean that window all over again."

She does this every time. I really don't know why she doesn't appreciate my efforts.

But at least I get a brand new canvas every day for my beautiful creations.

Hilary Taylor's Biography

I am Hilary Taylor, a 59-year-old newbie to this writing lark. Having retired two years ago after a long career in the NHS, I recently joined a creative writing class and have learned the joy of making up stories.

724: 81 YEARS

by Marco Cardoni

The grapnel wire snapped, sending my love and thoughts to their demise in the frozen depths below. Thud. I defiantly rammed my pickaxe into the rock face. It wasn't time.

Every muscle in my body screamed with pain. The remnants of my teeth ground themselves to dust like beached pebbles. Each pickaxe swing was more strenuous than the last, until…

My life's work – a human-shaped sculpture in the mountain – was finally finished.

Breath-taking.

But… who was it supposed to be again?

Marco Cardoni's Biography

Marco Cardoni is an MA student, studying English literature at De Montfort University. He loves reading dystopian fiction, writing (stories and pop culture reviews), making his own (somewhat amateurish) comic books and, most importantly, his crazy springer spaniel, Marley.

~

725: FORGOTTEN PLANTS WON'T ALWAYS DIE

by Liz Krogman

At first, I watered them on principle. Even though it was my brother's job to take care of his plants, not mine. And then I forgot about my principles and the plants. But they carried on living. Cacti, they're an amazing thing.

I noticed after a year, when I gave in. Poured the glass of water I no longer felt like drinking into one of the pots. I finally got close enough to tell. I'd be darned, but they were plastic.

Liz Krogman's Biography

Liz grew up in New Hampshire and attended school at Duke University in North Carolina where she received a BSc in biology. Much of her time is spent procrastinating daily life by writing instead.

726: THE THING THAT FLOATS

by Lee Holland

The woman walked along the lakeside. A light breeze swept through the trees, tickling the leaves. She looked over the lake and gasped. She immediately dialled 999.

"Help, there's something floating on top of the water."

She waited for what seemed like hours.

The officer finally showed up. The woman pointed at the floating body, bobbing on the water.

She watched as his face turned from friendly to confused.

He turned back to her and said, crossly, "That is a duck."

Lee Holland's Biography

Lee is a Welsh author, currently residing in Eastbourne. He uses writing, in addition to running ridiculous distances, as therapy for his anxiety and depression.

~

727: A SUDDEN EXPRESSION OF UNSUDDEN THOUGHT

by CompletelyBoofyBlitzed

"How can you even look like you're enjoying it? You know I have spoiled it, I can taste it."

Cassidy had tried to make a fish pie with a creamy mash that David had wanted for a long time, but she'd burned it.

"I almost believe you. You know, you could be an actor?" She giggled. "You are really good."

He was quiet for a moment and then he uttered, "I think my most successful role is loving you."

"What?"

"Nothing."

CompletelyBoofyBlitzed's Biography

I don't want to say much about myself but rather let my work speak for itself. What I will say is that I am 23, a computational linguist and a quiet indigenist.

www.linktr.ee/completelyboofyblitzed

728: SUSAN'S BENCH

by Jill Lang

The Lutyens style bench was made out of solid wood – probably oak – and had been dedicated to Susan Sitwell.

I knew Susan Sitwell. Sadly, her surname never sat well. At school, she was constantly chastised for fidgeting, whispering and worse – daydreaming.

It was daydreaming that brought about the dedication. She was found face down in the pond in front of the bench, a sodden copy of *Wuthering Heights* on the bank.

She never went anywhere without a book in her hand.

Jill Lang's Biography

Now retired, Jill is enjoying pursuing her interest in creative writing, Scrabble with her father, an enthusiasm for letter writing shared with her grandmother and two inspirational foreign language teachers who gave her a passion for words.

~

729: THE ELECTION

by Ibukun Keyamo

The election was short; violent, yes. I look at the upturned tables and chairs. Fatal even.

I try to avoid looking at Toby, whose severed head is still lying a few feet from his body. It's unbelievable.

My cup of tea sits untouched as I stare scathingly at Mimi and Lucy. Because of them, my beloved purple giraffe doesn't have a head and, by a vote of 2-1, out of all my dolls, Mirabelle had become the queen of the dollhouse.

Ibukun Keyamo's Biography

My name is Ibukun Keyamo. I'm a 16-year-old university freshman from Nigeria. I absolutely love writing and you can almost always find me lost in a good book.

730: MAKING PEANUTS AT THE FRUIT FACTORY

by Paul Rhodes

Nothing made sense.

There was a raid. Immigration took the Afghans but left the Iraqis.

The Iraqis stole satsumas. Stuffed them down their trousers, shoelaces tied around the ankles to stop them falling.

My boss was mid-forties but had acne. He wanted to promote me with no extra pay.

Said it'd be good for my development.

"I'm just doing this until I get a proper job," I said.

"I thought this was a proper job," he said. "It is for me."

Paul Rhodes' Biography

After years of considering himself a writer, Paul Rhodes decided it was time to stop scribbling on beermats and get serious. His short stories have been published by FTB Press and are available from Amazon. He lives in Faversham, England.

~

731: A WIFE, A MOTHER AND A DAUGHTER

by RL Comstock

A father and a son, while waiting in the park, were watching a mother and a daughter crossing a street in the dark.

Their glances would suddenly turn to a frightful stare, observing a bus going fast and people shouting, "Beware."

Later in the hospital, a husband appeared. He found his wife who was struck, just as he feared.

Earlier, from the park, came her father and her son. You see, the wife, mother and daughter were all the same one.

RL Comstock's Biography

RL Comstock is an artist, designer, writer, inventor and seeker who has worked on others' books as a designer and illustrator, as well as working on his writings of children's books and historical fiction novels.

www.rlc3nine.com

732: MOTHERHOOD

by Marsha K. Hanson

It was definitely not what anyone thought. The wolf they had tracked disappeared into the night. Her mouth was covered with fresh blood; she had sustained several fresh paw cuts.

Quietly, the thick brush covered her trail. Following her was the only option. No one could be safe if she was left wounded, able to attack again.

After several thousand yards, it was discovered: a den, a fresh kill and several pups whom she had returned to nurse. All was well.

Marsha K. Hanson's Biography

I live in a rural town in southeastern Idaho. I love to write and have written and published two children's books. I am currently working on a self-help book on my journey during having breast cancer.

www.kiddbooks.com

~

733: IT HAPPENS

by Muriel Garvis

I stared out the window, waiting.
Always waiting.
Soon they will come.
I know they will, they said they would.
Waiting still, another day.
If only they knew, I need them.
Time goes by so slowly without hope.
Today the car comes. They get out.
The door opens. I feel life is good.
Their presence fills my soul with hope.
Children, pictures, hugs and kisses.
Time goes by so quickly. Now I am alone again.
Waiting, staring out the window, waiting.

Muriel Garvis' Biography

Muriel Garvis works as the director of nursing in a local nursing home and as a nurse practitioner. Her passion is caring for people and being inspired by human nature. Her greatest accomplishment is raising nine children with her eternal companion.

734: LAND OF CANDY

by Kaelin Lee

On a dangerous quest to arrive at the colourful kingdom before my enemy, I trudged through a forest blanketed in fluffy snow. Suddenly, I stepped into a gooey pit that pulled me in.

Determined, with the sun setting, I pushed myself out. Sprinting along the path, I encountered one nutty lady and an icy land. Panting, exhausted, in the corner of my eye, I spotted the shadow of an enormous monster approaching.

"Aah."

My friend said, "Geez, we're just playing Candyland."

Kaelin Lee's Biography

Kaelin Lee likes pandas and the TV show *Friends*. She also took an absurdly long time thinking about what she likes.

~

735: TEAMBUILDING LOGIC

by Tony Lawrence

None of us is smarter than all of us.
But some of us are less smarter than others.
And some of us are smarter than the rest.
So split us up into smarter and dumber teams.
By putting the smartest person with the dumbest group.
And the dumbest one with the more smarter others.
Is the smartest person still smarter than the rest?
And is the smarter team now smarter than before?
Which team is now the smartest of the two?

Tony Lawrence's Biography

I'm a retired businessman, living in North Yorkshire with my wife and our two cats, plus a lodger cat who likes our place better than his owners' house across the road. I am new to writing, and enjoy playing drums.

736: ROLLERCOASTER APOCALYPSE

by Kate Miller

The world was ruined, but I was the only one who could see; the sky bright red, buildings burning. But the world still seemed normal to everybody else. Overgrown carousels with faded creatures and bumper cars mocked with the inability to move, carrying instead a ride into fear. The wind rattled the swaying signs – 'you must be this tall to ride' – but it doesn't matter now.

While you drown in fear, I will be joyfully laughing in all but creaking memories.

Kate Miller's Biography

I'm a postgraduate law student from Manchester, new to writing and grateful for any appreciation my writing receives. I love to read/write flash fiction and I love horror films. My first piece of writing was published online by *Ellipsis Zine*.

~

737: DARK MARK

by Clarrie Rose

Maggie stood at the copier and stared at the dark smudge on the wall. Was it coffee? Ink? Blood that dripped from someone's nose?

"Mike, what's that?"

"Dunno." He sighed as he lurched out of the copy room.

The whirring of the machine filled Maggie's ears, making her feel oddly settled. She gnawed on her nails, the red varnish sticking between her teeth.

She stood there, distant, as the copier spat out its last piece of paper and fell into silence.

Clarrie Rose's Biography

Clarrie Rose is a writer from Manchester, England. Having recently completed her MA in creative writing, Clarrie is now editor of *Hypnopomp Magazine* and enjoys reading and creating experimental fiction and poetry.

738: THE HARE & THE OWL

by Jordan B. Jolley

At six the hare woke.
    At seven he went out.
    At eight he saw nothing afoul.

At nine the hare stopped.
    At ten he took off.
    At eleven he was caught by an owl.

At twelve the owl left.
    At one I came by,
    following a coyote's howl.

I saw the hare's words.
    He had written his story,
    of how he was killed by the owl.

These words I have read.
    They are all around.
    They speak for fur and fowl.

Jordan B. Jolley's Biography

Jordan B. Jolley, author of *The Tales of Draco*, has lived most of his life in the small town of Dayton, Idaho. He is currently continuing on *The Tales of Draco* series and his second collection of fairy tales.

~

739: COMPULSION

by Emily K Martin

I won't do it again. The last time was the last time. I'm not bulimic. I don't purge often enough to be diagnosed, anyway.

The binge lasted only minutes, or seconds; did it even happen? I don't feel full. I slip into the kitchen and dig through the trash, finding a plastic tray shaped to cradle three rows of fudgy cookies. I lick the chocolate smears before tossing it back.

My legs and backside grow as I run to the toilet.

Emily K Martin's Biography

Emily K. Martin is a nurse who would rather be a writer. She has a blog and writes YA fiction. When not nursing or writing, she can be found running, cooking, and raising three sweet girls in northern Virginia.

www.ekmartinauthor.wordpress.com

~

740: A FATHER'S PERSPECTIVE

by Jonathan Pacheco

Raining down are the reflecting shards, as I see the crystal lights from all around. All the pictures from each memory show from the miniature mirrors. On this ground is only me, for everything is only magic left, which even when passing can her beauty show.

The tears shed, but I beg to not grieve. This little angel I always picked up and hugged before school started and now I see a grown woman.

A smile is on my face, happy.

Jonathan Pacheco's Biography

Hello, my name is Jonathan Pacheco. I come from a small town of Ukiah right in California. I am known mostly in my town for performing stand-up comedy, but I do writing more than anything else imaginable.

741: THE COLOUR RED

by Lisa Reynolds

When quarantine ended, she drove to the store and purchased hair dye.

For three days it sat on her bathroom vanity, untouched.

Each time she entered the room, the pretty redhead on the box said, "Do it. You know you want to."

With renewed excitement, she opened the box, followed the instructions, then stared at the result.

Her grey hair was gone, but the sparkle in her eyes had returned.

She struck a pose and giggled, her eighty-two-year-old lips spread wide.

Lisa Reynolds' Biography

Lisa Reynolds is an internationally published writer living in Eastern Ontario, Canada. She wrote the story 'The Colour Red' while under quarantine during the COVID-19 pandemic.

~

742: OUR NEW PET

by Chloe Testa

"Honey, guess what I got."

"Milk?"

"No."

"Eggs?"

"No…"

"Chicken?"

"Shoot, I knew there was something else…"

"The kids from school?"

"We don't have kids."

"Good job really, or you'd forget those too."

"You're missing the point. Guess what I got."

"OK, fine, I give up. What did you get?"

"I got a cat. Isn't she gorgeous?"

"Love of my life, light of my world, you know I love all of your quirks, but that's not a cat. That's a badger."

Chloe Testa's Biography

English teacher, passionate writer, cat enthusiast having grown up with one foot in the white sands of Malta and the other on the rugged hills of Gloucestershire.

743: BUS

by Clare Owen

Step on. Pay money. Get shoved. Fall forwards. Say, "Oi." Turn round. Glare sourly. See gang. Eyes fall.

Gang push. Gang threaten. Driver shouts. "Clear off." Gang laugh. Bus quivers. Sense doom.

Boy moves. Raises fist. Hits window. Driver shouts. Hits again. Hits again. Window shakes. "Stop now." Police radioed.

Hits again. Hits again. Window smashes. Glass flies. People duck. Gang laugh. I tremble.

All quiet. Look up. Eyes meet. Teeth smile. Teeth bared. Raises fist. See exit. Leap forward. Escape.

Clare Owen's Biography

Clare Owen is a writer, poet, journalist and visual artist. She has written for the *HuffPost* and *TES*, as well as academically on East Germany. She remains proud that her first published poem was a haiku about hedgehogs.

~

744: REMINISCENCE

by S. Rupsha Mitra

The twilight glimmered on her visage as she opened the window. The zephyr was zestful. It caressed her rosy cheeks, plunging her deep in reminiscence.

She recalled how she had relied on her subconscious, praying to meet him. Then he appeared, but fleetingly...

Suddenly, she woke up from her daze. John asked her, "Won't you have coffee? I made it for you. Still walking down the memory lane?"

She grinned, and her heart whispered: *what seems illusive can later come true.*

S. Rupsha Mitra's Biography

S. Rupsha Mitra is from India. She is a student who loves writing poetry and short stories. She is drawn towards writing about emotions and motivations.

745: THE BRISTLECONE PINE

by Taylor Moore

Thwack.

"It's a shame this beauty's coming down." *Thwack.*

"It's just a tree, and we need the land." *Thwack.*

"Yeah, but a cool tree. Shame." *Thwack.*

With one last swing of the axe, the pine tree crashed to the ground, its 5,000 year legacy ending. The woodcutters surveyed their work with something akin to pride. It's not every day you cut down the oldest living thing on the planet.

"Anyways, what do they want the land for?"

"Golf course, I think."

Taylor Moore's Biography

Just a high-schooler from Nevada who likes trees and writing prompts.

~

746: ILLUSION

by B. K. Bolen

Sitting on the sidewalk, Noah laboriously sketched out a picture of a tiger, using chalk. Now looking up, Noah saw a miniature dog approaching, limping as though it was hit by a car. Seeing the dog struggle caused Noah to wince.

He got up and went over to the crippled canine. The dog reacted suddenly and leaped into the air, eagle-like wings sprouting out, and took flight. He watched the animal fly as it evaporated into nothingness.

Noah woke up sweating.

B. K. Bolen's Biography

Brian Bolen is a clinical psychologist, licensed marriage therapist and addictions professional. He lives in Wesley Chapel, Florida, with his wife and editor, Erin. During his spare time, he plays the saxophones and flutes, preferring smooth jazz and R&B.

747: DRY HANDS

by Christine Reeves

My hands were changing as I looked at them.

All colour leached from the skin until it was pale and transparent, papery and thin. The sinewy blue veins became more prominent, the finger joints knobbly.

Small cracks appeared as my nails turned into claws.

Finally the flesh fell away, leaving just white bone.

What was happening?

"I'm sorry," I screamed out, remembering my light-fingered habits. "I'll put it back."

Then I woke.

Whether nightmare or retribution, theft was not the answer.

Christine Reeves' Biography

After retiring, I started attending creative writing classes. I've always wanted to write a novel but the classes revealed my limitations. Now, instead of that 'best seller', I stick to flash fiction and short stories.

~

748: THE FOREVER NIGHT

by JS Cline

All is dark. Two days have gone by, but San Francisco remains warm. Where did the sun go? What caused the Forever Night?

Not the most pressing question. Scientists shifted their focus towards retaining what little heat we have left, and inventing new methods of creating heat. We have several weeks trapped in the valley, retained by the bay.

Several weeks. Or less. Other cities have gone cold.

We check the news constantly, hoping for hope. It's all we can do.

JS Cline's Biography

Frantically trying to capture a squirmy eel-like premise with a pen or wrangling a bit of world design skittering about like a greased pig, is the thing of crazy people. And JS Cline is a crazy people.

749: A NIGHT TO REMEMBER, OR NOT

by Sebastian Cowen

It was a night to remember, yet I don't.

All I can remember are the sequences of nine.

The blotchy nine seconds of sobriety and of clarity.

However, there were twenty-seven seconds of respite where all my mind converged on a single point, and all the secrets of the universe became clear to me.

To write so much, to wonder if I even ate that night, and to publish a book all myself.

And yet, I don't even remember writing it.

Sebastian Cowen's Biography

Sebastian Cowen is an aspiring American author with not many merits to his name, but he has a growing interest in music and flash fiction writing.

~

750: DAUGHTERS AND MOTHERS

by G. Gaurav

"Want to join our revolution, Ma?" my 15-year-old asked.

"Revolution?"

"A real one."

"Real?"

"Not on FB, Twitter, Insta."

"What do you want?"

"First, smash my face."

"Why?"

"It begins at home."

I punched her face. Blood dripped from her nose. She stood steady.

I told her to hit me too. She did.

"We are ready."

We followed our children.

You heard it right. A billion died.

10 years ago.

The wild bees are back. I talk to the rivers again.

G. Gaurav's Biography

G. Gaurav is a freelance writer based in Ontario, Canada. Originally from India, he relocated in 2018 and now divides his time between being a full-time dad to twin boys and doing household chores. He writes in his spare time.

www.facebook.com/gaurav.ghose.9

751: DATE

by Doug Hawley

I tried to get a date with the girl at the grocery store. Because I was a little nervous and wasn't ready, I asked where the bananas and apples were.

She said, "Aisle 26."

Ashamed of my cowardice, I got a cart and picked up some bananas and apples.

I got up my courage to ask her out and, when I saw that no one else was in line, I boldly asked, "Now, how about a date."

She said, "Aisle 15."

Doug Hawley's Biography

The author is a little old man who lives in Lake Oswego, Oregon, USA with cat Kitzhaber and editor Sharon. He was an actuary, now writes, hikes, snowshoes and volunteers.

www.sites.google.com/site/aberrantword/

~

752: THEY ARE COMING

by Sylvia Ketchum

"What are you doing, Gregg?"

"Prepping," he said, his voice muffled behind a gas mask.

"Whatever for?"

"Them," he said, pointing to the stars.

"Seriously?" I rolled my eyes. "Get inside, dinner's served."

"Nope."

"Suit yourself." I slammed the door.

I picked the bones from my fried fish as his went cold.

Search lights flashed through the window. I peeled back the curtain. Nothing.

I opened the door. "Gregg, where are you?"

An alien spacecraft beamed him up. Gregg was gone.

Sylvia Ketchum's Biography

Sylvia Ketchum is an avid reader, writer and consumer of gluten-free snacks.

753: AN EXPLANATION

by B.C. Ong

"Mum, why can't we go out?"

"Well, it isn't safe outside."

"Why isn't it safe outside?"

The mum sighed heavily. She didn't know how to explain the new reality they were facing, especially to a three-year-old girl. She took her time regaining her composure – something she had to do more often these days. She then took a deep breath and said, "Honey, we could get very sick if we leave the house."

Her daughter looked confused, then asked even more questions.

B.C. Ong's Biography

B.C. Ong is a Filipino-Chinese college student from Manila, Philippines. He is currently taking a BSc in applied corporate management at De La Salle University, Manila.

www.linkedin.com/in/brian-cedric-ong-194b021a2/

~

754: NAUROZ IN THE TIME OF SOCIAL DISTANCING

by Mahek Khwaja

I served the egg pulao on a silver tray, a smaller tray this year. Before 2020, Nauroz was about festivity-fret; the blouse must befit the bosom aptly, excessive water must not make the rice soggy, we must reach Jamatkhana for the prayers timely and what not.

I snugged on the dining-chair in cotton pyjamas and wished Nauroz to my family. I took the first spoon of pulao smelling irresistibly of nuts, egg and saffron, slowly if not civilly. This was new.

Mahek Khwaja's Biography

Mahek Khwaja, MA in English literature, currently works as editorial assistant at Paramount Books (Pvt.) Ltd. Being a scribbler, she has previously published with *Zau Literary Magazine* and *Hektoen International* and she occasionally performs spoken word for private YouTube channels.

755: NEW LIFE

by James Northern

"I got the job," I say. "The one in Australia."

Carla squeezes my hand beneath the table. I finally told them. Patterned crockery and silver cutlery lie on bamboo placemats before us.

"When do you start?" asks Mum.

"February. For three years."

Mum stares at the sideboard where an Arabian dagger lies beside a photograph of my cousin with her baby. Strips of moist turkey fall beneath Dad's quickening blade. Mum's mouth opens.

"Did you see the Liverpool score?" asks Dad.

James Northern's Biography

James Northern (@JNorthernWrites on Twitter) is a Gloucestershire-based writer of short stories. His work appears in the 2020 and 2019 *National Flash Fiction Day Anthology*, the *Stroud Short Stories Volume 2* anthology and issue 19 of the *Riggwelter Journal*.

~

756: LIFE

by Madiana Dethan

Not knowing why, or rather not *wanting* to know why, he fell to pieces, again and again. The actual truth was that he knew full well what was going on, but was apparently stuck in an endless circle or an impossible labyrinth. It felt horrible, he was drowning, no one could help him...

It was what it was, though. Confused and lost, he had to deal with it, lock horns with it, live with it. Much ado about nothing, really. *Life.*

Madiana Dethan's Biography

I am 48. I live in Bordeaux, France. I play, dance, take pictures, compose songs, play the guitar and the drums, draw, puzzle out words, explore everything in every direction. Now I'm trying something new: 81 words in English.

757: CAMPING INSOMNIA

by Miriam Hurdle

"How was your sleep last night?"

"Awful. I'm not the camping type."

"You slept in a cot. Didn't it help?"

"Not having walls around gave me a nightmare."

"The tent is the wall."

"I could see the moonlight through the tent."

"That should be soothing."

"But… it's like, transparent. It felt like sleeping in the open air. I heard growling and saw a bear. It chased me."

"The bear didn't chase you. It visited and stole our food last night though."

Miriam Hurdle's Biography

Miriam Hurdle writes memoir, poems, short stories and flash fiction. She earned a Doctor of Education from the University of La Verne in California. Her poetry *Songs of Heartstrings* was published in 2018. She enjoys blogging, gardening, photography and travelling.

www.theshowersofblessings.com

~

758: LIFE IN LOCKDOWN

by Sarah Brown

Monday: Did nothing.

Tuesday: Had a shower, then did nothing.

Wednesday: Had a cup of tea, had a shower, then did nothing.

Thursday: Got dressed, had a cup of tea, had a shower, then did nothing.

Friday: Cut toenails, got dressed, had a cup of tea, had a shower, then did nothing.

Saturday: Read the paper, cut toenails, got dressed, had a cup of tea, had a shower, then did nothing.

Sunday: Did nothing.

Do you think I shower too often?

Sarah Brown's Biography

My name is Sarah Brown. I am 54 and live in Oxford. I have twin daughters, who are 29, and 2 grandchildren. I used to be a teacher, but now I write and enter competitions to pass the time.

759: SWEET TALK

by Hullabaloo22

It's been a bit of a long journey, but now I've found my destination.

I can smell the sweetness on your breath. I'm not interested in reality, facts. I live for the syrup that accompanies lies.

You talk the kind of talk I love to hear.

Feather-like, my footsteps on your lips. I wonder if you realise I'm here. Don't swat me or you'll just hasten it.

I'm prepared to indulge myself on lips sweet as honey, before delivering that sting.

Hullabaloo22's Biography

Hullabaloo22 is an established writer on Booksie. She lives in West Cork, Ireland, and writes short stories, poetry and the occasional longer work.

www.booksie.com/users/hullabaloo22-171418

~

760: IT'S NEVER ENOUGH

by Siegfried E Finser

"Do you love me?"

"Of course I do."

"You have to say it."

"How can you doubt me?"

"I don't doubt you. It's not that."

"Then what is it?"

A pause.

"Do you still love me in the same way?"

"The same way?"

"You know, like when you proposed? It felt so strong."

Another pause.

"You keep giving me more reasons to be with you."

Comfortable pause.

"I wish – just wish – some things could stay the same."

Pause.

"I love you."

Siegfried E Finser's Biography

I'm 88, published some seven books and written fifty short, short stories without publishing them. The one above is a distillation of a much longer short story. This was a great exercise. I'm not too sure anymore which version is better.

761: PLEASE GO ON

by Mark Pritchard

Please go on. I'm asking kindly. Official parts should fit precisely. With special grease you should slide in nicely. Perhaps too gentle, then try and push harder. Jiggle, wiggle, muttering with gentle taps.

Video experts ease these things on, smiling. Some video trickery may be included. Not one mention of special clamps, black magic or dynamite.

Reaching for my biggest hammer, I warn you, this won't end kindly.

Push hard here, then hit just there.

WACK, WACK, SNAP.

I hate you.

Mark Pritchard's Biography

Hello, I'm dyslexic so writing is a challenge for me, but I like to have a go. I drive a lorry and have a YouTube channel. Weekends, I'm sorting out tractors, Land Rovers and bikes at home in Ellesmere, Shropshire.

www.youtube.com/channel/UC_xMJhBESNFvAwbJvYVyYDA

~

762: KITCHEN AND DISASTER

by Lee Foley

Dave was going through his kitchen cupboards to see what he had left. He picked up the bread and found it was still in date. *Excellent.*

Soon, he had everything he needed: bread, cheese, ham, pickles, tomatoes, mayonnaise and English mustard for that extra kick. That was when he saw on the news that an asteroid was heading for Earth and everyone only had a few minutes to live.

Oh well, he thought, *at least I have time for a sandwich.*

Lee Foley's Biography

Lee is a creative person with a lot of ideas but a short attention span. He can often be found making music, painting pictures and writing stories when he is supposed to be working.

763: A FRAGILE BOY

by Rudy S. Uribe Jr.

I babysat my five-year-old nephew. He loved playing draughts. My sister always let him win, hoping to bolster his self-confidence. He was a great kid, kind and gentle, and self-confident.

"King me," I said.

The boy hesitated. Slowly, he placed his piece atop mine. His eyes looked downward, his fragile self-confidence slipping.

"It's your move," I said.

He made a mistake. I looked him in the eye. Do I let him win, or teach him to lose?

I moved my king.

Rudy S. Uribe Jr.'s Biography

Rudy is a copywriter and sales trainer. He is twice published in *Alfred Hitchcock's Mystery Magazine* as the winner of The Mysterious Photograph Contest.

~

764: THE 10TH STEP

by Oliver Lynton

Steps one to nine are an easy hop, skip and jump. Number ten is wider though, so the gate can swing inwards. In easier times it was always left open, inviting people to enter and admire the secret gardens within.

Life was simple and carefree then. Strangers came to chat and left as friends.

Today, as I pull open the gate, my heart fills with sadness. Fitting my mask and gloves, human intimacy precluded, I step out into the deserted street.

Oliver Lynton's Biography

Spent most of my life travelling, much of it living and working in developing countries. Humbled, enchanted and occasionally angered by the people I met. Currently semi-retired, I am enjoying life as a trained, though novice, freelance photographer.

765: LAST SEEN

by Bert Velthuis

1943. Darkness. Light from the Lievendach's open hallway on the other side of the street is the only illumination. A grey Wehrmacht truck next to the pavement. Soldiers with rifles. An officer shouting into the house, "Schnell, beeil dich."

The Lievendachs appear. Yellow armbands. Mr Lievendach, a suitcase. Mrs Lievenbach with little Samuel, toy horse under his arm. Louis, my friend, last.

"Einsteigen." Open tailgate. Dark interior. Mr Lievenbach climbs in. Soldiers assist his wife and sons.

The truck drives away.

Bert Velthuis' Biography

Born in Holland in 1935, I worked for 38 years as a tea planter in Malawi. Since my retirement in 1995, we live in an old farmhouse on Ibiza, far from the madding crowd.

~

766: PECKING ORDER

by Gordon Williams

He watched through the kitchen window as blackbirds bullied the chaffinches, robins and blue tits away from the bird table. Then two magpies commandeered the food as the blackbirds fled.

Annoyed at these interlopers stealing the small birds' food, he went outside and threw a handful of gravel at the black and white bullies to frighten them off.

Indoors, his wife watched him and shouted, "Michael, leave those birds alone."

Once again, he obeyed her angry command and skulked back inside.

Gordon Williams' Biography

Gordon Williams was born near Manchester when the M6 was still cobbled. He moved to Northern Ireland in 1984 for the peace and quiet. The current lockdown has allowed him to fulfil his ambition to become a full-time recluse.

767: A LOVE THAT DEFIES DEATH

by Madeleine McDonald

The dying woman knew peace, for she would see her beloved husband again. Long ago, a Mongolian shaman had foretold their reunion. They were newly married then, exploring the world. Despite the tourist trap flummery, she treasured the prophecy.

"When you die, someone waits for you, with love that defies death."

The portal opened. The woman stepped into the light and recoiled, fighting the grip of a guy she had slept with twice at university because she felt sorry for him.

Madeleine McDonald's Biography

Madeleine McDonald lives on the Yorkshire coast, where the cliffs crumble into the sea. Her latest novel, *A Shackled Inheritance*, is available from Amazon.

www.amazon.com/dp/B01BBCBX38

~

768: ANDY THE ANT

by Andrew James Spence

Andy Ant looked up. A long way, but he smelt honey.

Up, up, up he climbed. The stalk was slippery, down, down.

More ups, what a view.

No branches, but he managed.

He was an athletic Andy Ant. He was high. Up he went.

Is this stalk metal?

He saw a hundred miles. There were discs, wires, cross-pieces.

There: a dropped slice of bread, honey. He filled up.

So tasty, he ate more.

Didn't pay attention.

He slipped, down, down...

Down.

Andrew James Spence's Biography

Worked in TV, advertising, imported Austrian tractors. Started removal company in 1969, sold in 1986, built car race engines. Wife and I raced cars 1978-2005, broke back at 130mph at Spa, now in wheelchair. Wife flies plane as it's safer.

www.youtube.com/user/skizzysmith

769: FOOTPRINTS IN THE SNOW

by Dave Firth

A gentle fall of snow caressed our sleeping village. Footprints left the village square, crossed the street and scaled the library wall. Onward, over the roofs of houses they marched, then they climbed to the top of our church steeple and simply disappeared.

A man with four toes on each foot, or two feet short one toe, who can walk up walls and vanish in the night. It seems to me that such a man could not be one of us.

Dave Firth's Biography

Recently retired from a late-flowering career as a solo singer. Have always wanted to write but have never given it the time it needs. Left it a bit late but looking forward to the challenge.

~

770: FREEDOM

by Fabio Crispim

I wake but they're still asleep. Their snoring echoes through the halls of the dark building. No food until they wake, so I wait.

Hours later, there's movement. Doors open and close, footsteps thump the floor and they whisper. From a distant room, I hear the clang of a steel bowl. It's filled with chunks of processed meat – the only thing I can eat.

They leave, slam the door, and I eat alone. Nine hours until they return. For now: freedom.

Fabio Crispim's Biography

Fabio is a Portuguese professional writer in the UK who loves video games and spends time with his part-time editor and full-time cat, Ripley. He's recently started writing more creative work, which he hopes can be enjoyed by many.

771: GOING VIRAL

by Adrian Hallchurch

"It's about planet Earth," said St Peter.

"What's the problem?" asked God.

"The new species, the humans, they're getting a bit full of themselves."

"How so?"

"Flying in planes, polluting everything, wrecking it for everyone else."

"Mmm…" said God, rummaging in his toolbox. "I've got these."

He held up two small packets. "Viruses – one will shake them up a little and the other will wipe them out completely."

"Maybe the first… let's just remind them who's in charge."

"Here goes, then."

Adrian Hallchurch's Biography

I've been writing short stories and novels for a lot of years between day jobs and raising a daughter, and recently published a collection *Last Voyage of the Dunces and other stories*, twelve tales of love, lust and despair.

www.amazon.co.uk/dp/B0878WSWTP

~

772: THE MOST DELICIOUS TURKEY LEG

by Peggy Gerber

Marianne first saw it on *Alfred Hitchcock Presents*. A woman kills her philandering husband with a frozen leg of lamb, later serving the meat to the police.

Marianne sneers as she scrutinizes her husband in front of the TV, with his beer belly and halitosis, thinking about nineteen long years of being called fat, dumb and useless. As she walks into the kitchen, she wonders if the frozen turkey leg will work as well as the leg of lamb. It does.

Peggy Gerber's Biography

Peggy Gerber began her writing career to fill the void created when she became an empty nester. She has recently been published in *Spillwords, Daily Science Fiction, Reedsy* and *Poetry in the Time of the Coronavirus*.

773: THINGS

by Christian Andrei Nuez Laplap

I have always wondered what it was like to die.

I gaze at the dim sky above me as thunder echoes below. I am not fascinated with death, but lying here does kind of make me question things. Things I have never thought of before. Things I seem to take for granted.

Things like how impactful just a few seconds are to a simple change of a stoplight.

Feeling the shards of glass around me, my consciousness slowly fades into darkness.

Christian Andrei Nuez Laplap's Biography

C.A. Laplap is a 20-year-old BA psychology student at the University of the Philippines-Cebu. He is an awardee of excellence in the WYEC 2018 and has written for *Yellow Pages Singapore*, *Creative Copywrite Solutions Singapore*, *PhilippinePassers* and *OneCebu*.

~

774: THE HEIRLOOM

by Karen Waldron

My great uncle Herbert left me the time machine. He was quite the writer in his day. Nobody knew he owned a real machine himself, and who knows if that famous novel was based on his own experiences.

I've had it all these years and I'd love to be able to tell you about where the machine has taken me, and how far into the past and future I've travelled. But, I've absolutely no idea how to work the blessed thing.

Karen Waldron's Biography

I'm a freelance copy editor and proof-reader and, in between times, write stories and poems for pleasure. I live in Woking with my husband and three children, and a cat who occasionally deigns to join us.

775: MARVELLOUS

by Ross Lowe

My final magic trick was an absolute world-changer.

One minute, I was stepping confidently into my Mr Marvellouso Disappearing Box at the Bull's Head, in front of a crowd of bored, unimpressed punters. The next minute, I stepped into a field of bemused cows in what looked like Switzerland. *Ha.* That showed them.

Hmm. Problem was, that showed me too.

Unfortunately, I hadn't brought my wallet or my Disappearing Box (which had disappeared) to what was now clearly my new home.

Ross Lowe's Biography

Originally from Derbyshire, England, Ross now writes from Berlin, Germany. When he's not writing, he's in the German countryside in ridiculous shorts, or flying home to cheer on his beloved Derby County in a ridiculous waste of time and money.

www.rosslowe.co.uk

~

776: THE DETAIL'S IN THE DEVIL

by Alison Wren

Dad says wasps are evil, the work of the devil.
Pointless little critters, with no purpose in this life.
So the empty jam-jar sits on the windowsill with a hole in the lid.
It's half-full of water. Or half empty, as he says.
Either way, it's half-full of dead wasps.
You see, they're not devious like Dad.
They just like strawberry jam and crawl in the top.
They buzz, bloat and bubble to death
So who's the devil and who's not?

Alison Wren's Biography

A self-confessed hermitess, Alison likes nothing better than to hide in her shed in her pyjamas and write. She also likes to eat. And tap-dance. Write, eat, tap-dance – in that order. Oh, and sometimes she listens to Bowie.

777: SCEPTIC

by Phil Maud

It came at me, a distended deathly white.

Pox-ridden face marking an ancient pestilential suffering.

Those vacant cataract eyes held a deep menace, kindled in their milky depths.

Its glowering animated corpse loomed above me, from which came a voice like the creaking of one-thousand rusty hinges. "Despair, I have found thee."

Dimming lights attended this utterance, the only clue to an unfathomed netherworld power.

I shrank back at once, cowering in fear.

Then I realised.

I don't believe in ghosts.

Phil Maud's Biography

Phil is an entirely new writer. His interests are fantasy and science fiction but at the moment a lot of his stories are to do with Hell. Very occasionally he will write something at www.magic-phil.co.uk. Why not take a look?

~

778: MAN, WOMAN

by Nili Roberts

"Difficult, man, woman," a young gardener once told me.

He didn't mean to be so concise; that was the extent of his English.

Fitting, I thought. This was the country of the haiku and the bonsai tree after all. But I would have preferred a more detailed report. Even in Japanese, a verb and perhaps a subordinate clause would have gone a long way.

Versed in the art of pruning, did he think a frank breakup talk would have been uncouth?

Nili Roberts' Biography

I'm Nili Roberts. I love scribbling stories in cafés around Osaka. I came here 15 years ago to practise a martial art. Home was Istanbul, Paris, London. It sounds like a posh shopping bag, but I'm not posh.

www.instagram.com/niluferplum/

779: THE LARK ASCENDING

by Bridget Yates

Her golden voice soared to the rafters, echoed round the ancient stone walls, ricocheted from the carved columns and embraced the dark, gleaming wood. The thrilling, exultant notes brought tears to the eyes of the three people in the congregation. Eyes blinked away the feelings and suspicions they might be hiding, but she was triumphant as she followed his coffin down the aisle with measured steps.

He hadn't liked her singing.

But he had liked the way she made his coffee.

Bridget Yates' Biography

I am a retired teacher who spends all her time and money on as many holidays as she can. In between holidays I write, embroider, knit, crochet, spin and play the harp. Ah, this wonderful life...

~

780: IS THIS THE END?

by M Anthony David

Sam sat dozing. His bus would arrive home in ten minutes. He yawned, stretching out. His four hour long journey was ending. He thought of what awaited him.

The bus swerved violently. It whirred back, with a screeching noise. And then, there was stillness.

Moans and groans broke out. His life played out like a video. *Is this the end?* Sam wondered.

His neighbour howled in pain, arm hanging loose from his shoulder. Shell-shocked but unscathed otherwise, Sam paused, thanking God.

M Anthony David's Biography

M Anthony David teaches at medical school. A passionate communicator, he has written a couple of books and some articles. He loves to speak and write creatively. Married to an educator, Rebekah, he has two grownup sons, Abiathar and Abishai.

781: IN THE DETAILS

by *John James Morris*

Yuri stood upon a plate of trembling rock, surrounded by plumes of fire and blazing waterfalls.

Winged demons used jagged pitchforks to torture Hell's denizens, trapped within dangling metal cages, their tormented screams echoing throughout the chasm.

Sitting, in a towering throne of skeletons, was she: a hundred-foot tall manifestation of evil.

She grasped a handful of writhing bodies using her talons, then spilled them into her splintered mouth, crunching their brittle bones.

Her black hole eyes noticed Yuri.

She smiled.

John James Morris' Biography

John James Morris is a writer from Nottingham, UK. He has a penchant for writing science fiction, though dabbles in the 'other' genres from time-to-time. He currently works in politics, but don't hold that against him.

@JohnJamesMorris

~

782: AUTUMN'S ARRIVAL

by *Sachin Prakash*

It was the season the house moth had been waiting for – autumn. He couldn't wait to hear the ignorant humans crunching the umber leaves, disintegrating them into nothing but dust that fairies would like to collect, thank you very much.

The fields, like green canvases filled with leftover ginger pieces and flecks of molten bronze, seemed much politer to tenants and much happier. He wished the world was like this all year, not just gentle, but filled with amber leaves drooping.

Sachin Prakash's Biography

I have always had a passion for writing, crafting stories of all different genres. It has only been in recent months that I delved into the 'industry' of writing 50 word stories, which has now become an uncontrollable hobby.

783: JOY OF SUMMER

by Farzaneh Hajirasouliha

It was a sunny evening of summer, with the shiny blue sky full of moving cotton clouds. Behind the window, I was able to see people laughing, running, biking, walking, even shopping.

But it was not a perfect time to go out and lie on the grassy ground, enjoying the breeze on your face.

The joy of summer is to lie down on your sofa, open a packet of cheese-ball snacks, excitedly staring at the TV until the football match starts.

Farzaneh Hajirasouliha's Biography

I am a PhD student, loving art and science, and I think that writing is a way to combine these two ingredients to make a tasteful thing for the mind. I also play a musical instrument called the Persian santoor.

~

784: THE EMPTY HOUSE

by Vicki Sinclair

The house is quiet without him, more still. Like it fed off his energy and, without him, became dormant, waiting for that single flicker of life to awaken it.

Slowly, his possessions are boxed up, the materials of his existence destined for the skip, or, if worthy, the charity shop.

The dusty floors mopped, cobwebs cleared, the pantry cleaned out.

All traces of his story wiped away.

Then, the exchanging of keys. The beginning of a new chapter.

The house stirs.

Vicki Sinclair's Biography

Vicki grew up in the Midlands countryside and moved to London for university – hasn't left since. At 27 years old, she works in advertising but hopes to build a career in conservation. Finds comfort in reading; endeavours to write.

785: IMPOSTER SYNDROME

by Lucy Lucy

I'm sure you won't believe me when I say I wrote a children's opera and put it on in Alaska, went to Hull University, married a farm manager who pretended to be fifty four but was in fact fifty six, taught Saddam Hussein's nephews, ran a charity for asylum seekers, had an American friend who was nuts about Istanbul, hitch-hiked to the Arctic Circle in Finland and spent yesterday working on Chopin's 'Polonaise in A Flat'.

Not necessarily in that order.

Lucy Lucy's Biography

All the above is true. I am 64, straight, a good amateur pianist interested in contemporary classical music and live in Yorkshire. I have written plays, most of which have been performed, and short stories.

~

786: NO WORDS

by Rebeccah Yeadon

London was mesmerising, relentless.

She had to retreat into cafes to process it all with a notepad and a hot drink. Every borough, every square, every cobbled street held a unique character that she tried to memorise.

Yet later, saturated with sights, she could never capture their essence. The life and colour slipped out of reach like a sunset melting into black. She would push the pad away, resigned to sit, full of unwritten stories, hoping someday the words would come.

Rebeccah Yeadon's Biography

I moved from Yorkshire to London in my early twenties. After five years here, I still struggle to put the magic of the city into words. I have a passion for stories, avidly reading them and aspiring to write my own.

787: HANGOVER

by Julie Mayger

I turned on the shower and tentatively stuck my head under the sprinkles of water.

The pain was terrible; it felt like someone was throwing needles at me. I closed my eyes and felt around for the shampoo, flipped up the lid and felt nauseous from its smell.

Zombie-like, I let the water trickle over my head and slowly began to massage the shampoo over my aching scalp, nearly passing out from the fumes.

I squinted at the label: 'Hair Remover'.

Julie Mayger's Biography

Restless by nature, I have travelled extensively, lived in South Africa for 15 years, and have had a varied but sound career. I currently work as a professional pet sitter. Writing, walking, animals and environmental topics motivate me. And the sun.

www.facebook.com/JulieMayger1

~

788: GRIEF

by Mariam Bibi

She dropped into the middle of the ocean, barely having a chance to breathe as she struggled and fought against the waves. The undercurrent tore through her. She let it, just like the water filling her lungs.

There was no point fighting against nature. Nature is terrifyingly beautiful and will always win. She learnt to work with it, learning not to fight but to accept the inevitable.

She closed her eyes, took a deep breath and got out of the car.

Mariam Bibi's Biography

A new writer, who is working on turning the volume up on her emotions.

789: THE BAIT

by Neil Renton

I put all my energy into catching that mouse. I'd sit in silence jumping at the slightest of non-existent movements or jerk my head in the direction of a sound that didn't happen. I put traps out with peanut butter as the bait.

One of the traps was empty. No bait. No mouse. I'd been outsmarted by a brain the size of a peanut.

I went to bed and kissed my sleeping wife. Guess what I smelt? That's right. Peanut butter.

Neil Renton's Biography

I've done a bit of writing in the past, ranging from football reports to short stories. I'm now looking to do more. I've got a million caterpillar ideas that are crying out to be turned into fully fledged butterflies.

~

790: METROPOLITAN MEMORIAL

by Kirk I. Holden

These waters had always been notoriously treacherous and I had wagered all I had on this tattered old map.

The sun beat down on the boat and I wiped the sweat from my brow. I wondered if this trip would be worth it.

Then I saw them, two metal fragments, waves crashing violently against them. This was the spot that had been crudely scrawled on the chart: 'The Shard'.

Somewhere in the depths an ancient city, all of its treasures waited.

Kirk I. Holden's Biography

Kirk I. Holden, based in Leicestershire, England, has been writing fiction for over 10 years, mainly writing fantasy or science fiction stories, as well as some website articles. Outside of writing, he's an avid tabletop, board game and RPG player.

791: TIMBUKTU

by Zoey Rowan

She had only meant to stay over the long weekend. But situations changed; she changed. She wore pink now.

The plants in her apartment drooped, wilted and died. Her neighbour kept the cat. Bills addressed to Mrs Leonora Hill went unanswered. After a long overdue outstanding balance and countless unreceived phone calls, her apartment had been gutted, but Nora didn't know that.

If Nora had still been Elly, she would have calculated her cost. Now she couldn't imagine who would care.

Zoey Rowan's Biography

Zoey Rowan is a copywriter, content writer and translator living in Berlin. When she isn't writing short stories, she can be found trying out new recipes or biking around her city.

~

792: A PRICK OF PAIN

by Jose Luis Torres

The young man raised his hand and pointed to the free space. The old man obeyed the rest of his indications until the car was finally parked.

The parking assistant waited patiently before performing his usual low-head and extended-palm approach. That cane tip made him look up and recognise Mr Rogers, his now retired teacher. The same who kept repeating he wouldn't get far in life.

Alone, still evoking those words, he ducked down by the tyre and opened his knife.

Jose Luis Torres' Biography

Spanish English teacher. Half-dozen non-fiction self-published books. Flash fiction writer from time to time.

793: AN INVITATION

by Michael Lane

Dear Prince,

You came to me that day in the forest. Come to my palace and be my king. So you don't get lost, I have ordered the trees cleared. Oh, and my friend, the woodsman, has wandered off somewhere.

I tend to fall asleep suddenly, but you are in my dreams. I don't mind the gap in reality.

Our dwarves sing too much. They refuse the apples I offer for their health. You order them properly.

Your loving,
Princess Snowy

Michael Lane's Biography

Michael Lane was a drama teacher. Since then, he has written plays and short films. He runs the Clarendon Park Community Cinema for his locality in Leicester, UK, and is happily writing short stories and scripts.

~

794: LETTER FOUND IN A DRY-STONE WALL

by Rob Bray

Emmot,

I sat quietly by our stream all morning, though you didn't come. I burn for your embrace. My sister says you should flee, let the rats eat themselves and the plague with it. From our farm we can see the graves multiply. I say Eyam's reward will be in Heaven. She laughs. The rich have left, she says, the vicar's children too. Those who remain have nowhere to go.

But I know that you stay for me; for us.

Rowland

Rob Bray's Biography

I'm a Leicestershire writer currently writing historical fiction and, in between the frustrations of research, short stories. I am a member of Leicester Writers' Club and have had stories published in anthologies and shortlisted in competitions.

795: PUMPKINS

by Holly Webster

My pumpkins are the best – round, plump and sweet – not like those tasteless monstrosities from across the pond. I'm the envy of every plot, they all want to know my secret.

Sometimes I say it's plenty of fresh manure dug in deep. Sometimes I say it's consistent watering. When I'm feeling whimsical, I tell people I dance naked through the pumpkin patch every full moon.

One day someone will find out, but not soon. After all, people rarely dig that deep.

Holly Webster's Biography

Holly Webster is a writer of urban fantasy and horror based in Leicestershire, England. Published in Mantle Lane's anthology *Songs for the Elephant Man* and member of the Leicester Writers' Club, she's currently working on her first full-length novel.

~

796: MEDITATIVE AWAKENING

by Linda Smith

Emerging gently from sleep, I keep my eyes closed. Calm and relaxed. My days are often so intense that I fall asleep at the drop of a hat, but now I can't think where I am. I can feel I'm lying flat so not on the sofa. No pillow, so not in bed either.

Something I feel under my fingers sparks a memory. *Mat.*

Oh yes, now I remember. I'm in my yoga class. And I just know I was snoring.

Linda Smith's Biography

I am a granny who loves reading, especially reading to my grandchildren, but I have never written a story before.

797: ALTERNATIVE HISTORY

by Michele Witthaus

We don't know it yet, but it's our last working lunch. We hesitate over the menu, contemplating a glass of wine. Bad idea, we agree, both thinking of afternoon responsibilities.

What if, instead, we'd ordered a bottle and let the conversation roam? What if, then, we'd strolled out into the cold, bright London air and walked, diving into one of those tiny Italian cafés that's been there forever to sip espressos before at last releasing each other into our separate lives?

Michele Witthaus' Biography

Michele Witthaus has a journalistic background and her writing has appeared in a variety of anthologies and other publications. She has been writing a poem a day about the lockdown experience since March 2020. She is an active member of Leicester Writers' Club.

~

798: ISOLATION

by Gwyneth Williams

You told me as a child I wouldn't eat. They sent me to hospital, in isolation, only some buttons to play with. They said no visitors, but you insisted. When I saw you, I held out my arms for you to pick me up. You told them I'd die and they moved me.

Now, we're thirty miles apart and you're in isolation. Every day, we talk on the phone and I hear in your voice, your arms held out to me.

Gwyneth Williams' Biography

Gwyneth is 57 years old, widowed, and works part time as a scientific officer in the medical school at the University of Leicester. She began writing stories and poems as a child and had her first novel published in 2015.

www.facebook.com/GwynethWilliamsAuthor/

799: CURSED

by Ivan Richardson

I wake to see a ghostly figure sitting on my bed.

"You have been cursed." A bony hand points from beneath black robes. "You will die this time tomorrow. But I will grant you a chance for vengeance." Laid out on the bed are a key, a glove and a photo. "Discover what links these items and you shall know your killer."

I pull the covers back over me. Forget revenge, this is my last chance for a good night's sleep.

Ivan Richardson's Biography

My name is Ivan Richardson, 35 years old. I work as an engineer in Leicester. I'm an amateur author writing short stories for the last four years, mainly sci-fi and horror.

~

800: GAIA'S LAMENT

by Julia Wood

Today, I'm sad. The grey carpet is re-gathering itself above me, waiting to cover me as though I am an unsightly thing to be hidden away.

My holiday is coming to an end. And you know how it is with holidays? You never want them to end. I don't want my flourishing flowers, my rejoicing creatures, smothered.

The humans are returning, rolling out the grey carpet, token of my unimportance. Soon, I'll be hidden again. Neglected. Forgotten. No one will cry.

Julia Wood's Biography

Julia Wood is a novelist and short story writer, whose stories have been anthologised. One of her novels is currently being considered by an agent. She is also a multi-media artist with a YouTube Channel: Julia's Novelty Bloomers.

www.youtube.com/channel/UCs943xiDLNBS6Q6mr7ldabg

801: THEY MET BY MOONLIGHT

by Ros Masterson

"Did you hear that?"

"What?"

"A sort of scratchy sound."

"Scratchy like an itch?"

"No, scratchy like a shut-out cat."

He listens. "No."

The moon goes behind a cloud.

"There it is again. You must have heard it. There's a really big fox round here." She clutches his arm.

"Don't be scared if it's only a fox."

She swings round. "It's behind me. Not scratchy, swishier than that, like a knife cutting through silk."

"Oh, that was me. Is it silk?"

Ros Masterson's Biography

Ros Masterson lives in Leicester and is a member of the Leicester Writers' Club. She has published a number of academic works, including a successful textbook, and is now working on a novel.

~

802: COCONUT SHY

by Louise Goulding

The Monday after the fair came to town – I'd gone with Andrea, and we rode the Waltzer twice, and got toffee apples – that Monday, Gus Webster – who sometimes came to school with dirty clothes and sometimes had no lunch and sometimes wasn't there at all – Gus Webster had a black eye, and he told us it happened at the fairground – he said it got hit trying to win at the coconut shy, and I thought, *Well, I never saw him there.*

Louise Goulding's Biography

Louise Goulding's work has appeared in anthologies from Mother's Milk Books and Kunsthalle Cromer, and in the *2019 Olga Sinclair Prize Collection.* She lives in Norwich with her husband, their son and their secondhand cat.

803: -1

by Sihaam Osman

This is nothing new.

If only I hadn't forgotten that the remote had fallen behind the sofa. I mean, I did manage to lose the keys a few days ago. And the plants do look a bit limp. With regards to the neighbour's cat, well, Linda isn't back for another week. The dishes in the sink have become a kitchen ornament.

Now, I am wondering where I've parked my car. It's 3:30 and I have a feeling I'm forgett—

"THE KIDS."

Sihaam Osman's Biography

Sihaam is a student who enjoys reading books and creative writing as well as learning as much as she can about the workings of the world.

~

804: UNCLE DONALD

by Kudakwashe Chirapa

Uncle Donald never said anything to anyone on any particular day. He would always sit on his veranda and would nod to anything that passed by.

That is why everyone knew something was wrong the day he died. As usual, he was smoking a cigarette when he noticed Timothy the rapper passing by and called out to him, "Let's collaborate sometime this year."

Astonished by this, Timothy drew closer, only to notice that the old man had breathed his last breath.

Kudakwashe Chirapa's Biography

Kudakwashe was born in Harare in 2000. He loves poetry and stories. One of his poems has been published in the *Songs of Peace World's Biggest Anthology of Contemporary Poetry*. He is studying actuarial science at the University of Zimbabwe.

805: THE KID

by Benjamin Noel

Sixteen years ago, a sneaky, conniving but angel faced boy was born.

At the dinner table, he smiles and giggles like every adorable kid, but under the table, something is afoot. While his parents are distracted, his foot, armed with the sharpest toenails known to man, inches closer and closer to his big brother. And without a flicker in his puppy dog face, he swipes at the legs of his brother, slashing around for maximum damage.

He is my little brother.

Benjamin Noel's Biography

I am a college student who enjoys writing, hopefully enough to make some money from it one day.

~

806: PEOPLE WATCHING

by Charles Murphy

"You reckon she has low self-esteem?" Doug asked, nodding at the woman across the road in the beer garden.

"What do you mean?" replied Jason, taking a long draw on his cigarette.

"Well, you know. Big hair, heavy makeup and the clothes she's wearing. All there to compensate for a lack of personality."

"Yeah, I guess so."

Doug swiped his finger down his phone screen again. Damn, still no more likes.

Different filter? he thought. *I'll check again in a minute.*

Charles Murphy's Biography

A man-shaped person looking to try and break into writing. In a recent period of reflection, I asked myself what is it that I actually enjoyed during school? The answer was writing stories. So here I am. Bon appétit.

Twitter: @Mrccmurphy

807: THE REALITY SHE DESERVES

by Robbie Brown

Now that he had helped avert yet another apocalypse, it was finally time for Murf to be rewarded.

"You may live on the timeline and the reality of your choosing."

He decided that his mum deserved happiness even more than he. He let her be with her one true love, thereby writing himself out of all existence across all realities.

The world reset itself to 1976 and Belinda Murphy caught the eye of the man who could offer her the earth.

Robbie Brown's Biography

Robbie Brown, professional cook hanging up the apron to focus on making up stories, or how to live on meagre rations.

www.dovetalesscotland.co.uk

~

808: MOVING TARGET

by Seth Turner-Higgins

Exhilaration.

Sweat running, heart pumping, target met.

I'm still young. Still strong.

I climb off the machine, wipe down, drive to work.

Sweat running, heart pumping, target achieved.

Still top of my game. Still strong.

Lockdown.

Sweat running, heart pumping, target gone.

Too still now.

Dusty bike, rusty bike.

Barely running, tyre pumping.

Target?

Still able.

Sweat running, heart pumping.

It's spring... glorious, abundant, alive. Light and speed surround me.

The bike moves. I am still, inside. Still in awe. Exhilarated.

Seth Turner-Higgins' Biography

Seth graduated in 1991 and began his working life at Central Television as an assistant director before finding his real vocation. For the last 27 years he has enjoyed teaching drama and theatre to a variety of inspirational individuals.

809: HUMANS LEAVE EARTH

by Grace Turner-Higgins

Through the portal they step. One by one by one. Feet drag. Reluctant eyes linger regretfully on the barren wasteland they once called home.

Creator watches from above – exasperated. Today, humans leave Earth.

But maybe they've learnt their lesson? Maybe they won't destroy the next planet.

Creator rubs their temples. Unlikely.

With a sigh of resignation, Creator gets back to work.

A little air, some plants – some water? Hmm.

Creator scratches their chin. What next?

Some birds. Creator rather likes those.

Grace Turner-Higgins' Biography

Grace (17), is currently studying business at college and is hoping to go on to do a degree in creative writing at uni in a year's time. Grace has written many stories, however this is the shortest of them all.

~

810: THE LOCKDOWN TREPIDATION

by Eileen Baldwin

Come on, you'll be fine, Jane thought to herself.

Her heart pounded as she closed her old wooden front door.

She donned her mask and walked the few minutes to her appointment. The birds were singing, their sweet voices a treat to hear. The air smelt fresh, but Jane was dreading her first trip out after lockdown.

Finally, she arrived at Jane's Hair Salon. Her first client, Mrs Jones, was waiting for a perm.

Both women were thrilled to be back.

Eileen Baldwin's Biography

Married 52 years. 3 children, 4 grandchildren, 8-week-old great-granddaughter. Writing is a joy since I got over writer's block. Poetry in print. Prize winner on National Poetry Day 2020. Love crochet, music. AotFFWC member.

811: WHAT MOTHER SAID

by Isabel Flynn

Five years old and she peeled the banana, one section at a time, just like monkeys did. Or so her mother said. She'd never seen a monkey eating a banana. But she loved bananas and ate it.

Fifteen years old and she peeled the banana. Rubbing the skin insides onto your face freshens it like a spiny mouse. Or so her mother said. She'd never seen a spiny mouse and certainly didn't want spines, so passed. But she ate the banana.

Isabel Flynn's Biography

Isabel Flynn. A late writer, late to start, late to bed, late to get up, but loving it.
www.gallimaufryonblog.wordpress.com

~

812: LIAISON

by Jeni Lawes

"Will you accompany me? I'd feel better if you came."

He turned to face me, watery eyes squinting in the sun. Slowly he got up, creaking as he did so.

We walked in silence to our destination. He waited patiently for me to collect groceries, watching the world go by around him. When we returned, she was there, red faced and fierce. "Stop luring my cat away," she shrieked.

We shared a secret look that said, "Until next time." I smiled.

Jeni Lawes' Biography

Jeni lives in the magical city of Norwich, England, with her husband, two cats, a dragon and a snake. She enjoys watching horror movies, reading, going to heavy metal gigs, getting tattooed, working out and, of course, writing.

813: INFECTED

by David Viner

"Damned thing's infected."

"Didn't you do something to stop that?"

"Yeah, thought I had."

"Well?"

"It went bang…"

"Weren't you expecting that?"

"Yeah."

"So?"

"Carbon. You never know what it's gonna do next."

"Thought it was going to be simple."

"That was the plan. Pretty lights here, some quantum stuff there. Then this."

"So, what now?"

"Look down there, that planet. The damned infection's become self-aware. That does it. I'll have to scrap this cosmos and build another one from scratch."

David Viner's Biography

David Viner has had several short stories published since 2007. He is currently using Wattpad to showcase some of his work, one of which, 'Wisdom of the Ancients', reached the science fiction number one spot in May-July 2020.

www.wattpad.com/user/dvdvnr

~

814: VILLAGE VIGIL

by Glo Curl

Japan had surrendered seven weeks since, and men were returning from the camps, broken from the horrors they had endured. Whenever the train stopped at this station, he would listen for the church bells from the village two miles beyond; his village, his son's village, waiting.

Skilfully bringing the steaming giant to a halt, he leant out of the cab. The wind lifted his cap from his smoky brow and, in that instant, he heard them. He jumped down and ran.

Glo Curl's Biography

Glo dabbles in poetry and flash fiction, enjoying the discipline of brevity. Moreover, she's lazy and anything longer than 500 words would be a chore.

815: TOY GUN VERSUS FINGER GUN

by Dr. Sriharsha Sripathi

A rather interesting situation I witnessed recently suggested that perhaps tots enjoy imagining toys rather than having real ones.

I observed my 2.25 year old son pointing out his forefinger, pretending it was a gun. He then threatened to shoot. Because of this, I decided to purchase him a toy gun that fired darts up to 15 feet away.

After receiving the toy, he continued to enjoy pointing out his forefinger and pretending it was a gun. *He enjoyed that more.*

Dr. Sriharsha Sripathi's Biography

I'm Dr. Sriharsha S, an assistant professor in the Department of Mechanical Engineering at Ramaiah Institute of Technology, Bangalore, Karnataka, India. My entry is actually a personal experience I came across recently.

~

816: MEMORY TEST

by Joseph Mould

"Damn door, it's stuck again."

"Do you know, Ken, you're like a broken record. You'd never make a burglar."

"Honestly, love, it's bad this time, won't budge an inch. I'm going to chop the damn thing to pieces."

"Idle threats, dear."

"What do you mean? When I get out to the shed, it's history."

"Good luck with that, could be tricky."

"Will you stop being such a patronising old bag?"

"Very well, my love, here's the key. Best try that first."

Joseph Mould's Biography

My name is Joseph Mould, I am 34 years of age and live in North Lincolnshire. I am a new writer and what I lack in talent I hope I make up for with enthusiasm.

817: ONLY YOU CAN SAVE HIM

by Pappo Nindo

He had always been the protagonist, but one day he woke up and suddenly wanted more.

A plan emerged, to break out of the narrative, by making the reader lose interest in him.

So he waited and waited, doing nothing noteworthy, to make sure that nobody would read to the end.

Weeks became months, years and decades, but the story just skipped to the interesting part.

Now, only you can save him, dear reader, by not reading this story's last...

...word.

Pappo Nindo's Biography

Pappo Nindo is an anthropomorphic cardboard figure, scientist and artist. He came to this world as an ambassador to improve the relations between humans and cardboard. On his countless adventures, his main goal is to make those he encounters smile.

www.papponindo.de

~

818: ALONE

by Dianne D. Pingalo

"Why did you leave?"

"I never left."

"You did. You left me alone."

"But I did not."

"I was sad, you know. I thought I was going to be alone again. You left. But that's OK, at least you came back. Are you here to stay?"

"Of course, though I never left. You just never talked to me."

"I did. I received no answer."

"Well, I'm here to stay."

"That's good to hear."

She smiles and walks away from the mirror.

Dianne D. Pingalo's Biography

Dianne Pingalo is a 20-year-old aspiring writer from the Philippines. She dreams to publish her imaginations someday. She is currently taking BA Communication at the University of the Philippines, Baguio.

819: THE CAT WITH THE LEMONY CLAWS

by Iris & Phil Hatchard

Selma was a scratchy cat. Kitten, actually. Very small. Smaller than a small rock. (Not that small. Think of a slightly larger small rock.)

She particularly liked scratching lemons and noses. Her parents found this hilarious. It's not clear why, but as they had nine hundred children, it's unlikely they'd find time to explain.

Every bath-time, Selma would run and hide, and her parents would coax her back with treats. Until the treats ran out, whereupon her claws remained lemony forever.

Iris & Phil Hatchard's Biography

Phil is a doodler, scribbler and teacher, and has dabbled in acting and stand-up comedy. Iris is four. She likes cats and princesses and baths. Selma is a cat. Phil and Iris know better than to try and bathe her.

www.twitter.com/evilflea

~

820: FOUR WORDS

by Joe Brothers

I remember sitting in Year 9 English and Mrs Geary telling us that some writers might spend a whole day only writing four words. They'd be the four most well-crafted, fit for purpose words you could possibly imagine, but only four words.

I was sitting there thinking, *Oh, getting paid to only write four words a day, I wouldn't mind me a slice of that cake, thank you very much.*

No wonder I found writing these 81 words such a struggle.

Joe Brothers' Biography

Joe Brothers, like director Danny Boyle, studied at Bangor University. Joe, too, works in the film industry – as a barista in a cinema's coffee shop. When not spelling people's names wrong on cups, Joe can be found enthusiastically writing.

821: ROCKY TOP

by Charles Lee

Call it Marshmallow Mountain, or call it Rocky Road, but the thick chocolate, chewy ice cream was all William ate when he was young.

When he learned about climate change, he cried. Mountains with workers chipping away at chocolate chunks of boulders were in peril, about to be lost to landslides of muddy mocha.

He tried to warn them and was surprised when he read no stories of chocolate avalanches and casualty counts in the newspaper. Probably another Rocky Road conspiracy.

Charles Lee's Biography

Charles Lee is a high school student from Livingston, New Jersey. He enjoys spending time with friends and going to the beach. He's passionate about sports, in particular tennis, football and wrestling.

~

822: DARE TO CROSS THE LINE

by Sreedevi Ganti Mahapatra

Uff. What made me enter this terrible kitchen? Couldn't I control my greed? I ran after a bluebottle fly.

I was trained to catch tasty insects, easily available and edible. Why do we always run after aliens? White tiled walls. A sink with brass taps that looks like a dissection table.

No one could be more stupid; I jumped on the post-mortem table when alive.

I am the stupid garden frog who ran after the forbidden fruit, abandoning my green paradise.

Sreedevi Ganti Mahapatra's Biography

High school teacher in the tribal district of Seoni, Madhya Pradesh, India. Seoni is also known as Mowgali Land. Passion for reading, writing, travelling and spending time on nature trails. Would like to spend more time with students, teaching and learning.

823: TEMPTATION

by Helen Aitchison

It was too much to bear, the teasing, the temptation unfaltering. Her senses in overdrive, anticipation like electricity pumping through her veins. She tried to resist the seduction. Her willpower presented in waves of determination, only to retract as desire engulfed her. Knowing it was sinful, her fingers lingered, itching to undress the delight mesmerising her.

"Damn it," she exclaimed. Still three days until weigh in, she rationalised, ripping the packaging off the chocolate and frantically shoving it in her mouth.

Helen Aitchison's Biography

Helen Aitchison began writing in 2019 after winning a place on Introduction to Playwriting with Live Theatre. She has since had poems published with Slice Of The Moon Books and been shortlisted for the Story Tyne Award.

www.helenaitchisonwrites.com

~

824: BEST OF TIMES, WORST OF TIMES

by Mohit Dass

A man in his late 30s was sitting by a fireplace in icy-cold December, recollecting the best of times from his youth.

"Mac," called his mother. "What happened to you, my son?"

It seemed he'd lost all hope and, likewise, most of his friends and cousins, either to death or to the selfish reasons they had.

Once a lively character and inspiration for others to look upon, he'd now become clueless and despairing because his love had left him in pain.

Mohit Dass' Biography

I'm from India and writing is my longtime awaited passion. I want to see my name in print one day. Reading has now become my new hobby since the lockdown started. Love travelling. If not, then watching travel videos.

825: NEVER SAY CAN'T

by Matthew Gooch

"I can't do that," I said.

I looked down at the piece of paper in front of me.

"I've never written a story before."

"And why not?" said Anne, the head teacher. "What makes you think you cannot write a story?"

"I'm no good at anything."

"Never say can't," said Anne. "Just write about what you enjoy and make sure that you are certain of what you are writing."

I took the pen from my head teacher carefully.

"But I can't."

Matthew Gooch's Biography

My name is Matthew. I am a mathematics graduate. I have grown up with galactosemia, a rare metabolic condition. I love writing and have written a story about my grandma who passed away last year from cancer.

~

826: BONE BREAKER

by Jimmy Doom

"You're not the least bit repentant."

"No, I'm certainly not."

I returned to my sandwich, or, should I say, attempted to return my mouth to it in order to consume it, but she wasn't done scolding me.

"You broke my brother's wrist."

I took a bite of sandwich for sustenance and time. Her face turned the relative colour of the salami between the bread, sans mustard.

After swallowing, I said, "When you learn what he did, you'll break his other one."

Jimmy Doom's Biography

Jimmy Doom is an actor and writer from Detroit, Michigan. He gets beat up and shot at on film quite a bit, in real life only occasionally. His micro fiction can be found online.

827: THE SEASIDE CARAVAN

by Hannah Cole

Liz could barely lug the wheelchair up the steps, or carry Jack through the narrow doorways.

Emily talked about last year, next year, "we always…", but this would definitely be the last time.

Leaving Emily cocooned in her sandy towel, Liz carried Jack to the water.

He laughed, trying to kick.

As Liz heaved him higher on her hip, a wave knocked them sideways.

Jack spluttered, choked.

Liz screamed, "Towel, Em."

But Emily was far down the beach. Walking with someone.

Hannah Cole's Biography

Hannah Cole is a teacher and writer, currently blogging about an elderly bear surviving the COVID-19 crisis (www.vulnerableteddy.com). She has lived in Hammersmith and Oxford. She grows easy vegetables and colourful weeds.

~

828: A LONELY WRAITH

by Ripunjoy Borgohain

"You are too young to be here. What are you doing at a place like this?"

"What does it matter? Why don't you mind your own business?"

"Little girls like you shouldn't be wondering alone at night."

"What can go wrong? Why are you out so late?"

"I am the night guard at a factory nearby and I always come here to smoke a cigarette."

"I know, which is why I came here. I felt so lonely the past 60 years."

Ripunjoy Borgohain's Biography

Hello, my name is Ripunjoy Borgohain. I am from Assam, India and I am currently pursuing my BA in biotechnology. I love reading and writing poems and stories. Nothing feels better than bringing out happiness in others through my tales.

www.instagram.com/rip_van_winkle3/

829: THE UNKNOWN

by Matthew Dawson

"It's coming and I'm scared."

"What's coming?"

"I don't know and it's scary."

"When is it coming?"

"I don't know."

"Why does it scare you?"

"Because I don't know what it is."

"Why is it coming?"

"I don't know."

"How do you know it will be scary?"

"I don't."

"So maybe it is something to look forward to?"

"But I don't know what I am looking forward to, my future is unknown."

"So is everyone's."

"Yes, and the unknown scares me."

Matthew Dawson's Biography

I am an aspiring writer of young adult fiction from the concrete jungles of Milton Keynes. I live with my wife, 10-year-old daughter and an array of pets.

~

830: DON'T ASK

by Tonia Nem

When she opened the door, she wished she'd never introduced herself to Miss Charlton. Her old neighbour was always covered in cat fur, which she sprinkled all over Kiara's place while tirelessly chattering about old-lady nonsense.

This time, Miss Charlton had a serious expression on her face.

"Did you see the morning newspaper, Kiara, or whatever your name is?"

Kiara, or whatever her name was, put the friendliest smile on her face, opened the door wide, and invited the woman inside.

Tonia Nem's Biography

My name is Antoniya Nemtserova but Tonia Nem is easier to remember, hence Tonia's born. I'm a Bulgarian living in the USA. I love writing flash and micro fiction and never limit myself with a certain genre. I follow my inspiration.

www.medium.com/@antnem

831: CLEARING UP

by Pam Knapp

Shirts were hung crisply in the wardrobe, a wayward crumb swept, invisible dust wiped, used crockery put back in cupboards. She mustn't leave anything unattended. Everything must be perfect. But the bathroom towels were yesterday's. Would Tom notice?

Her colour drained, recalling how she'd used the towels and placed them on the heated rail. Her gut rolled.

Reason shook at the bars that kept it from breaking into reality. Of course he wouldn't notice. She'd change them when the blood dried.

Pam Knapp's Biography

Pam Knapp @pamcountonwords is a secondary school teacher from East Sussex who loves anything to do with words. Sometimes publishers have been kind enough to print her stories. This has made her very happy.

~

832: WIZARD

by Paula Lacey

A woodcarver has been at work in this forest glade. In one trunk, an owl wisely surveys the scene while a red kite is caught in the act of landing on the next. The surrounding fallen trees are covered by a host of frogs, lizards and butterflies.

My favourite carving is a wizard with flowing robes, a pointed hat and a long beard. I gaze at him for a long time, then turn to leave. Did he just wink at me?

Paula Lacey's Biography

After a somewhat varied career, I recently retired and am now enjoying taking my first steps into the world of writing. Mainly, I find myself most attracted to writing about the natural world and about feelings and relationships.

833: MUM AND DAD

by Vishnu Nandan

I snuck into my house after another secret night party. I kept silent, trying not to wake my strict father. As I approached the door, the lights came on.

My mother looked worried. She asked whether I'd eaten. I convinced her I had and proceeded to my room.

I'd forgotten my keys, so I returned to the living room. From my parents' room, I heard, "Has he arrived? Nights are not safe."

Dad always hid love behind a veil called strictness.

Vishnu Nandan's Biography

Vishnu Nandan is a Keralite who started writing when his pen prompted him to worlds he never knew before. Hailing from the picturesque lakeside of Alappuzha, he also cultivated interests like photography, gardening and learning trades.

~

834: THE FINAL COMMENCEMENT

by Richard Stanley

The heatwave mercifully departed New England just one day preceding the 246th commencement ceremony of the Massachusetts Institute of Technology. The usual opening pomp was absent. MIT's president expressed her profound sadness and regret that the class of 2115 would be MIT's final graduating class.

After the ceremony, this august institution would close its doors for ever. The 18 students solemnly received their diplomas in the 108 degree heat. It went without saying that all of them majored in environmental engineering.

Richard Stanley's Biography

Emeritus Professor of Mathematics at M.I.T. and Arts and Sciences Distinguished Professor, University of Miami.

835: SOCIAL DISTANCING

by Manda Riehl

"If you want something done, ask a busy person," they chuckled, dropping several more folders on her desk. They headed to lunch without her.

She was the hardest worker in the office. Everything done early, the obnoxious teacher's pet. Who wanted to be around that?

It showed on her face – the lines on her forehead echoing the cracks from the constant white-knuckling and the relentless crush of her perfectionism.

"Are you OK? You look tired," they said, not wanting an answer.

Manda Riehl's Biography

Manda Riehl is a biomathematician and mother.

~

836: DINNER FOR SOME

by Caiden Lang

Fatman stood by an open flame, with steaks slowly sizzling.

Hard at work, he wiped his brow. And then he couldn't move.

With his head wrenched back and his eyes pulled wide, the light was all around. Needles entered and little heads bobbled; a conference had begun. He couldn't scream; couldn't feel the touching or the sounds.

Of little things that hovered, now there was no trace.

So he probed and he cut, and he wondered what flying men might want.

Caiden Lang's Biography

I am a high school teacher and aspiring editor from South Africa. I enjoy knowing that there is truth beneath my feet – it allows me to read the weird and wonderful without getting lost.

837: AN OBSCURE TECHNICALITY IN THE LAWS OF THIS STATE

by Michael Hardy

Once upon a time a man robbed a bank of eighteen dollars that he needed to buy a book of short stories that he had seen in the window of a bookstore.

He was acquitted of the crime because of an obscure technicality in the laws of This State, but that income put him in a higher tax bracket. The IRS called this to his attention and he paid. The IRS lived happily ever after, but the District Attorney did not.

Michael Hardy's Biography

I have a Ph.D. with a major in statistics and a minor in mathematics and I have taught those subjects at nine different universities. I have some competence in English, Esperanto, German and a bit of Italian.

www.math.stackexchange.com/users/11667/michael-hardy

~

838: THE INTERVIEW

by Lyndsay Lomax

Huge globules of moisture dropped from grey clouds. I'd forgotten my umbrella.
A bad omen?
I was hustled into a room to contemplate rehearsed answers to imagined questions.
A navy-suited man entered, papers in hand, a forced smile stretched over his lips.
He looked familiar, like yesterday's dream. Had I seen him before?
Rapid-fire questions followed the pleasantries; I answered as best I could.
Suddenly, it was over.
"We'll be in touch."
Outside, the menacing clouds had retreated.
A good omen?

Lyndsay Lomax's Biography

Originally from North West England, Lyndsay Lomax is an aspiring writer who lives in Switzerland, where she spends her time reading, baking, spending time outdoors and, of course, writing. Her website is:

www.lyndsaylomax.com

839: JANET

by Medeia Sharif

They all feared Janet. The girls whispered amongst themselves every morning, seeing what she wore in her hair that day.

Janet wore barrettes when she was in an OK mood. A headband indicated anger. A ponytail meant she was after revenge.

Monday morning, Janet wore a red bow on top of her head. The girls hid in hallway recesses in fear. They tearfully backed away from her. They avoided her in class.

A bow... who was she going to kill today?

Medeia Sharif's Biography

By day, Medeia Sharif is a middle school English teacher and by night she's a multi-published author of novels and short stories for all age groups. She can be found at:
www.medeiasharif.com

~

840: DOODLING CURSE

by Emily Knight

We're through. That is what you said to me as I boarded the train at Waverley Station.
We're done. That is what drummed through my head to the beat of the train.
My hand. That is what I noticed when brass cogs and coiled springs grew from the page.
Distress. That is what I felt when the carriage filled with my unconstrained scrawls.
Unchecked. That is what has become of my doodling curse.
All because of those simple words, we're through.

Emily Knight's Biography

I'm Emily, a recent convert to the manipulation of words for the sole purpose of creative fun.

841: TRAVELLING GNOME

by CL Wearne

The garden gnome's fishing rod was pointing north now. *He's definitely moved again*, thought Katherine. She looked at the bedroom windows of next door, expecting the kids to be there sniggering, but they weren't. She sat down on the bench and drank her tea.

Back inside, she mopped the kitchen floor. Mud seemed to just appear.

That night in bed, she thought she heard tiny footsteps but dismissed it as the pipes. The tug on her blanket was real enough though.

CL Wearne's Biography

I am a disabled author from SE England where I live with my scientist partner and two cats.

~

842: SAFE HARBOUR

by Debbie Rolls

Submerged, I follow the harbour wall. Sound muffled by watery wrap.

Below, a ray glides across sand. Mussels jut from weathered stones, amongst clumps of green. I weave between jellyfish, unsure whether they are benign. I flick strands of severed grass away from my mask. Silver slithers of fish flit in and out of crevices.

A tap on my head makes me shoot upwards. The edge of a wing slips past, as the cormorant heads for a more secure landing strip.

Debbie Rolls' Biography

I am an educator and freelance writer. I am studying an MA in travel and nature writing. I enjoy writing for children and adults. I love to swim.

843: EYES IN THE DARK

by Gwynne Weir

Eyes in the darkness, just beneath the shadows of the trees. I watched them and they watched me; those unblinking amber eyes. Every time I tried to move, the eyes flashed; small fires that burned into my soul.

I shifted, fumbling around for something – anything – I could use. I wasn't paying attention.

Looking back in front of me, the eyes still shone; a rotten yellow glow. Behind me, a putrid stench rose as I felt the hot breath on my neck.

Gwynne Weir's Biography

An avid reader, Gwynne has often found herself creating worlds and has several short stories published in a range of genres and themes. She is currently honing her skills by working on an MA in creative writing.

www.tgwenllian.wixsite.com/aweiredworld

~

844: TRACKED CHANGES

by Jan Courtney

The boy – around six years old, blond ruffled hair – scoots down Corsham High Street, a maroon schoolbag banging against his knees.

His mother senses the widening gap between them and starts to call, "Harry, Harry." As he becomes smaller and more distant, she shouts louder, edgy, almost desperate, frantic, "Harry, *Harry.*"

But Harry scoots faster, yelling, "Albert, wait. Albert, Albert, wait for me." A chain gang of urgency, like a tube train rushing down a non-existent track on the cobbled street.

Jan Courtney's Biography

Juicy crone. Writer of non-fiction. Lover of wild places and the centeredness of emptiness. Foggy themes reoccur, exploring the universal struggle we embrace to find what lies within.

www.jancourtney.co.uk

845: TIME TO FIGHT

by Aerin Bernstein

The wind whistles in my ears as I plant my feet in the ground.

"You're done for, Zimora," I say coldly.

My nemesis smiles. "No, I don't think I am."

My dark brown curls whip around my face as I draw my sword. "Really?"

The sides of Zimora's mouth curl and she frowns. "Samara, drop that. You know… join me and I'll spare you."

I cock my head. "Not going to happen."

She advances, twirling her blade. "Time to fight, sister."

Aerin Bernstein's Biography

I'm Aerin B, a sassy tween writer. I'm about to publish my first novel *Color Quest* on Amazon; I'm so excited. I love reading, writing, eating and laughing. I'm also a grammar nerd. Lastly, I am absolutely obsessed with rainbows.

~

846: MUM'S HAND

by Karen Bevan

He studied her hand in his own. Long, slim fingers, the neat natural nails. Even her thumb was elegant. Blue, gnarled veins beneath thin wrinkled skin. It was a beautiful hand that held the story of a long life.

Once young and strong yet soft, it caressed him lovingly, gently when he was a baby and she a young mother. He remembered it soothing him when he was a small child after a fall, reassuringly wiping tears from his chubby cheeks.

Karen Bevan's Biography

My name is Karen. I love my children, this beautiful planet and all creatures great and small, to coin a phrase. I try to see the positive in everything and I believe the best time to be happy is always today.

847: STARLIGHT

by Gemma Bevan

I look up over the rooftops in search of the stars, admiring how such small things can glisten with a fierce, yet quiet, intensity. It is a kind of feeling that can only come from the twinkling of a thousand suns. I pad silently over the tiles of my roof, basking in the early morning air. Feeling completely alive, finally.

I feel a struggling beneath my foot before I hear a heart wrenching yowl. I have trodden on Tibbles' tail again.

Gemma Bevan's Biography

Gemma Bevan is a small-town girl with a passion for fiction. She enjoys consuming all types, including books, TV, films and games. She has never written a story this short before but had great fun doing it.

~

848: WORTH LIVING?

by John Bevan

He had been diagnosed with an incurable disease, one that would rob him of the things he loved doing most.

He had to decide whether it was worth carrying on. He battled with his demons and, every day, he thought of reasons to continue.

He loved his family and this was the overriding reason not to do anything 'silly'. He tried many different options to improve his life, some not pleasant.

Eventually, he decided life is precious and so should continue.

John Bevan's Biography

John Bevan, father of two wonderful children, married to a wonderful person, semi-retired now and trying to help where I can with the extended family.

849: REDEMPTIVE

by Adam Bevan

He knew – inevitably – he had messed it all up. Again.

That familiar emptiness delved into the very pit of his stomach and resided there with familiarity.

Finally, he arose with weakness and wandered the streets, weeping.

He was lost. He was fearful.

At that very moment, the sun soaked onto his skin: a warm embrace. The crisp air filled with birdsong, and a flock of white wings gloriously soared overhead.

Emptiness became fullness.

"Do better with your day, TODAY, my son."

Adam Bevan's Biography

English teacher for 10 years. Avid traveller. Vegan for 7 years. Love the natural world.

~

850: GARDEN FRIENDS

by Rebecca Hubbard

First, we searched the lawn for daisies, gathering those with the fattest stems. Then, cross-legged in the lilac's shade, we sat and made, one by one, slits in the juicy stalks with our thumbnails. Next, we coaxed one stalk through another, squinting like mother threading a needle, the hairs bending as stem slipped through stem.

As shadows lengthened, we went in for tea; two fairy queens with garlands round our necks, daisy bracelets at our wrists and thumb nails rimmed green.

Rebecca Hubbard's Biography

Rebecca Hubbard is an experienced and inspiring writing tutor and published poet. *The Garden of Shadow and Delight* is her collection of prose poems on gardens (Cinnamon Press, 2014). She has a deep connection with landscape, art and words.

851: GLIMPSE OF RUSTED STEEL

by Joseph Lancaster

A creeping fluorescence invited itself over the windowsill, now possessed by the meandering ivy and untamed bonsai that peeped through the glassless stone hole.

I resided, a still, rusted blade in the hands of the unworthy, felled by a beast of equal strength. I gathered fragile dust and the falling debris of the ornate ceiling.

A scent of death lingered, but did not repress the sound of footfall. A warm hand grasped my dormant hilt, a new warrior holds my steel...

Joseph Lancaster's Biography

I am a third year film and TV production student at York St John University, originally from the Newcastle area. I'm always trying to improve my writing skills and potentially pursue it as a career if I can do so.

~

852: THE CORONER'S REPORT

by Campbell Hinshelwood

"No signs of foul play, Henry. Just another one wandering too close to the edge, I reckon."

"Yes, most likely, and to think – the breeding season has only just started."

Finster's Pass is a precarious coastal path, part of a large network of bridleways that connects Zennor and Boscastle. Fertile waters attract large colonies of nesting seabirds, including guillemot and razorbills, famed for their pointy eggs.

During summer, it's not uncommon for greedy egg collectors to traverse away from the path...

Campbell Hinshelwood's Biography

Campbell is a writer, photographer and avid surfer from Sydney. He lives in Australia for the reliable swell, but his heart belongs to England. The inspiration for his work often involves friends sitting-room-stories told during fleeting moments.

www.campbellhinshelwood.com

853: EGGS

by Brittany Holmes

I can't get in the front door fast enough, away from the freezing rain. I'm careful with the bags, don't want to break my eggs when I have three cakes to bake.

I unpack and leave the eggs on the side to get to room temperature. They're cold from being squashed against the fish fingers in my bag for life. I'm terrible at packing.

I dry off, change and preheat the oven. I hear a crack from the box of eggs.

Brittany Holmes' Biography

My literary interests lie in fantasy and my current project is a feminist pirate story dabbled with magic. I teach creative media and media studies at York College, UK, while searching for the ideal PhD topic.

www.linkedin.com/in/brittany-holmes-1a4005b9/

~

854: THE RETURN

by Karen Western

Repeatedly, she swallowed the acid bile that rose from her stomach. Concentrating hard, she stared at the silhouettes in the darkness, imagining another world. One where she could travel in daylight. Maria had never thought she would return. Had she made the right decision?

She listened, head tilted, straining to capture the sound and heard the soft night waves of the ocean. Almost unexpectedly, piercing turquoise eyes appeared.

She had arrived. She clutched her growing bump and prepared for the greeting.

Karen Western's Biography

My professional and educational background includes a varied sprinkle of career changes, a BSC and MA in education. I am a trustee for Seasons for Growth and enjoy seeing those who have experienced trauma progress and enjoy life.

855: SAME OLD

by Sharon Pinner

"Good morning," he said to the pigeon that was always looking at him from the window ledge. He directed a nod to cars, bikes and pedestrians dashing by on the road beyond. He leant over his stick to watch a furry bee emerge from a hole in the soil.

"It's like the world is starting afresh," he said, but the pigeon had moved off. Familiar voices beckoned from the television indoors.

"See you tomorrow." He waved as a butterfly wafted by.

Sharon Pinner's Biography

I am a writer from Cambridgeshire whose interests include birds, running, football and pondering. I am a Bath Spa University MA travel and nature writing student (2019/20).
www.wildlifeontherun.wordpress.com

~

856: OBOL

by Jacek Wilkos

Tom put a coin in the man's mouth before sliding the body bag tightly shut.

"You really believe this?" his companion asked with a grimace on his face.

"Yes. He will need it."

*

Peter woke up, choking. He sprang to a sitting position and spat out the thing from his mouth. The sound of metal hitting the floor echoed in the room.

This place, unknown to him, was illuminated only by screens of gaming machines, each displaying the words 'insert coin'.

Jacek Wilkos' Biography

Jacek Wilkos is an engineer from Poland. He lives with his wife and daughter in the beautiful city of Cracow. He is addicted to buying books. He loves black coffee, dark ambient music and riding his bike.
www.facebook.com/Jacek.W.Wilkos/

857: NEITHER USE NOR ORNAMENT

by R. J. Kinnarney

Clare held the cup up above her head. "Look, you can see the light through it."

"And what use is that?" Steve swirled the amber around his chipped glass.

Clare didn't respond. She placed the cup back on the shelf.

*

The van's engine rumbles outside the front door. Clare puts the bone china cup in the final box and steps outside.

Steve is sitting on the stairs, chipped glass in hand. "I'm sorry."

"And what use is that?" The door closes.

R. J. Kinnarney's Biography

R. J. Kinnarney is author of children's novel *Abigail Aces Acting*. R. J. Kinnarney's short stories and flash fiction have been published by *100 Words of Solitude, The Daily Drunk, 50 Word Stories, Daunt Books* and *The Write In*.

~

858: A PENCIL TEST

by Tim Warren

Take an ordinary HB pencil and place it behind your right ear. If the pencil remains firmly in place while your ear falls off, something is definitely wrong in the world.

If you overvalue symmetry, repeat the test on your left ear. Then put the pencil back exactly where you first found it. If everything had seemed just fine beforehand, there is every chance this pencil was the one thing holding everything together...

And perhaps – just perhaps – it's not too late.

Tim Warren's Biography

Tim Warren is a writer of mostly very short things. His work can be found most recently in *Overheard, Serious Flash Fiction: Vols. 5 & 6, Paragraph Planet*, the *VSS365 Anthology* and on Twitter. He lives in Cornwall, UK.

www.twitter.com/FredTweetzsche

859: SCREAM

by A. A. Rubin

The figure looked around. Something had definitely changed. His world, constantly spinning for as long as he could remember, had now become totally still.

He sniffed the air suspiciously and noticed that it was drier as well. On all sides, there were boundaries where, once, there were infinite possibilities.

He called out to his creator, Mr Munch, but the glass was soundproofed. He raised his hands to his face, grabbed his cheeks and screamed silently, forever trapped inside his gilded frame.

A. A. Rubin's Biography

A. A. Rubin's work has appeared in *Cowboy Jamboree, Kyanite Press* and *Pif*. He roams the galaxy seeking adventure, but can be reached through his website:

www.aarubin.wordpress.com

~

860: FAREWELL TO GRIEF WHILE FINDING LOVE AND LIFE AT THE EDGE OF THE WORLD

by Michelle Weaver

As I dig my fingers into the gilded grain, my toes sink deeper. Tepid waves wash over them, gently, lovingly. I once belonged there, submerged beneath its depths, the sunlight obscured.

Teardrops no longer glisten, dried salty by the sea breeze. Memories surge; crystalline. He'd promised to meet me at the tide's edge, where the afterlife would merge with my own.

As I reach for the burnished horizon, his touch elevates me, easing my pain. I promise to live, for now.

Michelle Weaver's Biography

Michelle Weaver is a 46-year-old primary school teacher from Leeds. She lives as she loves, with passion and determination. Her twin 11-year-old daughters and husband make her life interesting and meaningful. The outcome of her childhood: resilience and resourcefulness.

861: THE UNPREMEDITATED PLUM

by Diana Senechal

Harriet bought a plum at the open market on Friday morning but forgot to squeeze it slightly before giving it to a prospective boss as a foolish bribe.

Said boss received it with a grimace. *I get too many of these*, she seemed to say. But the seeming overrode the saying, and the interview went well.

"You have a lot to offer," she said.

"So do you," countered Harriet, which, she realised later, sounded a bit condescending. But not excessively so.

Diana Senechal's Biography

Diana Senechal is the 2011 winner of the Hiett Prize in the Humanities and the author of two books. She teaches at the Varga Katalin Gimnázium in Szolnok, Hungary.

~

862: PAYBACK

by Kathryn Smith

Something is horribly wrong.

Foxes with bloodied faces are swaggering up to my grade two listed Cotswold cottage.

Hares carrying jugs are bounding close behind, slopping out a red carpet.

A fanfare of shrieks has started up and is getting louder.

There is a pheasant in the porch eyeing the shotgun, carelessly picking at the trigger with a claw.

Then, as I step over my snakeskin shoes and alligator bag, I hear the click of teeth; about eighty I would guess.

Kathryn Smith's Biography

Kathryn writes and paints stories in the gritty north of England.

863: SPEAKING OF LOVE LOST FOR WORDS

by Kate Leimer

A taciturn man was beloved by a loquacious woman.

"Brevity is necessary," he advised.

"I must vocalise, soliloquise, fill my world with wordfulness. May we not live together in symbiotic, systolic harmony?"

"No."

Disappointed, she wed a musician instead. He spoke little but set her lyrical words to music and made himself a fine career.

The taciturn man maintained his silent solitude. Occasionally, at his fireside, he lifted his head and smiled, reading the words of the books she had written.

Kate Leimer's Biography

A lapsed writer, I'm returning to fiction after many years. Having published features and local news, I'm used to being concise but this is the shortest story I've ever written. I work in a library in the Cotswolds.

~

864: DUST ON MY DANCING SHOES

by Emma Robertson

I hover by the door as smiling pairs waltz past. Ted was right, I shouldn't've come. My dancing days are over.

"Hello. Here for ballroom?" The teacher is only about thirty, younger than my grandchildren. Younger than the sparkly shoes in my bag.

"No, I—"

"Come on." She introduces me to the curious, friendly regulars.

Ted laughed when I said I wanted to go dancing, but here I am – braver, now he's gone. Shoes on; I'm ready. Better late than never.

Emma Robertson's Biography

Emma Robertson is an emerging fiction writer with her first two short stories being published in autumn 2020. She is also a performing arts tutor living in London, with nonfiction articles published in dance magazines under her maiden name.

www.twitter.com/emmadancetrain

865: RECYCLING NOT DISPOSING

by David Don

We are all hoarders, keeping items never to use again. There comes a time to dispose of them. How we do this is important for us all.

Instead of disposing them to landfill, take your unwanted items to a charity shop where they can help others, supporting the charity to raise funds to help people in need.

Another benefit of recycling is a small step towards reducing pollution, so we all benefit.

Working together, we support ourselves along with our planet.

David Don's Biography

My name is David Don. I'm in my mid-sixties. I recently started writing to keep active during the pandemic and discovered I enjoyed doing so. I'm now working on a plan of action for my first novel.

~

866: IT HAS TENTACLES

by Eleanor Dickenson

"What do you mean, a tentacle?"

"It was right there under the pier, round that pillar. You can't see now the water's higher."

"Can't have been. There's nothing in these waters that big. What film were you watching last night?"

"No, really, look."

"I am – see? Lean out and you can see there's nothing there."

"There. It's there."

"You're just being silly. I should've worn a coat though, it's raining. I just felt a drop of water run down my neck."

Eleanor Dickenson's Biography

Eleanor Dickenson is a Yorkshire-based writer with a fascination for the ocean and its inhabitants, both tentacled and otherwise. Her work includes poetry and fiction.

867: TRUE LOVE

by Alicia Yau

I seldom talk, but I did whisper to you, "Wear this, eat that... please survive to make me happy."

You almost died, then were rescued by my doctors. This repeated endlessly in your life. Do you remember? Do you care?

You are not made for the other side, which always announces, "You all are now free to do whatever you like." From there, I can only hear screams of ferocity and pain, not happiness.

Now, stay calm and survive, my love.

Alicia Yau's Biography

Alicia loves to read and write fiction and science fiction. She has been published in *365 tomorrows*.

~

868: THE LIVING STATUE

by Rosalind Adam

With his gilded hat and death-mask smirk, he assumes the pose. His heartbeat slows. He tunes out the lad who yells in his ear. He braces against the drunks who push and cajole.

Neither cheek-muscle twitch nor cramping leg betray the illusion until a passer-by offers a coin. He stirs, sucks air into DVT-prone lungs and morphs into a brief jerk-jive routine. Then, with slowing breath, his blood pressure returns to near-death low, taking street art to the limits of life.

Rosalind Adam's Biography

Rosalind Adam, of Leicester, UK, has had her poetry published in anthologies and online sites. In 2018, she was a G. S. Fraser poetry prize winner and was awarded a distinction for her MA in creative writing.

www.rosalindadam.blogspot.com

869: IN A DEEP CHAMBER

by David S Mitchell

In a deep chamber, his ridiculed life's work was vindicated. The elusive treasure was finally in Edward's shaking hands.

Tearful, he smiled with an impossible joy. No eyes had seen this golden statue for four thousand years. This glorious moment would be savoured for ten deep breaths.

On seven, the tunnel collapsed. The roof above too.

Crushed, Edward clutched the statue and continued to smile in his last moments. He would be eventually found and finally respected, in a deep chamber.

David S Mitchell's Biography

David S Mitchell is a new Scottish writer hoping to share many tales. Enjoys long walks and spotting birds on the coast whilst dreaming up new story ideas exploring the ancient past and potential futures. Guilty of minor ukulele crimes.

www.davidsmitchell.xyz

~

870: DIVE IN

by Andrew Carter

We jumped into a life raft just before our trawler went down.
We watched it sink – booms, nets and catch.
The boat sank, leaving a white box afloat.
The ocean was terribly rough.
We were very afraid.
We were hungry.
We were so cold.
A raging sea calmed.
A white box floated near us.
I reached towards the box with a paddle.
I managed to bring it in, and what was inside?
Wet matches, toothpicks, floss, diving helmet and dive tables.

Andrew Carter's Biography

Andrew lives in Newcastle, Australia, and has published poetry and stories in *Xpressions Magazine, Australian Writers' Centre* and *Cairns Post*.

871: I COULDN'T SLEEP FOR TWO, THREE NIGHTS

by Lauren M Foster

I want to dismiss it as a dream: a rap on the door, no one there. Clattering from the garden. I seize my alpenstock, venture out, into the moonlight.

"Meow."

"Oh, it's just you Claudius." As I bend to stroke him, a hand clamps over my mouth. A chemical taste, then blackness.

I come round, bound and blindfolded, on what feels like a comfortable bed. A man's voice, arrogant, aristocratic. "That's not my wife, you morons."

The hand, the taste again.

Lauren M Foster's Biography

Lauren M Foster is a writer based in Charnwood, UK. She has been published in *The New Luciad, Ink Pantry, DIY Poets* and more, and plays drums in a garage punk band called The Cars That Ate Paris.

~

872: A LIFE BEYOND

by Karen Rust

The boy is gone, the house too quiet. I sit at my laptop but cannot write. His father works upstairs, ploughing through endless Zoom meetings.

My *world* is negotiating an unknown city two-hundred miles away.

Is that all I am? Was? Still am?

The phone rings. Tea spills in my haste. He seems fine, happy. Not all his new friends are coping so well. He must go; a socially distanced event awaits.

I mop up, open a new document, and type.

Karen Rust's Biography

Karen has just completed an MA in creative writing at the University of Leicester. A lead writer for Writing East Midlands, she ghost-writes biographies for StoryTerrace and is published in literary journals including *Cabinet of Heed, Ellipsiszine, Mookychick* and *Inkpantry*.

www.bloominglateblog.wordpress.com

873: WHISPERS FROM THE GRAVE

by Thomas Belmar

A recently widowed woman named Mary would visit the cemetery every evening, where her husband was buried.

One dark, misty night, a young boy was standing, dressed in white, crying uncontrollably over a grave next to where she usually mourned. She had never seen him before and, as she approached her husband's grave, she felt a great chill in the air.

"Why are you here alone?" she asked.

He turned with grey lifeless eyes and whispered, "Nobody came to my funeral."

Thomas Belmar's Biography

My name is Thomas Belmar and I serve the city of Liverpool. Helping people on their travels as I daydream about my next short story, my goal is to capture people's imagination and share mine with the world.

~

874: JUST TO SAY...

by Ella Wilson

To whom it may concern,

I just wish to enlighten you. I am not stupid.

I notice the sly looks, the snide comments, the mocking laughs.

I see it all.

Why don't I retaliate, you ask?

No, it's not because I'm too shy or embarrassed.

I'm not self-conscious or in the least bit fearful.

The honest, plain and quite simple truth is, frankly, I do not care.

Why not, you ask?

You can figure that one out.

Best wishes,

Ella x

Ella Wilson's Biography

Ella Wilson lives in the south-west of England and currently studies English literature, drama and classical civilisation at A level, and the creative writing AFA. She aspires to be an actress and screenwriter.

875: THE HARDEST WORDS

by Katerina Hellam

The silence was deafening, or so they say. Words said can't easily be taken back. She sat there and glared instead. My visage showed I wouldn't be moved.

The silence continued. It was her fault. Well mostly, anyway. The events of the last hour replayed in my mind. She sighed at me and her eyes looked at me in that way.

Maybe some of this was my fault. Maybe.

The silence continued until finally we said those words together.

"I'm sorry."

Katerina Hellam's Biography

Katerina Hellam is a TG author in her 50s based in the UK who has two books published via Amazon to date and is currently working hard on a third.

www.katerinahellam.wordpress.com

~

876: NIGHTMARE OF 2020

by Betty J Burton

Gretchen woke with a start. Her heart was racing. She took a deep breath, hoping it was only a dream.

She shivered, remembering masses of dying people, street riots, wildfires, rationed food, being quarantined. Gretchen donned her slippers. She wanted to look outside.

"Stop that," her mother cried. "It's too dangerous."

"Why?" Gretchen asked.

"Don't you remember? This world has gone mad." Tears filled her mother's eyes.

"Will things ever get better?" Gretchen asked.

"Only God knows..." said her mother sadly.

Betty J Burton's Biography

I'm from Virginia. My dad taught me storytelling, sitting on our front porch. I have been writing my entire life. I've had a few poems published and a couple short stories – one in *Behind Closed Doors* called 'The Ghost Within'.

877: TOO MUCH TO ASK

by Boakesey

Sue sighed. Creating a story that was *EXACTLY* 81 words long was much harder than she'd expected it to be.

She was a professional author, published in several different countries and languages, books selling in droves. She could easily write 3,000 words a day when the muse struck, so 81 words should be a doddle. Only it wasn't.

She had the perfect story arc, great setting, sympathetic characters and... 200 words. Too many, no matter what she did.

She gave up.

Boakesey's Biography

I'm an ex-teacher, on the scrapheap due to PTSD, SAD and mobility challenges following a mini-stroke. I took up 'Writing for Well-Being' to help with my mental health and now facilitate a writers' group on the Isle of Man, where I currently live.

~

878: ACCORDION-PLAYING DONKEYS ON THE CHEESE MOON

by Jonathan Hunter

Whilst wolfing down the cheese of the moon, a solemn looking donkey approached me with an accordion hanging around his neck. He dropped his accordion by my side and simply stared at me. A whole stillness and silence fell around.

Slowly touching one note, I listened. Instantly, amidst clouds of smoke, hundreds of donkeys appeared, circling me. Their accordion playing was so deafening I tried to run, but it was too late. I fell over as my legs turned to cheese.

Jonathan Hunter's Biography

I'm a librarian from the Midlands, UK. Since lockdown, I have found the fun in writing flash fiction as a hobby and have posted some stories on *Friday Flash Fiction*. I support the mighty Solihull Moors and the lesser known Manchester United.

879: PURPLES

by Swi Neo Mary Yap

"What are you cooking, Ming?" Her future father-in-law, coming to dinner, loves purple.

"Purple carrot, cauliflower, cabbage, on purple plates." Her staccato voice increases in pitch.

Her furious fingers slice, peel, chop, fry. Her breath blasts toxic fumes. Yet the delicate aroma of the purples permeates my being and I imagine turning into Barney. Dessert is purple plums and grapes.

"Sis, I'll prepare a cocktail of gentian violet, soda and vodka." The table setting for seven is now set for six.

Swi Neo Mary Yap's Biography

Singaporean Swi Neo Mary Yap is a retired educator. She enjoys reading books of all genres and writes short faction stories – fiction based on facts. She has had two short stories published.

~

880: THE LAPTOP

by Michael J. Lowis

"Ken, is that you laughing?" George shouted.

"No, but I heard it too. It's coming from your laptop."

"I've only just bought it. It's the most advanced of its type. It seems to have a mind of its own."

The lid was open and the camera lens glowed red. Demented cackling was coming from the speakers, but stopped as they approached.

"Maybe it's been laughing at us," Ken suggested.

George closed the lid. "I doubt it. It's not human, you know."

Michael J. Lowis' Biography

Michael J. Lowis is a retired academic who has published nine books to date, embracing non-fiction, memoir and historical fiction. He targets general readers who enjoy thinking about some of the bigger issues of life. See author.to/MichaelJLowis for more details.

881: BRIDGE 81

by Tanya Hill

Balanced on a bridge, I wait for a train; a ghost train with Blinky and Sal, IED blasted in Helmand, and Tommo broken by screaming nightmares. Save me a seat, lads.

There: piercing headlights, a horn. My train: it doesn't need to stop.

Scuffed footstep behind. Turn, snarl, "Leave me, go."

A woman cop – ice eyes, sunshine hair, corrugated burn cheeks. She offers her hand, whispers, "Step back. I did. Come see the sunrise with me."

Another ghost? Or a chance...

Tanya Hill's Biography

I'm a woman who chooses to live as a man. Often this hurts, but I do it for those who don't understand. A former soldier who loves trains, I have never considered destroying myself on one.

~

882: KIND REGARD

by Meghan O'Brien

With kind regards,
   The Department of Justice.

Laying the letter down after reading those final words, Sharika wondered to herself who the hell designed these damn letters anyway? What type of monster pummels any human being with endless reasoning as to their lack of value, removal of self-worth and application of indignation in response to a letter requesting a stop sign? And how the hell did it end up at the DoJ?

She doubted there was any kindness in their regard.

Meghan O'Brien's Biography

Meghan O'Brien is an upstate New York native who enjoys writing, horseback riding, cooking and gaming. She and her husband reside along the Mohawk river with their three cats.

883: CORONA TROUBLES

by Klaus Gehling

"This mask doesn't fit," said the customer.

"OK."

He came closer and whispered, "My nose grows when I lie. So, it needs more space."

"I understand your problem," I stated. "Are you, perhaps, a member of the family of Pinocchio? Please, don't... umm... well... lie."

He nodded.

"I can help you," I assured him. "Take this colourful toy. Then, just cut a hole in the mask and attach this to it."

He nodded again. "Thank you for the balloon; very versatile."

Klaus Gehling's Biography

I'm retired but still working as a clinical psychologist occasionally. Writing odd stories is one of my passions, as is playing chess, archeology, history and music. I live in Germany and South Africa.

~

884: IN THE KNICKER TIME

by Patrick Moorhouse

My friend said to me, "Time is elastic, like in your knickers. So, the next time a good moment comes along, grab it and tie a large thing like a brick or a television to it. Hold on to it, then the moment will become longer. Carry on holding it until it is as long as you want."

I thought he was finished, but he had one more comment.

"But caution, don't do this when you have horrible neighbours for tea."

Patrick Moorhouse's Biography

Patrick Moorhouse has lived most his life in Milton Keynes, a city of great inspiration for him. He has a sparkling family and a jewel shining grandling, Eli.

885: RACE DAY

by Yvonne Mastaglio

Nervous and ready to go, waiting for the lights to change to red. I'm off round the track faster and faster. The spectators cheer as my white Porsche speeds past.

Oh, the thrill of speed rushing through my veins. Passing the blue car, I'm in first place, the winner's trophy in sight. Round the bend a bit fast, wrong gear, can't slow down. The crowd gasp as I come off the track...

Time to put the Scalextric away for another day.

Yvonne Mastaglio's Biography

Married to Paul. Live in Cullercoats with our cat, Toby. Enjoy archery, skiing, walking and reading. In my younger days I was a ballerina and roller-skater.

~

886: HAUNTING HANDS

by Clara Baird

It's pleasant to watch him breathing.

He turns towards me, feet barely touching the tough footboard of his hospital bed. A soft yawn passes his lips as he nestles into me, ready to sleep.

I think that he knows what's coming next. It's the way his hands are so cold as they try to grasp onto mine, his breath shaking as it fans against my hollowed cheek. The only sound the flatlining of his monitor.

If only I could breathe too.

Clara Baird's Biography

Clara is a university student originally from Ireland, who tries to practise writing on her blog in her free time but often ends up playing with her dog instead.

887: WHAT'S THE TIME GRANDAD?

by Tom Gaunt

"Don't touch that clock," Grandad had said.

Me being me, I touched it, first having noticed that the time on his clock was wrong: 19:18 the digital display had read.

I looked at my watch, saw it was 15:20 and altered the clock display to the correct time.

I pressed the button on the top and suddenly felt like I was dropping down a very large hole.

Here I am, with my grandad. Two time travellers. The year is now 1520.

Tom Gaunt's Biography

Born in 1948 in Manchester and now live in Milton Keynes. Married in 1980 and have two children. Most of my working life in railway engineering. Retired for 12 years. Interest in reading and writing thanks to an inspirational teacher.

~

888: A CALL FOR HELP

by Ashley Kim

"Hello, 911, what is your emergency?"

"Hello, please help me. It's my mum. She's still stuck in the burning house. She's 81 and has Alzheimer's. Please help me. I can't lose her."

"Ma'am, I have just notified the firefighters. There are people on the way, please stay on the phone."

"She doesn't have enough time, I need to go in, I have to save my mum."

"Ma'am, please don't do that, you might get hurt."

"I have to go."

call ended

Ashley Kim's Biography

Ashley Kim is a junior at Union County Vocational-Technical School in New Jersey.

889: BUSBY

by Michael Farmer

Our dog, Busby, dug a large hole at the bottom of our garden and uncovered an ancient Roman necklace. The necklace was made of solid gold and valued at £50,000.

Busby was very pleased with his efforts, so we gave him lots of treats, including a luxurious new bed.

As a final tribute to his archaeological skills, we rang the English Kennel Club and tried to re-register him as a 'Gold Retriever'. The Kennel Club were amused but declined our request.

Michael Farmer's Biography

Michael Farmer graduated at Edinburgh University and then pursued a career in industry. When he retired, he joined a local writers' group and started writing short stories. He is married with five children.

~

890: THE AUCTION HOUSE

by Geoff Freedman

It smelled musky, like old peoples' houses. The items were the precious treasures of the recent dead. Edinburgh crystal from the 1960s and Reader's Digest books. The G Plan dining room suite and the caftan strewn around as reminders of the past.

The world is a cyclic machine and we are its visitors living out our little charade. The auction values are negligible, in line with the definition of the consumerist cycle. Today's young want different junk to clutter their house.

Geoff Freedman's Biography

At 74, I am still practicing as a bridge design consultant. Over the last 2 years I have been widowed and had sepsis and throat cancer, so cannot speak well. I have started to write short stories from my library of life.

891: THE AUTOBIOGRAPHY OF A MAYFLY

by Alistair Forsyth

I actually spent a long, boring time on the river bed as a nymph. The best bit was when I got to the surface and became a handsome mayfly.

I met up with some males and went chasing after good-looking females. I found a lovely one and we immediately coupled. I never even asked her name.

She then went off to lay her eggs and I crawled over to the bank, where I will shortly die of exhaustion. C'est la vie.

Alistair Forsyth's Biography

Alistair Forsyth is retired and lives in East Lothian. With a degree in English literature from Edinburgh University, he spends much of his spare time writing short stories with a small group known as the Fidra Writers.

~

892: TOO FEW TO MENTION

by Richard H. Argent

I think you'd approve. I know you've always liked the trees but, well, the effort it would've taken to hack through the roots. At least you have the view. It's a nice spot. We always used to enjoy coming for a walk, with no one else around. Happy days.

Like a fool, I've gone and made an extra cuppa. You would've laughed. Maybe I was a bit rash, but too late now. It's funny, but I regret not leaving a headstone.

Richard H. Argent's Biography

Richard lives in Nottingham with his wife and two daughters. He is a member of the Sutton Bonington Campus Creative Writing Group and attempts to write sci-fi in his spare time. He has contributed to *Nonsensically Challenged Volume 3*.

893: WHERE'S GEORGE?

by James Crerar

Robert and Mary left their country cottage in Inverness-shire for the 150 mile journey back to their home in Edinburgh, in their separate cars – necessary as he used his for fishing and golf – she, hers for shopping and the hairdresser.

Arriving on their doorstep, they each said simultaneously, "Where's George? I thought you had him."

George was their black Labrador.

"Well, I'm not going back for him," they both said.

It was the final straw. The following day, divorce proceedings started.

James Crerar's Biography

I am an 85-year-old retired lawyer living in Edinburgh. I have been happily married for 55 years, but my wife and I have only one car, no country cottage and no dog.

~

894: JENNERS, THE IMPRESSIVE EDINBURGH EMPORIUM VERSUS AMAZON

by Elaine Carlyle

Jenners – I *love it*.

From the moment I enter the store, the interesting musky perfumes assail my nostrils. Attractive sales ladies smile in the hope that I will whisk out my credit card and purchase their enticing skincare products and perfumes. Usually I do, as I adore being pampered and persuaded.

I remember my wedding gown, complete with sweeping train, from Jenner's bridal department. My wedding presents were from there too. However, I fear efficient Amazon will strangle this utopian lifestyle.

Elaine Carlyle's Biography

Elaine has had an interesting life with many twists and turns, which has provided her with plenty of material for story writing, which is a recent hobby. Elaine lives by the sea near Edinburgh, has a son, a daughter and three grandsons.

895: LOST BEAUTY

by Rosalind Newton

"Granny, please can I see your Sarah Lily photos?" I asked.

She was the same age in those model photos as I was now.

Her jaw set. "No."

"Why not?"

"I destroyed them."

I was grief-stricken.

"How could you?"

"You'll understand one day."

She was a beauty when she posed for the photographer in his studio in 1922. The wrinkles that now etched her face showed the total loss of her youth.

"I threw them all in the bin," she said.

Rosalind Newton's Biography

Rosalind Newton writes poetry and memoir. Her favourite pastime is international travel. She loves classical music, sings in a choir and enjoys safaris. Her favourite animals are cheetahs and lions in Africa, and wild tigers in India.

~

896: LEARNING ENGLISH

by John Vandore

Little Johnny was learning English, thinking one day, when he grew up, he'd know it all. But every time he thought he was getting a grasp of the language, along came something new.

He already knew about subjects and objects, verbs and adjectives and pronouns. He knew about adverbs, but then along came 'adverbial', and even an 'adverbially challenged anthology'. Whatever next?

Little Johnny was so exasperated that he resorted to intensifiers and nearly found out about negators and expletives too…

John Vandore's Biography

John Vandore, born and schooled in Scotland, going on to study engineering in Cambridge and later an MBA at Warwick. Lives in Wantage near Oxford, working on the Harwell Science & Innovation Campus in cryogenics, energy, food and quantum technology.

www.linkedin.com/in/john-vandore-23703b18/

897: A HELPFUL GRANDSON

by Veronica Crerar

Harold was fed up with the screen on his dashboard always nagging him. 'Check tyre pressure', 'A brake light is defective', 'You need new oil', it would say.

Tom, his technological whizz kid 15 year old grandson, said, "Let me fix it, Grandpa." An offer that was gratefully accepted.

Next morning, Harold started the engine. Up on the screen came, 'You need a haircut', 'Not that old shirt again', 'Clean your glasses'.

A furious Harold reversed the BMW into the wall.

Veronica Crerar's Biography

I am a retired solicitor living in Edinburgh. I have given up driving. I have 4 grandchildren, but the oldest is only 13 and lives in Milan.

~

898: PLUS CA CHANGE

by Sean Tobias May

James's phone beeped. 'Here.'

John knocked and shoved hard. The man pulled his trigger.

Kraaaakppppft.

Hotel fluorescents reflected from Jane's tablet.

"Police," Jackie shouted. "Open up, Brown."

Jane kicked, feeling sudden déjà vu as the gun spat.

Kraaaakppppft.

Zack's sensors watched police-bot Jeoff109 storm the dilated entrance. "Professor Brown – drop the portal-gun."

Kraaaakppppft.

Grayn scuttled forward, stinger deployed. Jruk hung down, antennae quivering. Fleeting memories of having fewer legs.

Prof Brown raised the gun gibbering, "Now, please – take me home."

Kraaaakppppft.

Sean Tobias May's Biography

Sean Tobias May (56) is a bio-scientist, parent of two and husband of one. He lives in Nottingham and has worked from home for nine looooooong months. His original zombie survival plan did not include quite so many online meetings.

899: A DOMESTIC

by John D Lary

She says, "The bathroom light's blown again."
He says, "So leave the door open and use the light from the hall."
Later, she says, "The washing machine's not working again."
He says, "So do the washing in the bath."
Later, she says, "The internet's crashed again."
He says, "So read a book."
Later, she says, "Rain's coming in through the ceiling in my bedroom."
He says, "So go sleep in the spare room."
Shortly thereafter, he says, "Is that thing loaded?"

John D Lary's Biography

John lives in Kent, England and enjoys flash fiction as it suits his attention span.

~

900: SHOELACES AND SHEEP

by Ashleigh Whittle

She tripped on her shoelace and dropped the bag. A panicked inhale echoed across the meadow. Sleeping sheep lifted lazy noses to smell the intruders.

"Quickly, Cheryl."

"I can't see anything."

"Shush now."

The dark blue sky was closing in quickly. "Ouch." Cheryl opened her eyes and closed them, opened them... Stars swirled in the sky...

"Cheryl, if you drop that bag again – Cheryl?"

Terry turned and saw her lying on her back. A hoof peeked out of the sprawling bag.

Ashleigh Whittle's Biography

Ashleigh is a fiction writer who prophesises technology bringing the end of the world. Ashleigh is also a software trainer in real life, where she convinces clients that technology will not bring the end of humanity, even though it will.

www.linkedin.com/in/ashleigh-whittle

901: NO RELEASE

by Natalie Marshall

"Sorry, you have been unsuccessful."

I had no reply.

I needed the tears and doubt blown away. Find a new course. Beginning again, starting from scratch. Painful and heart-breaking – these words just don't cut it.

I know the breeze and the sea are not people. But they are the most comfort. They embrace me and listen. All that can be done for me at the moment. All that will help to fix me.

Then, the beach was deemed out of bounds.

Natalie Marshall's Biography

Challenging myself to be creative at every opportunity. Day job, that I promise not to give up, in education.

~

902: IT'S WHAT I DO

by Phil Thomas

"Why are you waiting at the bus stop, George?"

"It's what I do. Every day. The 96A into town. Wait at the stop for an hour and get the bus back. It's the only chance I get to talk to anyone."

"But haven't you heard? They've cancelled the service. Nobody uses it anymore. The last bus was yesterday."

"Yeah. I heard."

"So... why are you waiting, George?"

"Like I said... it's what I do."

"Ah well... same time tomorrow?"

"I reckon."

Phil Thomas' Biography

Phil has been a music writer for over 25 years. He recently discovered flash fiction and now spends time in his 'studio' near Cardiff trying to answer the question: just how few words do you need to tell a story?

903: MAKING FRIENDS CAN BE SCARY

by Rosie Arcane

Freddy always makes me laugh and says I should dream big.

Jason reminds me to call my mum.

Michael gets me excited for Halloween and reminds me I should really learn to drive.

My little friend with orange hair and a foul mouth is incredibly childish sometimes.

One is really sweet, but I have to say his name at least five times before he listens to me.

Another is a fan of piercings, puzzles, and is a bit of a hellraiser.

Rosie Arcane's Biography

Rosie Arcane is from Edinburgh and started writing poetry and short stories as a teenager, but is only now sharing them with the world. Her work is influenced by her own personal experiences and a love of the horror genre.

~

904: MOUSE OR MARS?

by David Lowis

"After tonight, Mars won't shine as brightly again until the year 2035," I told my family during an afternoon walk in the woods.

My daughter held up her hand. "Shhh."

Rustling leaves heralded a mouse. It scurried from the undergrowth, then froze. We crouched, close enough to see its twitching nose and whiskers.

That night, we gazed at the sky, transfixed by the red planet's sparkle. We asked ourselves: What was more astounding? Which was more humbling? The mouse or Mars?

David Lowis' Biography

David Lowis lives in Surrey, England, with his wife, daughter and miniature schnauzer. When not doing his day job, he dabbles in writing. Someday, he hopes to publish longer stories. You can read more of his micro fiction at:

www.dlowis.wordpress.com

905: A MYSTERY

by Lim Swee Kim

Alas it is a mystery.
We thought learning
is safe, is social,
a normal part of life
for the young and youthful,
and with continual learning
for the middle-aged and seniors,
we would be on the right track.
Many would say boring,
somewhat unexciting,
unlike DH Lawrence's 'Mystery',
where the tall slim votaress
glimmers to fulfill the mystery
and brain exercises give good mental health,
especially with fun and friends.
Did we weave a tangled web?
Alas it is a mystery.

Lim Swee Kim's Biography

SweeKim enjoys nature, fitness, the arts and almost everything relating to her family, friends and community. A technology, finance and governance professional who is now transitioning to her 2nd half of life, these social spaces keep her sane and well.

~

906: OUR HAPPY PLACE

by Cheah Yin Mee

"Now, pick one place where you have been the happiest."

Her mind races off like a startled pigeon. *Kyoto? No, Istanbul.*

Frantically, she searches for that magical place. Finally, *aha*. Smugly, she looks across at her husband.

He smiles serenely. "All ready?"

"Yes, Machu Pichu. We married there." She looks to her husband for affirmation. "And you?"

"It's home," he says simply.

She felt the air sucked out of her lungs. Once again, she had let her head rule her heart.

Cheah Yin Mee's Biography

Cheah Yin Mee has been a teacher and a teacher educator for over 40 years. She has since retired to teach mindfulness to children. She enjoys writing and has been writing her memoirs and mindfulness stories for children.

~

907: BREATHING

by Christina M. Y. Chow

In the Corpse Pose, she takes a slow, long breath.

"Now hold for four," intones the yoga tutor.

She recalls her father's last breath, gasping into water's blackness.

And the midwife's calm voice, "Now pant quickly."

At night, peering into the Moses basket, she would listen intently to her newborn's soft breathing.

Years later, a breath's spaciousness coaxed her lower back to surrender its custodial spasms.

Breathing out, she counts to six very slowly.

Birth, Life, Death – cradled by Breath's hyphen.

Christina M. Y. Chow's Biography

Christina enjoys writing, has worked in adult education and community health advocacy. Curious about family stories, she hopes to share her late mother's journal in a forthcoming book *Red Packet with 20¢*. She divides her time between Singapore and England.

908: CHAI?

by Shahnaz Ali

"One spoonful please." Masala tea was never good without sugar.

"Monica, you must tell me how to make Punjabi masala chai," I said. In India, we had our variations to masala tea, and the Punjabis were best at it.

"Well, you grate in some ginger, add cardamom, clove and, of course, tealeaves to the mix of water and milk. Boil. Strain. Drink. Easy peasy." Monica smiled while handing me my cup.

I could smell the spices as I took a sip.

Shahnaz Ali's Biography

Shahnaz is a creative practitioner who indulges in art, creative writing, photography, cultural travel. She has written short write-ups in the format of stories, monologues, vignettes, free verse poems. Though originally from India, Shahnaz is currently based in Singapore.

~

909: GUESSTIMATE

by Jasmine Tan Chin Chwee

"How many teaspoons of garlic do we put in the pan to sautè, Mum?"

"Watch, don't keep asking."

"But what if I put too much, or too little?"

Mum gave me a look that warned me to stop talking.

Is cooking instinctive or intuitive?

The finely chopped garlic took forever to brown. But take your eyes off the sizzling suspension for a second and suddenly, all will be black and bitter.

YouTube videos make cooking seem easy, but Mum's reality bites.

Jasmine Tan Chin Chwee's Biography

Wannabe writer. Retired advocate, solicitor and design director. Passionate tourist guide. Grateful daughter, loving mother, mother-in-law and grandmother. Widow who has loved and been loved. Ardent collector of vintage culinary ware. Loyal Singaporean.

910: TEAM MEETING

by Jennifer P. L. Leong

Boss: Everyone, get ready to play your part.
  RL: Monumental task ahead, Boss.
  LL: Really tough with team members like RL, RA and LA.
  RA: Look who's talking.
  LA: We are all of one body, we can surely work together.
  Boss: Check with the others before you move a muscle.
  Boss (AKA Brain), RL (AKA Right Leg), LL (AKA Left Leg), RA (AKA Right Arm), and LA (AKA Left Arm): Co-ordination is the key to success.
  All exit for dance class...

Jennifer P. L. Leong's Biography

Jennifer the jellyfish loves stories and tries to see things from different perspectives. She has her tentacles rather tentatively dipped into these fields: some semblance of exercise, reading with young children and writing for fun.

~

911: ANDER

by Olatz Irigarai

The night is falling and the birds are quiet.
  Shhhh... Listen, Ander, can you hear Kilikili? He is flying to you again. Look, today he went first to Leire, Oier and Aamir's houses. All of your friends are already sleeping deeply on Kilikili's multicolour carpet, can you see them? Yes, they are approaching quickly to your window. Are you ready to hold the rope and get on? Soon they will be close to you.
  Good evening, Mum.
  Good evening, my love.

Olatz Irigarai's Biography

...a nomad, a daughter, a sister, a seed, a lover, a mother, a wave, an aunt, a breath, a friend, an apprentice, a believer, a woman, a drop, an artist...

912: THE DOG VOID

by Emma Nokes

No wagging or rolling.
No playing fetch.
No slobbering or salivating because you opened the fridge.
No hair on the carpet, sofa or armchair; no need for lint rollers.
No bin lorry barking or hailstorm howling.
No reason for mud all through the hallway or splattered on the walls.
No wet nosed sloppy kisses to gently push away from your face.
No click-clack sound from a yawn.
No sigh of content from a pre-circled resting patch.
No dogs?
No, thank you.

Emma Nokes' Biography

I am Emma, I am 33 and a new writer of poetry and fiction. I live on a cow farm in Dorset with my husband, two children and, perhaps unsurprisingly, three beloved dogs.

~

913: DONE WITH THE COMMUTE

by Rachel Wood

I reach my front door and let out a sigh of relief.
"Finally."
The 17:35 train from London was always grim, but someone had been hit on the line (read: jumped), and while it was obviously devastating, I am having a hard time remembering that in the cold November night.
I eventually locate my keys, turn the lock and trudge over the threshold to lock eyes with a perfect stranger.
"Who are y—"
But the gun fires before I can finish.

Rachel Wood's Biography

Rachel is a doctor in the UK squeezing flash fiction into life between shifts. Other hobbies include eating inordinate amounts of pasta and befriending the neighbours' toy poodle, both to great success.

914: THE CHAMPIONSHIPS

by Rob Vogt

As a child in an American suburb, he watched *Breakfast at Wimbledon* on his family's hulking Magnavox: Borg's Nordic grace, McEnroe's precocious artistry, Connors' double-fisted fury.

Today, he and a buddy have quaffed a few pints and slipped past a Centre Court usher into third-row seats. There he cheers for an Eastern European pixie wearing a tight skirt smoothed over her tight bum. She does not immediately fit into the montage of his youth, but he finds her image pleasing nonetheless.

Rob Vogt's Biography

Rob Vogt teaches high school English on Chicago's South Side.

~

915: CLIFF HANGER

by Janet L Davies

Ella walked to the edge of the cliff, looking at the view. She heard rocks fall and turned to walk back. The ground beneath her crumbled.

She screamed, grabbing rocks in her hands, nothing to rest her feet on. Ella looked down, wishing she hadn't. She was so high above the beach.

Time passed and she could hold on no longer. She prayed death would be quick. There was a great splash. The tide had come in. She swam to safety.

Janet L Davies' Biography

I live in Exeter, Devon, UK. I have several stories on Amazon KDP, write every day and am trying a few publishers now. I volunteered at our local primary school, helping with reading. I am also an artist.

www.artjandavies.com

916: SHE KNOWS ME

by Jane Fell

Leaning forward. Not touching. My mask covering my face. My muffled voice escapes. Can she hear me? Does she recognise my eyes, my voice?

Anxious, talking fast, agitated. I laugh. I sing. She smiles. Her shoulders relax. She hums.

"Who is this, Joy?"

"This is the lady who looks after me," says Mum.

She knows I care. That I love her. She knows that feeling. She knows me.

I mentally hug her, my arms wrapping around her.

"I love you, Mum."

Jane Fell's Biography

Jane Fell is grandmother to Lily and Matilda, both born in lockdown. 'She Knows Me' is a celebration of her mum's love. Despite all that has happened with her mum's deteriorating eyesight and dementia, Jane still feels her love.

~

917: THE AGE OF FEAR

by Catrin Rutland

The lake seemed a little deeper now. As the years progressed, I watched my children swimming and the sense of foreboding grew. I'd splash around carefree in that water as a kid, but now it was more dangerous. Come to think of it, most things were. From skating along the sidewalk through to rides at the fair, they had lost their innocence.

Is that what being a parent was, continuous fear? I think I'll ask my husband if we can move.

Catrin Rutland's Biography

By day, Catrin is an associate professor of anatomy and genetics, but by night she writes fiction, exploring the world and society from different points of view. Science fact to science fiction and everything in between.

www.catrinrutland.weebly.com

918: CHILD'S PLAY

by Annie Francis

"Shut the door."

"Yeah, quick."

Click. Then I heard murmuring only.

Small in size but not in spirit, the room soon couldn't hold them. They spilled out, shouting. The game complex, my part unknown, I watched them stream past me, up the stairs, smothering their barely suppressed glee.

"Careful," I said.

No reply.

"Who wants ice-cream?" I called.

"Ice-cream," echoed back. Then a thundering storm of feet on a new quest. Energy unabated, they braved the cavernous cold for sweet bounty.

Annie Francis' Biography

Annie is a creative: novelist, poet, gardener, artist and crafter. Also a full-time mother and part-time occupational therapist, Annie is working on her time management skills.

~

919: UNDERNEATH

by Marie Arbon

"Mummy, why do I have two mummies?" whispers Sebastian.

"Seb, Emily and I love each other and you, so very much."

"I know, I love you both too, but why do I have another *you*, Mummy?"

"You don't, silly. Come on, time for bed."

Mummy turns on the nightlight and closes the door. "Sweet dreams."

A shuffle. Mummy Shadow appears from underneath the bed.

She grips his hand tightly. "Remember, Mummy will love you forever."

Sebastian shivers, closes his eyes tightly.

Marie Arbon's Biography

Marie Arbon studied music at college and now works in the film industry. She enjoys writing short stories and poems. Marie is a big fan of Edgar Allan Poe.

920: BLOWING AWAY THE COBWEBS

by Andrew Dawkins

The wind tussled my hair as I stepped outside. The damp, dark evenings were setting in, however all my worries had disappeared and I was at peace with myself. The wind seemed to be blowing them away, stronger and gustier as I moved into the night.

It was strange how all the background noises of the day disappeared into the night; the transition from grey to black. The wind was really howling now as I fell forever faster towards the inevitable.

Andrew Dawkins' Biography

Living in a landlocked county in the UK, but born and bred by the windy seaside. I spend my time teaching, windsurfing and falling a lot in computer games.

~

921: SWIMMING IN NOVEMBER

by Ali Clarke

It's cold, but that's how I like it. The autumnal orange and red trees surround the lake. The sun reflects on the surface of the water. I take off my dryrobe and step in. It takes my breath away.

Immediately, I find myself immersed in this water world. Nothing else matters. I've heard we are capable of one conscious thought at a time. For once, my mind is firmly in the same place as I am. I feel part of nature.

Ali Clarke's Biography

In the early summer, a close friend took me to the lake. I've caught the bug for open water swimming. As the water gets colder, it gets more exciting somehow. One way or another, I plan to swim throughout winter.

922: WHERE THE WILD ONES SWIM

by Liz Howard

The fog hung low in the air, blurring the border between lake and sky. The mist enveloped everything in its path.

The swimmer stood on the shoreline. Excitement and apprehension filled her heart. She stepped into the cold, clear water, took a breath, filling her lungs with the cold, claggy air.

Not yet, she thought, tasting the deliciousness of the peace she knew she'd find.

Finally, she launched herself into the water, screaming profanities and giggling as she swam, finally, free.

Liz Howard's Biography

42, wild swimmer, bog snorkeler, lover of fun.

~

923: LOST

by Shobha Wilson

So, there I was, swinging my legs, waiting for my mum and dad to come and collect me. How does a child get lost in Marks & Spencer on her 7th birthday?

Worst of it was, I had been described over the Tannoy system as a little boy. Did they not see both my ears had earrings in them?

I was thinking, *What will happen if they don't come?* The shop would be shutting soon.

Finally (about time) they arrived. Relief.

Shobha Wilson's Biography

The above happened to me as I describe it. As a parent now, I can only imagine how my mum and dad felt at the time.

924: A HOME ED MUM'S MORNING

by Ceris Brewis

6:03AM: *Zub zub.*

Mad scrabble to mute alarm. Carefully disentangle myself from bedsheet and several night-time visitors. Tiptoe out of bedroom. *Creak.* Hold breath. (Note: remind husband to oil bedroom door again.) Breathe. Creep downstairs, yawning. Fill kettle, make tea, lean back into the sofa. Bliss.

"Mummy?"

Look up to see the four year old silhouetted in the doorway, dino tucked under one arm, a science book clutched in his hands.

"Mummy, how does gravity work?"

Yawn...

7:15AM: Drink cold tea.

Ceris Brewis' Biography

Ceris Brewis is a hobby writer and home-ed mum of three young boys.

~

925: SLAP

by Kay Sandry

I suck on gas and air.

You draw vile substance through hollow cheeks.

I pant – shallow, quick.

You pant – quick, shallow – junk suffuses your brain.

I grip an unknown hand, crush it with my own.

You punch a hole in the nursery door, tear at pictures hung on the wall. Slap down the mobile hanging over the cot and then you start to kick.

Our son is born in a slippery slithering of liquids and excrement.

You slump, spent.

Labour complete.

Kay Sandry's Biography

I write as Kay Sandry and am based in York, UK. I love to experiment with flash fiction as well as longer form. Examples of my work can be seen on Twitter:

@KaySandry

926: SEASONAL DREAMS

by Jodi Novak

Skin as pale as the fresh glistening snow that leisurely drifts onto her slim shoulders.
Cheeks that flush with a magnificent pink blush as the flowers bloom around her.
Heart as warming as the golden summer sun as it stands proudly against the blue sky.
Hair as fiery as the chestnut leaves that cascade and pirouette in the cool breeze.
She'll haunt my dreams again tonight, I know she will.
There she'll stay, frozen in my mind's eye for ever more.

Jodi Novak's Biography

Whilst working as a primary school teacher, Jodi Novak became inspired to write her own children's stories. She lives in England with her partner and her beloved husky, Luna.

~

927: TUNA CASSEROLE

by Tamsin Partington

It was one of those arguments that's like a little hangnail.
You take it between your teeth and tug. It's satisfying, you pull more. Then the whole, painful strip of skin comes off. You shouldn't have done it.
The door had been slammed, leaving a bellowing silence in its wake. I stared at the bowl, the remains that were left, contemplating what we had become.
Just because I hadn't eaten it yet, didn't mean he could.
Cats are obnoxious like that.

Tamsin Partington's Biography

Tamsin is a short story writer, cat-wrangler and child-tamer from Lancashire with a BA and MA in creative writing. She won the Edge Hill Short Story Prize for MA students in 2019 and has had several other stories published since.

928: LOVED

by David Brewis

It is hot cocoa on a cold day, warmth radiating into the coldest pits, filling tummy and heart with joy inexplicable.

The sunrise, pouring its light, like oil onto my skin, eases aches and worries while every nerve relishes the sensation of its soothing influence.

A celebration, making my heart pound, pulling the corners of my mouth so I cannot help but smile with foolish elation.

Sadness, now gladness. Fear, now freedom. Ashes, now beauty.

It is good to be loved.

David Brewis' Biography

David is a Christian, husband and father of three from the Midlands in England. While not being a writer or necessarily a creative by profession, he did very much enjoy this challenge and hopes that you will enjoy reading it.

~

929: LAVA RUN

by Maya Barnett

I bolted through the trees, the wind whipping in my hair. The heat from the volcano scorched every inch of me. I cradled my child close to my chest.

I made the mistake of turning around. I saw my house crumbling to the ground and all the memories with it. She squirmed in my arms. I held on to her for dear life.

I finally made it to safety. I collapsed into the fireman's arms and then everything went pitch black.

Maya Barnett's Biography

I'm 13. I live in the Boston area. I have two brothers and two pets. I heard about this challenge from my writing class. My favourite style of writing is horror stories.

930: MERGING

by Claire Schön

You put your dreams on hold.

"Best mistake I ever made," you'd lovingly say. "I'm still young."

Then time left your mind, or your mind left before its time.

Some call it role reversal, but I call it merging. My daughter is me long ago, I am you from the past, you've been her, you've been me, and now you don't always know who you are.

But sometimes you resurface.

"Don't you worry – you two have been my dream come true."

Claire Schön's Biography

Claire Schön is a marketing professional. When she's not running around with, and after, her two young children, she carves out small pieces of time to write and do yoga.

~

931: THE ONCE GREAT ATHLETE

by Danielle Linsey

"On your marks..."

Adrenaline rushes through me as I take a deep breath, preparing myself.

I place my right foot onto the block, shaking out my left, setting it down. My fingers hugging, but not crossing the line.

"Get set..."

I lift up my body, all my energy pushing into the blocks.

I feel a tightness in my calf and start to wonder: can I even win anymore?

There is only one way to know... I just have to run.

Bang.

Danielle Linsey's Biography

Danielle Linsey lives in Sussex, where she is a SEN teaching assistant. She has most recently had flash fiction stories shortlisted for Flash 500, The Michael Mullan Cancer Fund and Mum Life Stories.

932: RESISTING TEMPTATION

by Lena MacDonald

My humans come in from the kitchen.
    I smell meat and my nose twitches, identifying the scent.
    I watch them quietly, waiting.
    I sit close to them, closer still, my paw on their knee, big brown eyes pleading.
    "You've already had your dinner," they say, smiling at me lovingly.
    I sigh loudly, making my disappointment known.
    A stroke on the head, a tickle behind my ears that I like and lean into.
    I dribble on the carpet and wait for bacon.

Lena MacDonald's Biography

Lena MacDonald has been a storyteller and writer since childhood. She is an avid reader, preferring fiction, and particularly enjoys murder mysteries and adventure stories. Originally from South Wales, Lena now lives in Gloucestershire with her husband and dog.

~

933: NO MERCY

by Jenny Drury

He glared at the crouching man before him – there could be no mercy. Once again the advantage was his, but this time he would break him.

Drawing breath deep into his heaving chest, he turned his eyes heavenward, a mighty gladiator preparing his final blow. With a roar, he swung his arm, channelling the power that remained in his aching body, yet helpless as his adversary's stinging reply wrong-footed him, grazing his tortured face.

"Deuce," called the umpire.

Damn. Not again.

Jenny Drury's Biography

Jenny Drury is a frustrated novelist who seeks solace in writing flash fiction and poetry. A mum of two and lover of history and sport, she likes to write about the issues she cares about, especially the environment.

934: CLIMATE CRISIS

by Dorothy Francis

I sit in sweltering heat, watching the rocket take-off, loaded with the first global refugees.

Ugh, icy droplets start falling. Everyone pulls out umbrellas and jumpers. It's normal now: the threat of human extinction wasn't enough to fix our climate change incompetence. Giant puddles form rapidly around me. Everyone inflates their emergency lifeboats. Here comes the sweltering heat and water evaporates in clouds.

My ticket number is called. I board the ship, embarking on a journey to find our new home.

Dorothy Francis' Biography

Dorothy Francis is a 12-year-old girl who is passionate about climate change and loves writing. She would love to see people coming together to save planet Earth.

~

935: THE SINGER

by Duane L. Herrmann

She sang, dammit, and wouldn't stop. The ringing keeps going in my brain. I wish that she was dead.

Oh.

She is dead. I still forget that. It's something I cannot quite believe. She's been part of my life all of my life. How can she be gone now? She is, and yet her voice is still ringing in my mind.

It's not singing. It's screaming. Her screaming. She can't stop, because she has stopped. It's my brain that can't stop.

Duane L. Herrmann's Biography

Duane L. Herrmann survived an abusive childhood embellished with dyslexia, ADHD and now cyclothymia and PTSD. He knows whereof he writes. He grew up and remains on the Kansas prairie where breeze and trees calm him and help him write.

936: REGRET

by Marci Girton

She always caught household spiders and released them outside. "They are good," she admonished her phobic friends. "They look scary, but they kill bad bugs. They deserve to live."

Until the brown recluse infestation. They were everywhere: basement, bathroom, bedroom.

Sinister violin, spindly legs, dreadful poison.

"You are supposed to be reclusive," she cried, smashing the latest invader. She watched the threadlike legs wave slowly, then curl inward, and still.

Her heart no longer raced.

She regarded it sadly.

"I'm sorry."

Marci Girton's Biography

Marci Girton is a retired psychologist. Living in the Midwest, she has come to appreciate sunflowers, wheat fields and wide-open spaces. She enjoys green tea, quilting and cats, although not all in the same way.

~

937: ROOM AT THE END OF THE HALL

by Michele Kelly

I am about to walk into the room of my life's accomplishments.

I turn the metal knob, scorchingly cold, of a heavy wooden door. I expect a packed room. Like a hard-core hoarder in winter.

Scenes flash. Three children. The one man I ever loved. Words written. A business.

The door breathes a skinny whine.

The room is empty. Dead air.

"Have I done nothing?" I ask Him.

"The room is not empty."

"It is," I say defeatedly.

"You are here."

Michele Kelly's Biography

Michele Kelly is an Italian mother, corporate storyteller and fiction writer. She is co-founder of K+L Storytellers, contributor to *Today's Inspired Leader*, published ghostwriter and developmental editor. In 2016, she founded Your Extraordinary Story, a young authors' program.

938: HIGH STAKES

by Pamela Hibbert

Jodie flipped into the backstroke turn. Length fifteen.

Her father pounded the pool's edge, stopwatch in hand, clickety-clicking at every turn.

"Pull, Jodie."

Flip, twist, push, kick.

Her father's dream was at stake.

The final length.

And touch.

Jodie climbed out for the verdict.

"You need to focus, Jodie. We've only got one more year."

"What's this 'we'?"

Hot chocolate in the café.

"More commitment is needed, Jodie. It's the Olympics or bust, sweetheart."

Jodie stared him down.

"It's bust then."

Pamela Hibbert's Biography

Musician, artist and pillion rider. Former teacher and Morris dancer (someone has to do it). I've been writing for a number of years with successes and rejections to my name. Working on a novel like the rest of the planet.

~

939: THE MESSAGE

by Colleen Hue

Dear mum,

I just wanted to say sorry for yesterday so i actually wrote this letter because you say you're fed up with only ever getting texts, i even went to the post office... that was scary at first i didn't understand the queue but people were helpful and smiley... *where's emojis when you need one? anyway i didn't mean to come over all possessive and i am really glad that helen's going to be my step-mum.

Big love, jesse x

Colleen Hue's Biography

I have no literary credentials. My scribblings have been mostly corporate, until now. This is the start of my creative journey – first steps and all that. Like so many, I have numerous story ideas queuing up for my attention.

940: THE END OF IMAGINATION

by Ixai Salvo

The traveller got lost in a sea of imagination and came out being something else.

On the backs of whales he flew, and mountains he climbed as he went beyond sky.

Running back to fields of anthracite grass and forests of ash, the traveller discovered the end of imagination.

Thoughts of despair danced around the edge, waiting to jump and conquer.

Turning back, he looked, and decided everything was good; to try again.

Leaving, he continued, never giving hopelessness a chance.

Ixai Salvo's Biography

I am a PhD student of fisheries science in Spain. I always loved writing short stories and poems. As writing is part of my job and career, writing short stories helps me to evade while practising my English.

~

941: LUCKY NUMBER NINE

by Jennifer Hankin

You put down the phone and inhale deeply. Pick it up, dial and listen.

Ring ring, ring ring.

Nine times it rings. It's always nine times, never eight or ten.

You sigh and down goes the phone. You're never sure why you keep trying. You spin the dial again, for the ninth time. Maybe you'll be lucky.

"Thank you for calling Company Nine. Your call is very important to us. Please hold the line, you are number nine in the queue."

Jennifer Hankin's Biography

Jennifer Hankin lives in Loughborough with her husband and ridiculously large book collection. When she's not lost in a book, she enjoys writing poetry and prose, and sharing it with her colleagues in the Sutton Bonington Campus Creative Writing Group.

942: DREAMS DO COME TRUE

by Jake Cosmos Aller

In 1974, Sam had a dream that changed his life forever.

He fell asleep in a class and saw the most beautiful woman in the universe talking to him. She haunted his life for years. He went to the ends of the world to find her.

Then, one day in 1982, she walked off the bus, out of his dreams and into his life, to become his wife three months later. That is the beginning of the rest of the story.

Jake Cosmos Aller's Biography

Jake Cosmos Aller is a retired US diplomat living in South Korea where he blogs about the world sharing his poetic visions of the world. He served in 10 countries during his service. He grew up in Berkeley, California.

www.theworldaccordingtocosmos.com

~

943: A MOTHER'S LIFE

by Sarah Engeham

"Mummy, Mummy, Mummy, please can I—"

"Sweetheart, I'm a bit busy right now."

"Mummy, Mummy, Mummy, please can we—"

"Sweetheart, can you not see that I'm trying to sort the laundry?"

"Mummy, Mummy, Mummy, what can I do?"

"Sweetheart, what is your brother doing?"

"He's reading his book."

"Oh. Well, what is your daddy doing?"

"He's busy. He said, 'Not now.'"

"Give me five minutes, OK sweetheart?"

...

"OK, sweetheart, what would you like to do?"

"I'm OK now, thanks Mummy."

Sigh.

Sarah Engeham's Biography

Sarah Engeham, first and foremost a wife and mother to two young boys, but also PhD and science technician in a secondary school, which is a slightly different prospect during current trials and tribulations.

944: SCIENTIFIC MANTRA

by David Vargas Alfonso

Every sign looked insufficient. Even some messengers had died. Then, the cabildo called and the younger ranger took the floor.

"Today, I am a mediator. The orchids researcher asks permission to use the names we gave them."

The taitas concluded, after hours, the requirement was according to Komuya's will, a goddess hidden in the flowers. She answers health to contemplation and destruction to profanation.

'Orchidaceae Komuya', the common look to Nature's claim, new dialogue between theirs and the rest of humanity.

David Vargas Alfonso's Biography

David Vargas Alfonso is a library teacher and he has been a high school teacher. He has published some academic articles in index journals. He is a theologian, bilingual education specialist and philosophy magister.

scholar.google.es/citations?user=d7algSgAAAAJ&hl=es

~

945: WHERE? WHO? WHAT?

by Sarah Hoad

The streets were packed and Ivy needed to catch the bus to work. She squeezed through floods of people, tripping and pushing. She was already late and didn't have any time to waste. She jarred into a lady who came tumbling down.

Ivy reached out her hand to help, but the lady didn't acknowledge she was there. Instead, she was looking around for the person who shoved her. The lady got up and walked straight through Ivy, still not noticing her.

Sarah Hoad's Biography

My name is Sarah and I'm a school pupil in Year 6. I'm used to writing short horror / murder mystery stories but I decided to have a go at a different genre.

946: LOST IN WORDS

by Alison Reese

Authors often say their characters take on a life of their own, dictating their own story.

"Rubbish," I scoffed, "I'm writing it, I decide."

Apparently, my characters disagreed, as I find myself trapped within my words, a hostage to the characters I created. All attempts to break free have failed.

"What did you expect?" laughed my main protagonist. "You're the one who insisted that the author writes the story."

I pondered this. "But, if I'm here, then who's writing it now?"

Alison Reese's Biography

My name's Alison and I'm a primary school teacher from north London. I love reading and enjoy writing poetry and stories, although I never usually finish my stories. Challenges like these inspire me.

~

947: THE ENCLOSED

by Katie Singer

Suddenly, she awoke, her face dripping with sweat. She frantically looked around, pondering where she was and when she'd arrived there. The room had cracked floorboards that were as black as coal. *This is not my house,* she anxiously thought. *I've got to quietly escape.*

Soundlessly, she crept, her heart beating wildly. She tried opening the ancient, hazel door, but the rusty lock didn't open. Worriedly, she searched for a key on the floor, when an idea filled her whole mind.

Katie Singer's Biography

My name is Katie and I love dogs. I'm eight years old. I'm good at baking and I like to draw.

948: OUR FINAL THOUGHTS

by Julia Graves

His eulogy was perfect, just like the man himself. Always there with a pint or pound for someone down on their luck. Respected by us all, he loved the bookies, the horses and latterly the scratch card. He had a smile for everyone – even the wife. She had never cried once, just looked stern as he rolled into the fires.

"You try balancing the books when there's nothing to balance," she told us in the pub afterwards. "Great man, my arse."

Julia Graves' Biography

Despite my dyslexia and dyspraxia, I am currently studying creative writing with the OU. My writing is humorous, dark and usually unfinished. I failed my English literature O level with flying colours. I'm still writing after being told, more than once, that I should give up.

www.facebook.com/julia.graves.351

~

949: DEAFENING SILENCES

by Sam May

The sensation of Kikuko's motionless heart sent me back to the years of our childhood that we would spend together playing with our mother in the garden. We would all talk back to our eerie echoes down the well that we found when we first arrived at our house all those decades ago.

My eyes swiftly shot to my father, moments before he hit the ground with a soft thud. *He too,* I thought, *will succumb to the fugu's deadly poison.*

Sam May's Biography

Sam is 14, plays a lot of football and loves his dog (Sonic).

950: GOOD – YAWN – AFTERNOON

by Jeff Kemp

No free lunches when you sleep late. Calorifically, that gives the chance to experiment with fasting but were I interested in such a discipline, I'd start my day early rather than have two breakfasts at 5PM.

It does, however, give me eco-credibility since I've become a vegetarian. Well, a semi-vegetarian since it's only my first breakfast that lacks meat. But that's half way to saving the planet.

Since I sleep 12 hours out of 24, half way's good enough.

Good night.

Jeff Kemp's Biography

Living in Scotland, writing in English, born in Aotearoa, I mostly scribble poetry.

~

951: NIGHT ELECTRIC

by Elena Zhuang

Assassins hold the pleasurable weight of the lives they have taken. Be aware of the assassins lurking in the town, they are always watching you…

Oh, sorry for not introducing myself. Name's Loom, the sniper of *Night Electric*, and you have just been caught… toodles.

Survive next time, if there is one. Now, time to clean my katana.

Natsuk: "Loom, you're always so social."

Loom: "It's not my fault everyone is so… interesting."

"Get to France, your next mission is there."

Elena Zhuang's Biography

Hi, my name is Elena and I live on the planet Earth. Yes. I am a human who loves to watch anime and bother my brother. I also love baking, but not when I almost blow up the house.

952: HORROR IN THE BASEMENT

by Avery Pryce

The lights flickered in the basement just as Sophie took a peek. As quick as a flash, she dashed upstairs and told her family about her experience.

"Nonsense," her sister retorted.

When Sophie checked the basement... there was someone sitting in the corner with their back turned to her. Sophie tiptoed over to the mysterious person and tapped him on the shoulder...

Sophie trembled with fear. To her dismay, she was greeted by the abominable, creepy clown.

"I'M BACK," he cackled.

Avery Pryce's Biography

Hi, my name is Avery and I love writing stories. I also love eating chocolate. I'm a fan of horror stories, even though I find them to be so scary. Maybe one day, one of my stories will become an epic, blockbuster movie.

~

953: THE ZOO TRIP

by Arya Amlani

Dear Mum,

Today, on my trip, I saw a great, colossal gorilla. It narrowed its beady eyes right at me. Gradually, it got to its feet and advanced on us. It suddenly slapped the glass, hard. I panicked. I ran, but Miss Reese called me back and soothed me like a parrot with ruffled feathers, which I saw a zookeeper do. But the rest of the trip was boring, even though Miss Reese kept the commentary up.

Filled with love,

Arya

Arya Amlani's Biography

My first outing after the lockdown was to London Zoo with my mum. It poured with rain. We were drenched, but I would do it again everyday if I could.

954: TWO AND A MILLION IN THIS MARRIAGE

by Zoe J Walker

I put the plate in front of him. He doesn't look up. Just a grunt as he picks up his fork in his left hand. His right permanently occupied.

Dishes done.

He's slumped on the sofa. The TV isn't switched on anymore. His face glows blue and he scrolls and scrolls.

I'm all out of words. I sigh and go for a bath.

Brand new underwear unearthed at the back of the drawer.

Will he even notice my bags are packed?

Zoe J Walker's Biography

Zoe J Walker lives between Rome and Edinburgh. She's currently searching for representation for her novel. She won second place in November's 2020 micro fiction competition at Retreat West.

www.zoejwalker.com

~

955: BON APPÉTIT

by Cynthia Akagi

After 40 years of macaroni-Monday, taco-Tuesday and meatloaf-Wednesday, I am expanding palate and vocabulary – fish puff tart, melanzane parmigiana, antipasto penne. But oh how to pronounce gnocchi and quinoa? Yet the eatin's good.

My grocery bill is higher with my new culinary waltz, but everything tastes amazing with cooking wine and butter. Julia was right. Food is love and romance, but a tricky waistline challenge.

I refuse fish-Fridays. I delight instead in pesto-chicken-tagliatelle with porchini mushrooms and cream. No belching, please.

Cynthia Akagi's Biography

Cynthia Akagi is an education professor from Kansas, USA. In the '90s, she published two puberty books for parents to give to their children. In January 2021, she's publishing a healing journal for anyone healing from a major medical event.

956: BUMPY RIDE

by Myron Dunavan

The others crowd around. Harold flings the dice. Sevens: he's the winner.

Her tug reminds him not to ride the crest. He flags his money, turns and smiles. They will eat. Smart move. He hands the money to Mamma because she will manage it. It may last a few months this time.

Riding a dusty road home in an old pickup truck, he reflects about the bumps and twists in life. The bumps bind them more than money in Mamma's bag.

Myron Dunavan's Biography

Topeka, Kansas writer Myron (Max) Dunavan enjoys writing fiction and poetry. He participated in a Kansas authors club, the fine arts council, UN conferences, social work, vocational rehabilitation counselling advocacy issues professionally, and directed state agencies.

~

957: A CHOICE

by Kate Hamilton

The team of scientists sent by the Galactic Council was to (only) observe (yet another) planet on the verge of self-destruction.

They knew not to interfere with The Creator's quarantine for developing species, evolving through adolescence. But they were a bit tired of observing another beautiful world ruined by its inhabitants.

"ERRTH is doomed, but I really like butterflies and Beethoven," said the biologist. "Perhaps if we give them a well-designed virus, they will have time to… consider?"

So, they did.

Kate Hamilton's Biography

Katharine (Kate) Hamilton, BSW and MPA from Kansas University (Go Jayhawks) is a Baha'i and a retired social worker. She has worked in healthcare and United Way community development. She hopes to write a book from this story someday.

958: SWEET SEDUCTION

by Linda Hibbin

A pesky caterpillar nibbles the leaves of good intentions. My five a day on a good day. It wickedly wriggles in the chambers of my mind, taunting, reminding me of the bittersweet creaminess.

The monster in me consumes and spits out my resolve, which too weakly resists. I know what I want, to be seduced, surrender to unashamed depravity. I need a quick fix, quickly, and lift the lid.

A sexy hazelnut chocolate whirl. Mmmm. This is a deliciously good day.

Linda Hibbin's Biography

Linda is a septuagenarian who has written stories for her granddaughter but became seriously hooked during lockdown by attending Zoom writing courses. She loves the challenge of flash fiction. Is more Pam Ayres than Tennyson when it comes to poetry.

~

959: STEPPING UP

by Don Marler

Mary's head was dipped, and tears ran off her chin as she quietly confessed to her father, "I'm pregnant, Daddy."

The old man glared at her and shook his head. "Who's the father?"

Wiping away tears, Mary asked her father, "Do you remember Robert, the young preacher you introduced me to at your last revival?"

"Of course. He's the youth minister of my church."

Mary nodded. "Well… next Sunday, you're invited to our wedding. Robert is going to be your son-in-law."

Don Marler's Biography

Don Marler is a member of District 5 of Kansas Authors Club, winner of the 2017 short story award, author of the memoir *Laddie: My Four-Legged-Protector* for sale on Amazon and a photographer for the Wichita Wings indoor soccer team.

960: VEGAN BURGERS

by Jonathan Fryer

It had long been my dream to leave teaching, hit the road, and sell healthy food from one of those mobile cafe type things. And so I did.

Vegan burgers became my speciality.

And you meet all sorts of lovely people. Vegetarians, vegans – they are welcomed with open arms. I am not judgemental. And they make a good burger. The best, in fact.

The trouble is, it is hard to find a vegan around here these days. Time to move on...

Jonathan Fryer's Biography

I am an ex-biology teacher. I miss it. What a great career. I spent much time changing the way children think of the world and how to think differently, including the potentially sinister vegan burger.

~

961: CAREFUL WHAT YOU WISH FOR

by Richard Anthony Morris

I'd been telling my friends for years that I don't like surprise parties, but they insist. They spent the entire day acting casual, but I know they've found their way into my house to wait in the dark. May as well get this over with.

I make a lot of noise with the key in the lock. I take a deep breath, turning on the light as I walk in. Silence. Oh, OK, I guess I am alone on my birthday.

Richard Anthony Morris' Biography

My name is Richard Anthony Morris, I enjoy writing as a hobby and I'm based in the south-east of England.

962: WAITING

by Adam Waters

You'll be out tonight, holding court as ever, and you probably won't notice her hovering in the background. Even if you do see her, you'll assume she's weak and you don't have any time for a weak woman.

You haven't the measure of her, though. You can't see how excited she is because here you are, big, brash and wonderful. Eating a busy hole through her head. Making her mind drift off-line so that she can absorb everything about you, girl.

Adam Waters' Biography

Adam enjoys cats, music, cookery and writing recreationally.

~

963: NIBBLER'S ADVENTURE

by Sarah Charmley

Nibbler the hamster hid under the kitchen units where it was dark and smelled of food. He heard footsteps and stayed still, listening. He heard Jade's voice.

"Nibbler escaped. I left the door open."

Then crying.

Nibbler still hid in the dark.

He fell asleep.

When he woke, he smelled food. Following his nose, he found a peanut. And another. He followed them up a stack of books. He slipped down inside an orange bucket hamster trap.

The adventure was over.

Sarah Charmley's Biography

Freelance writer, editor, proofreader and storyteller, keeper of hamsters and guinea pigs (what they get up to), singer and puppeteer. Lives in Worcestershire, UK.

www.linkedin.com/in/sarah-charmley/

964: UNBELIEVABLE BUT TRUE

by Tamires Cunha

Hitchhiking from another city back to my hometown, I found myself thirsty on a desert road.

Hey, Universe, send me some water, I thought.

Nothing happened. Why did I think something would?

The few cars passing by didn't stop. When one finally did, I got in.

First thing I heard was, "Would you like some water? You can also have a piece of strawberry cake if you want."

As if the universe whispered, "Here's what you asked for, and even more."

Tamires Cunha's Biography

Tamires Cunha is a Brazilian lover of all types of arts, especially literature, which has been present in her life since childhood as a longtime friend. She deeply believes in the beauty of what is made through the heart.

~

965: WITCH STALKER

by L J McQueen

"She—"

"I don't care. You slaughtered her."

"Only once, Isabelle."

"We need to set this right. The witch queen will come for us."

"I have already come." Richard ripped off the skin from his face. The witch queen's violet eyes peeked from underneath.

"Have mercy," I said.

"Witch stalkers showed me no mercy."

"But I am half witch, half stalker."

The witch queen gave a gasp.

I placed the palm of my hand on her face and burnt her to ash.

L J McQueen's Biography

L J McQueen is a self-published author who stays up late reading secretly under the covers, has a normal job to pay the bills, and has an unhealthy obsession with chocolate biscuits.

966: R. U. BAIT

by Wyatt Payne

"Is your neighbourhood being overrun by rabid unicorns?"

"Yes."

"Then you need Rabid Unicorn Bait. Rabid Unicorn Bait is a human dummy that the rabid unicorns can chew on while you capture them and relocate them humanely."

"It looks really realistic."

"That's the point."

"I think it just said, 'Help me.'"

"If they do that, just hit them over the head with a bat."

"I think it's trying to move... did you tie someone up to be eaten by a unicorn?"

Wyatt Payne's Biography

My name is Wyatt Payne. I am 15 years old and if this is published it will be my first published work of fiction. That is all you need to know about me.

~

967: WORDS

by Tony Tremblett

"Whatcha doing?"

"Writing."

"Writing what?"

"Flash fiction."

"Huh?"

"A really short story, just 81 words."

"Why 81?"

"Why not?"

"Ha, funny. Seriously, though?"

"It's a submission requirement."

"Weird. Sounds like an occult thing."

"It's not an occult thing. A guy named Adam Rubinstein started it as a writing competition years ago. Now Christopher Fielden wants to set a world record for the most contributing authors published in an anthology of 81 word stories. I'd tell you more but I'm out of—"

Tony Tremblett's Biography

Tony Tremblett lives on Canada's pacific coast with a growing collection of books and DVDs, and a dwindling supply of dark chocolate. When not writing, he can be found exploring the great indoors of thrift stores and bookshops.

968: GHOST OR GHOSTIE?

by Neil Goodwin

Way down at the bottom of my garden, there be the scary shed. With resident ghostie, performing ghostly antics, clearly visible hanging around the bushes nearby. But, would ghost or ghostie best describe this creepy looking vision like something from an episode of *Scooby Doo*?

Proposal of distinction: Ghostie, a light-hearted fake ghost, usually made from white bedsheets with coat hangers and such, trying to imitate the other rather more serious, sinister ghost that has little or no sense of humour.

Neil Goodwin's Biography

Retired statistician, now writing memoir and short stories, specialising in silliness.

~

969: THE APOCALYPSE

by Penelope Henry

Before the shot was fired, everything was mundane. The grass was grey and so was the sky. Flowers began to wilt and things began to die. I felt trapped, wanting nothing more than to leave this wasteland.

And when the was shot fired, the war began. I would finally be free. I hurried to safety amongst a crowd of people destined to life in hiding.

I soon learnt that the shot would further ruin my life and I would never escape.

Penelope Henry's Biography

I am a fifteen-year-old American, living in England. I have travelled the world and lived on three continents. My three greatest passions are writing, drawing and my pure white kitten, Simon.

www.penelopehenry.wixsite.com/website

970: BECOMING A LEGEND

by N. J. Spencer

"I can't believe your husband hiked 485 miles on the Camino de Santiago in Spain. How long did it take him?"

"Thirty-three days."

"Did he enjoy it?"

"He did, except for falling on his face on day three."

"Was he injured?"

"He ended up with a purple face, which surfaced on social media. Later, on three occasions, strangers looked at him and asked, 'Are you Jerry?' Upon finishing, he received a Camino completion certificate and he has now become a legend."

N. J. Spencer's Biography

I am a retired English teacher. My current writing focuses on eating a whole food, plant-based diet. I hold certificates in plant-based nutrition from eCornell and health coaching from the Institute for Integrative Nutrition.

~

971: NIGHT

by Meredith Argent

Night prowled in, the moon in his hand and stars glistening in his fathomless eyes. A foreboding creature, he swept his shadow across the town, throwing his soul over the world, and the earth fell upon its knees.

Night kicked out Day as if she were a mere twinkle of dust and killed the sky, ripping it in half and exposing the black abyss behind. The sky had no choice but to obey him – Night had come to seize the day.

Meredith Argent's Biography

I am a 12-year-old girl who lives in Nottingham with my mum, dad and older sister. I am a Slytherin. I also like art, *Star Wars* and the K-pop band BTS.

972: ANGRY

by Brian Mackinney

I'm angry again. Someone's always pinching my pencil.

I'm not ready to work because my pencil's not there. It's happened every day this week.

My gran brought me a new one from New Zealand. It had a rubber on the end. I was ready for work. It was a great pencil. Wrote neatly. Spelt correctly. Teacher praised me all morning.

By dinner time, it'd gone. To New Zealand I guess.

I'll get the little one or the blunt one. Angry. Again.

Brian Mackinney's Biography

Brian Mackinney is an 80-year-old drabble writer whose stories can be found on:
www.clivef9.wixsite.com/macdrabble-tales

~

973: MY DYSTOPIAN DAY

by Mehak Vijay Chawla

There was hue and cry in our abode, tried to make a landscape that I saw on the road.

My mother's rebuke made me vexed, felt like I was a filcher who was under arrest.

My mother's high sound cried into my ear, I felt I was not her dear.

She is so stern that all the people in our neighbourhood are concerned.

Though she gave me tasty food to eat, thank God she was not in a mood to beat.

Mehak Vijay Chawla's Biography

I am published poet Mehak Vijay Chawla from New Delhi, India, studying in secondary school. I am most happy when I wrap myself into the tunes of Spotify. I hope one day I can be a famous young poet / artist.

974: FAMILY TRADITION

by Melissa Odom

Elizabeth breathed deep against the pounding in her heart as she tracked her prey with the barrel of the shotgun. Breathing deep, she pulled the trigger and watched as he went down.

Her mother, noticing the flicker of hurt in Elizabeth's eyes, reached down and placed a hand on her daughter's swollen belly.

"He outlived his purpose, just like your father and mine before him. It's tradition."

She had meant to be comforting, but her smile chilled Elizabeth to the bone.

Melissa Odom's Biography

My name is Melissa Odom. I am a single mother of two who lives in Gadsden, Alabama. I love to inspire and be inspired.

~

975: IN A LONE CUP

by Imogen Argent

Swirling in the tea, a lone cup, I watch the milk of the day frothing at their feet.

This world is dissolved, locks and chains binding the spoon keeper who dared to look under the sugar. These coatings aren't sweet. Their cardboard boxes are all soggy and the constant 'This way ups' are stark reminders of how we are all sombre teabags who are soon to be taken to this gritty exclusion.

We're unnoticeable, sitting in the doorways of the world.

Imogen Argent's Biography

I am 16 years old and currently live in Nottingham, England. My interests span from theology and opera to Eurovision and *RuPaul's Drag Race*. I live with my parents and younger sister.

976: MY FIRST DIARY

by Ankush Vijay Chawla

Anne Frank made my heart bulge-out to write diaries. So, I asked my father to buy a diary for me. The diary he bought became my favourite in a few seconds and my sister used to envy me for it.

The diary looked simple, consisting of two-hundred and twenty pages.

I prefer to write new things and events in the memoir. It has a fixed bookmark and, to make it interesting, I will write in calligraphy and fill it with poems.

Ankush Vijay Chawla's Biography

I am Ankush Vijay Chawla, hailing from New Delhi, India, studying in secondary school. I love to draw portraits, love shading. I am fond of reading about aliens and go through my space encyclopaedia. I hope to become a famous astronaut.

Instagram: @ankushvijayy

~

977: MY ENEMY'S FRIEND

by IR Belletti

If Xavier had to choose between winning and being safe, he would have taken off his cracked armour and gone back into battle with a broken arm.

This time, though, he cried. The next day, he was to fight his city's archenemy and his friends had just abandoned him.

His doorbell rang and his enemy was waiting on the doorstep.

"I came to cure you. If you won't be able to withstand me tomorrow, I won't win fairly." Xavier welcomed him.

IR Belletti's Biography

IR Belletti (sie/hir) is a queer writer and undergraduate in American literature. Hir previous publications include two poems in 2020 in *Adanna* and *Scorpion*, and a short story for non-profit organization StayAleeve. You can find hir writing on Instagram:

@oriorwriter_

978: EGGSHELL

by James Pemberton

The diary lay in the middle of the kitchen table, as solid and devastating as a brick through a window.

Ashleigh's mother sat next to it. Ordinarily, she never smoked indoors, or at all if pressed, but the open pack lay next to an ashtray with three identifiable butts amongst the ash.

Only the ticking of the clock could be heard in an eternity that aged them both, until one woman broke the silence.

"You know I've always loved you... right?"

James Pemberton's Biography

James Pemberton is a tall teller of tall tales from Oldham, England.

~

979: RATTLESNAKE BITE

by Sandee Lee

A yelp.

Brandy stood, staring at a grass tuft. Her head sagged.

I discovered fang marks on her nose.

I grabbed my cell phone from my left pocket. I looked at the time. The vet clinic closed in five minutes. We were fifteen minutes away. I called. I scooped Brandy into my arms and sped to town.

They said they'd be ready. They were. Efficient, caring, and willing to delay ending their workday on time to care for my precious companion.

Sandee Lee's Biography

Sandee Lee writes historical fiction and miscellaneous nonfiction from her rural Kansas home. She adores her border collies and working in the garden. You can connect with Sandee on Facebook @SandeeLeeWrites or on her webpage:

www.sandeelee.com

980: IN A WORD

by Alan Greaves

I provide tuition for two girls. Their dad – a hairy, sporty sort – writes stories.

"I'm writing one now, it's good." His grimy index-finger rummages the depths of a large, misshapen ear. "Eighty words max, can you?"

Aware that he would oblige me to admire his effort, I was desperate to do better. After all, if an all-in wrestler can do it, so can I.

Alas, he bested me. My splendid effort was rejected, spurned for being just one over the eighty.

Alan Greaves' Biography

I am a part-time piano teacher living in Nottingham. I retired from a varied working life as a policeman, itinerant musician, and cabinet maker. I am currently engaged in study with the Open University towards a degree qualification in music.

~

981: A WASTED LIFE?

by Robert Brewis

"But it's so hard when structure interferes with rhythm."

"What structure? Put eighty one words in a row.

"And rhythm? This is prose to write, not verse."

"Prose too should have rhythm, go with a swing.

"Nine lines of nine words each, structured like 'Furborg'."

"Think Occam. Why make it harder than needs be?"

"But I want both: nine nines are eighty one."

"Then you should have spent your life gaining skills...

"...with words, not dealing with numbers and flow charts."

Robert Brewis' Biography

Robert Brewis is probably retired after a career in accountancy and systems consultancy. He lives in North Buckinghamshire with his wife and about 120 primitive sheep. Most of his children and one grandchild beat him with their 81 Words submissions.

982: FADED FABRIC

by Fliss Zakaszewska

Jason stroked the fabric, its soft cotton familiar under his touch. How old was it now?

Glancing to the other side of the room, Grandma smiled down. He was thirty-five now and she'd made it when he'd been born, his name embroidered on it.

He pulled the patchwork quilt over his sleeping baby. "It's yours now, Jason Junior." He straightened her photo. "You said it'd help me to remember, didn't you?" he whispered, recalling childhood memories. "It does. Miss you, Grandma."

Fliss Zakaszewska's Biography

Born in Guatemala, Fliss has returned to her dad's homeland of Cornwall, UK. She'd write a ten-page essay when other kids wrote four. She's now learned both the meaning of the word 'brevity' and how it applies to her.

Twitter handle: @FlissZak

~

983: HEGEL

by Livia Furia

I was half asleep when I heard the bedroom door open and something jumped onto the bed.

"Hegel?"

There was no answer. I felt steps, perfectly measured, crossing the bed from one end to the other.

"Hegel?"

The intruder carefully climbed onto my chest and curled up. She was heavy and cold. She sighed softly when I moved.

I jumped out of bed screaming at the top of my lungs. I had buried Hegel in the garden almost two months ago.

Livia Furia's Biography

I am a Romanian author who published some science fiction and fantasy novels in the past. I work as a veterinarian in a small town. I like to read and write from time to time.

www.facebook.com/liviafuriaautor

984: A TRAIN OF SHATTERED MEMORIES

by Sophie Scriven

I saw the lights of the dining cart ahead.

I reached it with a sense of unease, but sat down for my meal. There were a few lone diners who passed smiles of condolence, although why they seemed that way is questionable. The rain had become fiercer and thrashed against the window, like a wild animal attempting to break free from its prison of normality. This trip was definitely a mistake. I checked the clock.

The train had crashed hours ago.

Sophie Scriven's Biography

My name is Sophie Scriven and I am 14 years old. I have always loved writing stories that leave the reader wondering whether the ending truly means what it means. I hope you will think hard when you read.

~

985: THE GOLDFISH

by Alex Fullerton

This morning I found the lonely goldfish resting on the floor.

"What are you doing down here, old chap?"

With a memory lasting three seconds, the creature was no doubt startled to find himself on this rather dry patch of carpet. Some journey, from those placid waters into the living room proper. I scooped the fellow up so as to return him to the bowl.

His scales were so wet and clammy, slipping right through my fingers. Just like last time.

Alex Fullerton's Biography

I live in Richmond and work for the Department of Health and Social Care on Test and Trace. I graduated from York and Oxford universities and enjoy travel, jiu-jitsu and writing, only one of which I can do right now.

My insta is: www.instagram.com/alex_fullertonn/

986: BATTLE OF THE SEXES

by Heather Haigh

"I convinced the wife she doesn't need to work," said Don Walker. "I provide the money, she provides for my needs."

"Stella would never agree to that," Mike replied. "Are you sure Judy doesn't mind an unexpected dinner guest?"

"She knows how important this project is to me. She'll rustle something up." Dan opened the door to show his boss in, and froze.

The house was stripped bare. Save for a single book on the floor. *Regaining Independence*, by Della Walker.

Heather Haigh's Biography

Heather always wanted to write, but life, and a near fatal accident, got in the way. Then she found that trying to learn and create was the best therapy for a damaged body after all.

~

987: KILLED THE MALL

by Ian Buzard

The doors slid open. It briefly amused him that the power was on.

Glass crunched on the tiled floor. Crisscrossing escalators now reduced to rusted stairs.

An entire community derailed and decaying.

The food court triggered his mourning for fries.

This was the only place he could think of. No longer an employee, no longer anything.

He knew the layout: lookout spots, safe rooms, escape routes.

He stood, bathed in neon.

Someone had spray painted: 'One nuke is all it took'.

Ian Buzard's Biography

I live in Glasgow, born in New Orleans. I have a BA in film and media from Stirling University and an MA in screenwriting from Screen Academy Scotland. Flash fiction is becoming my favourite hobby.

988: THE OLD LADY

by Mohamed Atta Amer

A thief entered the home of an old lady who lived alone. He stole clothes and some bread, then ran away beneath moonlight.

The old lady stood behind the window, watching the thief running between fields. She looked at her necklace and said, "Ah, if you'd sat for a while and talked to me, I would have given you this necklace even though you wanted to steal from me, because I haven't seen anyone who is interested in me for years."

Mohamed Atta Amer's Biography

Egyptian writer, 23 years old, nurse.

~

989: TO BE OR NOT TO BE AN ITEM? THAT IS THE QUESTION

by Geoff Holme

"Was that our last night together?"
   "You awake?"
   "Avoiding the question?"
   "Would you want a long-distance relationship?"
   "Can't you change your job?"
   "Why should I have to?"
   "Is your career that important to you?"
   "Are you serious?"
   ...
   "Will I see you again?"
   "Do you want to?"
   "Would I ask if I didn't?"
   "Can you give me some time?"
   "Haven't we wasted enough time?"
   "Has this week been wasted?"
   "What do you think?"
   "Bear with me, OK?"
   "I'll have to, won't I?"

Geoff Holme's Biography

Geoff Holme lives on the south coast of England, with two dogs and one long-suffering, extremely patient wife. He's been messing about with flash fiction for over a decade.

990: SPIDER HANDS

by Cheryl Buck

Do you ever get spider hands?

Do you ever have hands that want to twist and dance and tap?

You can't keep them still no matter how hard you try, so you hold onto something like you're afraid to let go. But you do, almost without noticing, as though you've forgotten, and your hands are dancing again.

Together and apart, on anything they can reach and through the air. Twisting and touching and flexing, never ever still.

I have spider hands.

Cheryl Buck's Biography

Cheryl writes and reads, and occasionally has to take breaks from one to do the other. More often she has to take breaks from her actual job to try and do both.

~

991: MURDER HE WROTE

by Roger West

"Do you have to use the hoover in here when I'm writing?"

"Write somewhere else then."

"I always write in the kitchen."

"We have other rooms, write in some other room."

"But I write best when I'm in here."

"So, what are you writing?"

"Turn the hoover off."

"No."

"I'm writing a murder story."

"What are you doing with that bread knife?"

"It's the murder weapon."

"In your story?"

"No, in your kitchen. Now turn the hoover off."

"Oh my god."

Roger West's Biography

I'm an experienced sports journalist/writer/reporter/commentator/broadcaster looking to get into fiction beginning with the short story. And believe you me, there's a whole world of a difference between fact and fiction. Here is a good starting point.

992: UGLY BRYAN

by Elizabeth Stanley

Bryan eyed the mirror. He was ugly and he knew it. No one liked him. Not girls. Not boys. No one.

He pulled his hoody on and slung his rifle over his shoulder. He walked to the door. The sound of groaning met his ears. He took deep breaths and pulled it open.

A hoard of zombies stumbled past. They were headed somewhere, but he didn't know where.

He lumbered out the door. At least he was the best looking now.

Elizabeth Stanley's Biography

Elizabeth Stanley is an author and artist living in Wales with her two girls and husband. When not creating, she enjoys reading and studying.

~

993: HUNTER WANTED

by Grannd Kane

Wanted: Hunter to protect the settlements of Orlando, Versin, Gallus, Anvil and East Welwyn. Accommodation and payment provided. Report to East Welwyn Town Hall if interested.

Wanted: Werewolf hunter to protect the settlements of Orlando, Versin, Gallus and Anvil. Accommodation and payment provided. Report to Anvil Town Hall if capable.

Wanted: Hunter of werewolves to protect the settlements of Orlando, Versin and Gallus. Accommodation and payment provided. Report to Gallus Town Hall if capable. Hunters who are werewolves need not apply.

Grannd Kane's Biography

Grannd Kane is a fantasy writer located in the north of Scotland. A passionate advocate of the Scots and Gaelic leids, he also enjoys Sudoku. He has been previously published by Aphelion.

994: THE TRIBOLOGIST

by Susanne Berger

I spent all my life researching the science of friction, lubrication and wear, but remained oblivious to the amount of interpersonal tribology that is happening all around me.

She's attractive alright – kind, supportive and very smart – but I cannot conceive what a woman could possibly see in me, a middle-aged workaholic whose hair is thinning and who is putting on weight round the middle.

If I had anything a woman could possibly want, how come I am still single at 48?

Susanne Berger's Biography

I've known that I wanted to be an author since the age of 14, when I had business cards printed that read 'Susanne Berger, Author'. 30 years later, I am finally working on it.

~

995: IN A PINCH

by Jaimen Shires

Frank keeps a large bag of peanuts beside the door.

Every night, before he goes out, he pulls a single shell from the bag and cracks it open. If it breaks cleanly like an eyeglass case, revealing two protein pills, he downs the medicine and lets the night take him wherever it will. If the break is rough or difficult, or if a peanut shoots across the room and is lost, he remains cautious and indoors.

The nut case knows all.

Jaimen Shires' Biography

Jaimen Shires is a Canadian author, born and raised in Leamington, Ontario. His work has been featured in a small handful of publications and his poetry has been recognised by the City of Maple Ridge, where he currently resides.

www.fb.com/jaimenshires

996: OF MEN & LOBSTERS

by Jessica Kirby

"But, what about the lobsters?"

No one had ever asked me that before. I thought I'd covered everything. Cuisine based questions made a change.

I remember the men feasting on lobsters with butter, washing them down with champagne until their cheeks turned red.

Two hours and forty minutes later, I floated away on a lifeboat in a sea of frozen bodies.

In the early hours of April 15th, the *Titanic* sank, and I guess the men went down with the lobsters.

Jessica Kirby's Biography

A creative writing graduate from Liverpool John Moores University, Jess was longlisted for the 2018 Yeovil Literary Prize and competes regularly in time restricted flash fiction, short fiction, short screenwriting and, most recently, micro fiction writing competitions.

~

997: LOVE OR LIMERICK

by CJ Nicol

Once, there was a man who spoke only in limerick.

Every morning, he would wake and say:

"Good morning, to the birds and the bees.

"Likewise, to the insects, the flowers and the trees.

"Blessed be I who wakes by sun or fine rainy mist.

"If only I had a lady, by whom I may be kissed.

"Perhaps, if I asked them nicely, please?"

Needless to say, he wasn't very good at making limericks. He died at eighty-three, lonesome and misunderstood.

CJ Nicol's Biography

My name is CJ. I'm from London and enjoy reading, particularly sci-fi and dystopian. Now, I am trying to get my foot into writing, by writing short stories in my spare time.

998: VENOM

by Charlotte Ella Read

I don't get angry,
    it's not like me.

I don't raise my voice,
    don't lash out.

But sometimes,
    my dear, sometimes my thoughts can scare.

My brain is venomous.
    Poison drips from my lips
    and hostility bleeds from my fingertips.

I'm small, delicate,
    use soft touches, kind words,
    but I can manipulate your thoughts,
    strike where it hurts.

My hands may not make you bleed,
    but the ideas that I feed to your soul
    will rot you from the inside out.

Charlotte Ella Read's Biography

Sleepless writer and university student, Charlotte Read, has practised putting words onto a page since young. From novels to haikus to songwriting, she won't back down at a challenge. However, poetry is the motivation that has kept her inspired.

~

999: SHE WHO LAUGHS LAST LAUGHS BEST

by Becky Benishek

My father invited the witch on purpose, but she cursed me anyway, before she'd even reached my cradle.

"A laugh that would end the world." Some prophecy that is. Wouldn't that kill her, too?

But life wasn't her aim, rather the ending of it, this world that abused her.

Being forbidden joy and delight abused me, too.

Was she the making of me, or were they?

They demand gratitude for letting me live. But life is no longer my aim, either.

Becky Benishek's Biography

Becky Benishek is the author of the children's books *The Squeezor is Coming, Dr. Guinea Pig George, What's At the End of Your Nose?* and *Hush, Mouse!* She's also contributed to science fiction and horror anthologies by Black Hare Press.

www.beckybenishek.com

~

1000: WHEN DOES ENOUGH BECOME ENOUGH?

by Anna Capstick

When does enough become enough? When the eyes, which once sparkled, are flooded with rain? When your inner lifeguard turns his back and leaves you drowning in your worries? Or when you begin to disintegrate under the merciless words that tear you apart?

Perhaps when the passion that once drove you burns out, or when you wither away at the thought of fighting that same battle continuously, or when staying silent becomes the easier option.

Maybe that's when enough becomes enough.

Anna Capstick's Biography

Anna enjoys playing sports, travelling, photography, learning languages (she's actually bilingual), reading and, of course, writing. She's constantly trying to improve her writing and can be a bit of a perfectionist.

A FINAL NOTE

Victorina Press and I would like to say one last THANK YOU to all the authors featured in this anthology. Their generosity is helping support a very worthy charity and it's an honour to present their stories in this unofficial world record-breaking collection.

Don't forget to check my website for more writing challenges. You will be able to find all the details here:
www.christopherfielden.com/writing-challenges/

There is an 'Authors of the Flash Fiction Writing Challenges' Facebook group that runs its own regular challenges. It's open to everyone. Please feel free to join here:
www.facebook.com/groups/157928995061095/

I bid you farewell Bristol-style:

Cheers me dears,

Chris Fielden

81 words

www.victorinapress.com

APPENDIX

Here are this book's contributing authors, listed alphabetically based on their first name or first initial. Alongside each name is their story number as it is presented in this book.

Name	No.	Name	No.
A. A. Rubin	859	Alexio Gomes	234
A. Gustafson	239	Ali Bounds	50
A.H. Creed	479	Ali Clarke	921
Aaron McDermott	293	Alice Hale	652
Abby Shue	500	Alice Payne	152
Abhi Shan	44	Alice Penfold	142
Abigail Rowe	178	Alicia McGrath	287
Abigail Williamson	20	Alicia Sledge	179
Adam Bevan	849	Alicia Yau	867
Adam Down	663	Alison Clary	489
Adam Rubinstein	97	Alison Reese	946
Adam Waters	962	Alison Wren	776
Adam Wright-Johnson	96	Alistair Forsyth	891
Adele Evershed	636	Allen Ashley	4
Adrian Hallchurch	771	Ally Cook	327
Adrian Nichol	137	Alyson Faye	409
Aerin Bernstein	845	Amanda Garzia	437
Ahmad Abu Sharkh	238	Amanda Huggins	102
Aigbonoga Omoh	501	Amanita Peridot Festoon	140
Aishwarya Harikumar	392	Amberlie Robinson	445
Akindu Perera	222	Amelia Brown	516
Alan Barker	25	Amisha Bansal	419
Alan Barker (Note: same name but a different AB)	414	Ana D.	115
Alan D. Przybylski	93	Anastasia Bromberg	511
Alan Dale	549	Anastasia Mosher	665
Alan Greaves	980	Andre Othenin-Girard	397
Alan Pattison	251	Andrew Ball	720
Alan Ridley	611	Andrew Carter	870
Alcuin Edwards	492	Andrew Dawkins	920
Aleah Bingham	268	Andrew James Spence	768
Alex Blair	496	Andrew Jones	458
Alex Fullerton	985	Andrew McGill	575
Alexandra Klyueva	18	Andrew Perry	342

Andrzej Christopher Marczewski	121	Benjamin Noel	805
Andy Langdale	603	Bernard Hicks	551
Angela P Googh	237	Bernard Muslin	686
Angelique Dusengimana	71	Bert Velthuis	765
Ani Martin	370	Beth Greenwood	703
Ania Kovas	215	Beth Kander	598
Anita Goveas	339	Betty Hattersley	161
Ankush Vijay Chawla	976	Betty J Burton	876
Anna Capstick	1000	Blake Holcomb	711
Anna Ferrar	464	Blerina Kapllani	407
Anna Sanderson	543	Boakesey	877
Anne Copeland	411	Brett Elliott-Palmer	30
Annie Francis	918	Brian Johnstone	256
Annika Franke	602	Brian Mackinney	972
Anu Roy	538	Brianna Damplo	426
Arlene Everingham	180	Bridget Blankley	285
Arthur KC Chan	581	Bridget Scrannage	177
Arya Amlani	953	Bridget Yates	779
Ash Gray	266	Brinkinfield	629
Ashleigh Whittle	900	Brittany Holmes	853
Ashley Kim	888	Bruce Millar	533
Ashley Scott	697	Bruce Wyness	262
Ashley Vohrer	633	Bryan Keefe	211
Ashutosh Pant	103	Byron Coulson	306
Austrian Spencer	671	C. H. Connor	462
Ava Groth	610	C.R. Berry	341
Avery Pryce	952	Caiden Lang	836
Ayesha Hassan	474	Caleb Jansen	588
B. K. Bolen	746	Cameron Crebs	354
B. P. Garcia	226	Campbell Hinshelwood	852
B.C. Ong	753	Carl Palmer	528
Barbara Eustace	647	Carla Vlad	707
Barnaby Page	568	Caroline Cowan	454
Barry Rhodes	29	Caroline Wright	46
Barry Smith	26	Carolyn Roden	228
Bart Elbey	714	Carolyn Ward	334
Bec Lewis	664	Carrie Hewlett	377
Becky Benishek	999	Cath Allwood	544
Bekk Escott	590	Catherine Broxton	19

Catherine Cade	404	Christine Reeves	747
Catherine Harkness	572	Christine Tapper	650
Cathi Radner	616	Christopher Fielden	1
Catrin Rutland	917	Christopher Searle	7
CB McCall	358	CJ Nicol	997
Ceris Brewis	924	CJ Wigg	674
Charles Bonkowsky	641	CL Wearne	841
Charles K Manila	442	Claire Allinson	136
Charles Lee	821	Claire Apps	168
Charles Murphy	806	Claire Gagnon	86
Charles Osborne	146	Claire Gee	613
Charlie Taylor	257	Claire Lee	135
Charlie Turner	289	Claire Schön	930
Charlotte Ella Read	998	Claire Taylor	195
Charlotte Farrell-Banks	666	Claire Temple	31
Charlotte Ward	337	Clara Baird	886
Charlotte West	427	Clare Owen	743
Cheah Yin Mee	906	Clare Tivey	188
Cheryl Buck	990	Clarrie Rose	737
Chip Jett	162	Cleiton Pinho	444
Chloe Frost	410	Colette Kriel	556
Chloe Nkomo	247	Colleen Hue	939
Chloe Testa	742	CompletelyBoofyBlitzed	727
Chris Black	446	Constance Bourg	374
Chris Cantor	205	Crilly O'Neil	33
Chris Espenshade	391	Cristina Bresser	267
Chris Green	428	Cynthia Akagi	955
Chris McLoughlin	260	Dan McConnell	561
Chris Pritchard	304	Daniel L. Link	34
Chris Tattersall	240	Daniel McClaskey	301
Christian Andrei Nuez Laplap	773	Danielle Linsey	931
Christian Obaitan	345	Danny Macks	706
Christianna Sahadeo	351	Darci-Leigh Robinson-Askew	313
Christina Burton	278	Darren Hackett	567
Christina M. Y. Chow	907	Dave Firth	769
Christine Bukania	712	David Batteiger	298
Christine Hursell	359	David Brewis	928
Christine Kingshott	393	David Conway	263
Christine O'Donnell	45	David Don	865

David Guilfoyle	297	Dr. Sriharsha Sripathi	815
David Heaton	386	DT Langdale	396
David John Griffin	628	Duane L. Herrmann	935
David Lowis	904	E. F. S. Byrne	186
David McTigue	382	Edmund Piper	138
David Rhymes	55	Edward Mortenson	453
David S Mitchell	869	Edward Rouse	199
David Silver	51	Edwin Stern	68
David Turton	8	Eileen Baldwin	810
David Vargas Alfonso	944	Elaine Carlyle	894
David Viner	813	Eleanor Dickenson	866
David Wright	191	Elena Zhuang	951
Dean Hollands	343	Elizabeth Lamb	547
Debaprasad Mukherjee	165	Elizabeth Stanley	992
Debbie Rolls	842	Ella Cass	128
Debbie Singh	486	Ella Wilson	874
Deborah Wroe	164	Elliot Cambrey	692
Dee La Vardera	124	Em Daurio	676
Dee Tilsley	254	Emily K Martin	739
Denis Joseph	504	Emily Knight	840
Denise Senecal	672	Emma Burnett	447
Derek McMillan	166	Emma Nokes	912
Devin Greene	236	Emma Robertson	864
Devon Goodchild	67	Emma Stammeyer	60
Dez T.	83	Emma Wilson	698
Diana Senechal	861	Erin Hardman	295
Diane de Anda	434	Esosa Kolawole	435
Diane Harding	23	Evelyn Hawke	668
Dianne D. Pingalo	818	Everest Pen	62
Dimiana Wassef	292	Evie Nicol	582
Dinesh Shihantha De Silva	635	Ezeh Michael Ogonna	518
Dionne Burton	521	Fabio Crispim	770
Diontae Jaegli	495	Farzaneh Hajirasouliha	783
Don Bartlome	700	Fay Franklin	58
Don Marler	959	Fee Johnstone	189
Dorothy Francis	934	Felix Castrillon	708
Doug Forrest	569	Femi S. Craigwell	48
Doug Hawley	751	Finlay Thomas Tweedie	318
Douglas J. Shearer	76	Fiona Aitken	562

Fiona Campbell	416	Hannah Brown	271
Fiona Flower	593	Hannah Cole	827
Fliss Zakaszewska	982	Harley Logan Thompson	314
Franca Basta	182	Harriet Payne	154
Frances Tate	687	Hazel Turner	204
Francesca Pappadogiannis	412	Heather Haigh	986
Francisca Staines	679	Heather Stuart Primbs	625
Frank Daurio	681	Heidi Lobecker	576
Frank Havemann	450	Heidi Vanlandingham	384
Frank Hubeny	99	Helen Aitchison	823
Frank Radcliffe	123	Helen Combe	98
G. Gaurav	750	Helen Matthews	323
Gail Everett	619	Helen Merrick	353
Gary Couzens	513	Hervé Suys	109
Gary McGrath	227	Hilary Taylor	723
Gavin Biddlecombe	134	Holly Garcia	558
Gemma Bevan	847	Holly Webster	795
Gemma Martiskainen	74	Huguette Van Akkeren	577
Geoff Freedman	890	Hullabaloo22	759
Geoff Holme	989	Ian Andrew	250
George Cornilă	150	Ian Buzard	987
Gillian M Seed	269	Ian James Stewart	347
Gillian Macleod	10	Ian Tucker	47
Ginger Marcinkowski	640	Ibukun Keyamo	729
Gitanjali Escobar Travieso	517	Imogen Argent	975
Glen Donaldson	104	IR Belletti	977
Glo Curl	814	Irene Banfield	275
Gloria Ames	507	Iris & Phil Hatchard	819
Glynis Ann Downey	270	Irving Benjamin	59
Gordon Williams	766	Isabel Flynn	811
Gowravy Ravanan	348	Isabella Rae Wharton-McLellan	357
Grace Turner-Higgins	809	Iuliana Khadyxa Filisanu	141
Grannd Kane	993	Ivan Richardson	799
Grant McKain	530	Ixai Salvo	940
Grant O'Townson	305	J. L. Harland	90
Gwyneth Williams	798	J. Rosina Harlow	415
Gwynne Weir	843	J.S Taols	40
Hajra Saeed	651	Jace Henderson	591
Haley M. Hwang	553	Jacek Wilkos	856

Jack Dabell	225	Jaz Leigh	130
Jack Dudley	69	Jeff Kemp	950
Jack Hanlon	78	Jeffrey H. Toney	259
Jack Purkis	390	Jeni Lawes	812
Jackie Batteiger	300	Jennifer Hankin	941
Jackie Hindmarsh	493	Jennifer P. L. Leong	910
Jacky Ellis	550	Jennifer Riddalls	272
Jade Swann	248	Jenny Butler	421
Jaimen Shires	995	Jenny Drury	933
Jaine Irish	52	Jenny Simmons	194
Jake Cosmos Aller	942	Jerome Parsons	499
James Braun	361	Jerry Wilson	3
James Byrne	350	Jessica Bowden	627
James Colfox	184	Jessica Everitt	274
James Crerar	893	Jessica Joy	57
James Hornby	80	Jessica Kirby	996
James Louis Peel	563	Jessica Richard	279
James Northern	755	Jessica Turnbull	371
James Pemberton	978	Jill Lang	728
James Sanders	27	Jimmy Doom	826
James Smart	400	Jo Howarth	185
Jamie Graham	11	Joan C. Hobart	122
Jamie Welch	378	Joanna Ball	158
Jan Brown	200	Jocelyn Wong	480
Jan Courtney	844	Jodi Nicholls	514
Jane Fell	916	Jodi Novak	926
Jane Imrie	512	Joe Bailey	149
Jane Sleight	328	Joe Brothers	820
Janet L Davies	915	Joe McMullen	363
Janet Lister	246	Johanna McDonald	221
Jasmine Hunt	252	Johannah Lipscher Simon	552
Jasmine Lee	148	John Bevan	848
Jasmine Tan Chin Chwee	909	John Cooper	331
Jason B	219	John D Lary	899
Jason Barbo	693	John Hannan	120
Jay Bee	112	John Holland	381
Jayanta Bhaumik	589	John Holmes	13
Jaycee Durand	684	John James Morris	781
Jayne Morgan	683	John L Bell	190

John Lane	658	Justine Quammie	457
John Mark Miller	283	Justyce Solomon	294
John Notley	9	K. J. Watson	534
John Rivers	596	Kaelin Lee	734
John Robertson	88	Kailin Guo	255
John S Alty	87	Kaitlin Ellis	634
John Vandore	896	Karen Bevan	846
Jon Drake	94	Karen McClure	424
Jon Spencer	470	Karen McDermott	174
Jonathan Fryer	960	Karen Rust	872
Jonathan Hastings	276	Karen Waldron	774
Jonathan Hunter	878	Karen Walker	669
Jonathan Inglesfield	145	Karen Western	854
Jonathan Martindale	91	Kate Hamilton	957
Jonathan Pacheco	740	Kate Leimer	863
Jordan B. Jolley	738	Kate Miller	736
Jordan Bahnub	296	Katerina Hellam	875
Jordis Fasheh	408	Katherine Kogoy	609
Jose Luis Torres	792	Kathleen E Williams	523
Joseph Lancaster	851	Kathleen Hearnshaw	548
Joseph Mould	816	Kathleen Keenan	77
Josephine Queen	564	Kathryn Dixon	198
Josh Joseph Dixon	316	Kathryn Evans	203
Josh Leeson	231	Kathryn J Barrow	395
Josie Gowler	118	Kathryn Joyce	718
Joy Thomas	143	Kathryn Smith	862
Joyce Bingham	648	Katie Chapman	172
Joyce Walker	207	Katie Labbe	119
JS Cline	748	Katie Pepper	497
Judi Edwards	600	Katie Singer	947
Judy Reeves	606	Katy Clayton	75
Julia Graves	948	Kavitha Yarlagadda	680
Julia O'Dowd	56	Kay Sandry	925
Julia T. Spano	531	Keian Murray	319
Julia Wood	800	Keith Pearson-Sandelands	310
Julie Goodswen	432	Kelly Van Nelson	481
Julie Howard	155	Kelsey Gallo	471
Julie Mayger	787	Kelsey Juean Irving	312
Julie Stone	106	Kennedy Meechan	715

Kenneth Cahall	620	Lena MacDonald	932
Kent Raddatz	601	Lesley Anne Truchet	28
Kerry Robinson	436	Levi Earl	308
Khamis Kabeu	484	Lewis Ayers	84
Kim Hart	571	Lexikon	466
Kim Montgomery	107	Liam Hogan	503
Kim Steindel	585	Liam Lawer	38
Kim Witbeck	580	Liam Rayner	487
Kimana McCallum	325	Libby Batteiger	299
Kimberly Owen	303	Lidia Giusa	366
Kira Inglis	368	Lim Swee Kim	905
Kirk I. Holden	790	Linda Foy	622
Kitty Litteur	468	Linda Hibbin	958
Klaus Gehling	883	Linda Jones	595
KM Arhel	524	Linda Lewis	653
Kolade Ajila	324	Linda Scogings	425
Kudakwashe Chirapa	804	Linda Smith	796
Kwame M.A. McPherson	229	Linda Taylor	15
Kylan Fedje	461	Lindsey Esplin	133
L J King	326	Lindy Gibbon	282
L J McQueen	965	Linn Kier	126
L. A. Cunningham	147	Lisa Miller	335
L.E. Daurio	673	Lisa Reynolds	741
Laila Miller	566	Lisa Stone	244
Laura Besley	472	Livia Furia	983
Laura Day	352	Liz Berg	473
Laura Foakes	597	Liz Howard	922
Lauren J. Phillips	688	Liz Krogman	725
Lauren M Foster	871	Lorna Dougan	545
Lauren Raybould	399	Lorna Stewart	608
Laurie Hicks	565	Lorraine Smith	281
Layla Ahmed	322	Louise Burgess	21
Layla Calarco	317	Louise Furre	214
Layla Rogers	491	Louise Goulding	802
Lee Foley	762	Louise Snape	224
Lee Holland	726	Lucinda Thelwell	218
Lee Kull	482	Lucy Camilla	355
Leigh Hastings	176	Lucy Lucy	785
Len Saculla	14	Lucy Morrice	398

Lumen Ros	689	Marilyn Rucker	612
Lydia Collins	574	Mark Burke	536
Lyndsay Lomax	838	Mark J Towers	527
Lynn Gale	356	Mark Johnson	460
Lynn Morcombe	605	Mark Pritchard	761
Lynn White	475	Mark Stocker	695
Lynn Zeleski	624	Marsha K. Hanson	732
Lynne Arnot	532	Martin Strike	233
Lynne Chitty	291	Mary Daurio	667
Lynsey Calvert	525	Mary Dharsi	699
M Anthony David	780	Mary Papageorgiou	379
Madamraj Mrinalini	502	Mary Prior	330
Maddy Hamley	24	Mason Bell	716
Madeleine McCabe	264	Matilda Pinto	100
Madeleine McDonald	767	Matthew Bines	719
Madeline Green	579	Matthew Dawson	829
Madiana Dethan	756	Matthew Galic	401
Madison Pickering	311	Matthew Gooch	825
Maggie Elliott	607	Matthew J Morine	586
Mahek Khwaja	754	Matthew Kerns	253
Mairead Robinson	372	Matthew Willis	429
Majella Pinto	127	Max Dobb	241
Malcolm Richardson	193	Maxine Smith	173
Manda Riehl	835	Maxx Dominic	66
Mandy Raywood	537	Maya Barnett	929
Mandy Whyman	526	Mckenzie Tompson	309
Marci Girton	936	Medeia Sharif	839
Marco Cardoni	724	Meg Gain	245
Margaret Bell	494	Meghan O'Brien	882
Margaret Davis	696	Mehak Vijay Chawla	973
Margee Unger	216	Melanie Goodell	192
Maria Carvalho	510	Melissa Odom	974
Maria DePaul	73	Melody Bowers	559
Maria Noble	364	Meredith Argent	971
Mariam Bibi	788	MF Mika	713
Mariam Mansuryan	441	Mhairi Bakertzi	535
Marie Arbon	919	Michael E James	101
Marie McGinn	367	Michael Farmer	889
Marieta Maglas	261	Michael Hardy	837

Michael J. Labbe	117	Niamh Burke	431
Michael J. Lowis	880	Nick Fairclough	49
Michael Lane	793	Nicole Loh	449
Michael Mclaughlin	37	Niina Olenbluu	232
Michael Rumsey	2	Nikki Butcher	560
Michael Swift	529	Nili Roberts	778
Michael Ward	209	Noel Alcoba	557
Michaela Mechura	433	Norm Veasman	39
Michele Kelly	937	NT Franklin	662
Michele Witthaus	797	Nurholis	163
Michelle Compton	649	Oghogho Odiase	599
Michelle Cook	682	Olatz Irigarai	911
Michelle Konov	35	Oliver Lynton	764
Michelle Weaver	860	Olivia Ackers	722
Micky Rowe	630	Olivia Magnuson	144
Mike Blakemore	64	Olivia-Ann Saxton	383
Mike Scott Thomson	116	Olusanya Anjorin	389
Miriam Hurdle	757	Oort Kuiper	346
Misa Hennin	394	Oriel Dobb	242
Mohamed Atta Amer	988	Oscar Kenway	405
Mohit Dass	824	Özge Göztürk	42
Muriel Garvis	733	Paige Murray	315
Murodova Marjona	413	Pam Jackson	196
Myron Dunavan	956	Pam Knapp	831
N. J. Spencer	970	Pamela Hibbert	938
N.B. Craven	690	Pamela Pope	362
Nam Raj Khatri	376	Pappo Nindo	817
Natalia Wojcik-Smith	643	Parzival Sattva	637
Natalie Marshall	901	Pat Hough	249
Natalie Wu	617	Patricia Mudge	422
Natasha Ali	554	Patricia Tarrant Brown	440
Natasha Nagle	594	Patrick Antonio	72
Nathaniel David Knox	131	Patrick Christian	485
Neil Brooks	156	Patrick Moorhouse	884
Neil D Cross	423	Patrick ten Brink	375
Neil Davie	584	Paul Mastaglio	290
Neil Goodwin	968	Paul Phillips	81
Neil Phillips	402	Paul Rhodes	730
Neil Renton	789	Paul Shaw	43

Paula Lacey	832	Richard Stanley	834
Paulette Pierre	656	Richard Swaine	167
Peggy Gerber	772	Ripunjoy Borgohain	828
Penelope Henry	969	RJS Cantwell	583
Pete Armstrong	522	RK	217
Peter Gregory & David Gough	456	RL Comstock	731
Peter J. Corbally	385	Rob Bray	794
Peter Loftus	451	Rob Vogt	914
Peter Stanton	615	Robbie Brown	807
Phil Maud	777	Robbie Porter	171
Phil Thomas	902	Robert Adams	469
Philip Charter	515	Robert Alan Ryder	286
Phoebe Tatham	220	Robert Brewis	981
PJ Stephenson	541	Robert Kombol	22
Prajith Menon	202	Robert Tucker	139
Prisha Gupta	53	Robert Wood	417
R. J. Kinnarney	857	Roberta Scafidi	717
R.A. Krueger	618	Roger Newton	459
R.J. Saxon	187	Roger West	991
Rachael Hinshaw	592	Rohana Chomick	175
Rachel Smith	373	Ron Smith	210
Rachel Wood	913	Ronald Hall	113
Rafe Bellers	626	Ros Byrne	54
Rajagopal Kaimal	212	Ros Masterson	801
Ray Sarlin	288	Rosalind Adam	868
Raymond E. Strawn III	632	Rosalind Newton	895
Raymond Sloan	539	Rose Farris	125
Rebecca Capel	439	Roshna Rusiniya	655
Rebecca Hubbard	850	Rosie Arcane	903
Rebecca Krohman	258	Rosie Cullen	506
Rebeccah Yeadon	786	Ross Lowe	775
Reed Markham	438	Rowan Lewis	508
Reha Tanör	604	Roz Levens	170
Renate Schiansky	540	Rudy S. Uribe Jr.	763
Rene Astle	6	Rui Soares	70
Rex Charger	702	Rupert Payne	153
Richard Anthony Morris	961	Ruth Pedley	332
Richard Freeman	639	Ryan Fell	321
Richard H. Argent	892	Ryu Ando	65

S Thomson-Hillis	338	Shahnaz Ali	908
S. M. Chiles	213	Shannon J Alger	223
S. Rupsha Mitra	744	Sharon Pinner	855
S. W. Hardy	41	Shaun Clarke	201
S.B. Borgersen	108	Shauna Elizabeth Murray	307
S.E. Taylor	646	Sheannah Guillemette	509
Sachin Prakash	782	Sheila Rosart	95
Sagar Jadhav	614	Shelly Teems	710
Sai Muthukumar	645	Shirley Muir	329
Sally Skeptic	208	Shobha Wilson	923
Sam Freer	403	Sidonie Baylis	570
Sam May	949	Siegfried E Finser	760
Samantha Gentzel	111	Sihaam Osman	803
Samantha Gunton	505	Silver Morris	36
Sandee Lee	979	Simone Wallace	333
Sandra 'Chas' Hines	430	Sivan Pillai	5
Sandra Orellana	16	Skylar Kim	420
Sandra Purdy	105	Smritirekha Talukdar	89
Sarah Ann Hall	418	Sophia Manubay	344
Sarah Brown	758	Sophie Henson	129
Sarah Burrett	243	Sophie Scriven	984
Sarah Charmley	963	Sreedevi Ganti Mahapatra	822
Sarah Engeham	943	Stefan Dimitrov	230
Sarah Everett	387	Stephanie Ngoei	340
Sarah Fletcher	465	Stephanie Potts	277
Sarah Hoad	945	Stephen P. Thompson	631
Sarah Jae Walsh	642	Stephie Simpson	546
Sarah Littleton	265	Steve Lodge	110
Sarah Mosedale	448	Steven Barrett	452
Sarah Stansfield	181	Stuart Atkinson	206
Sarah Stephenson	388	Sue Johnson	132
Saras Ojha	302	Sue Moos	455
Sarthak Das	638	Sue Partridge	183
Saskia Ashby	114	Sue Vincent	443
Scott Parent	654	Sunshine Tibod	519
Sean Bain	490	Susan Howarth	659
Sean Tobias May	898	Susan Wickham	644
Sebastian Cowen	749	Susanne Berger	994
Seth Turner-Higgins	808	Susi J Smith	380

Susie Frame	197	Tracey Maitland	32
Swi Neo Mary Yap	879	TS Lanchbery	159
Sydney Clarence	157	Ty Hall	587
Sylvia Ketchum	752	Umme Ammarah	677
Syreeta Muir	478	Val Chapman	406
T. Luxton	705	Valerie Fish	365
T. W. Garland	704	Valerie Griffin	61
T.L. Shenkin	235	Valerie J Shay	670
T.N.M. Sheppard	488	Veena Rah	678
Tamires Cunha	964	Veronica Crerar	897
Tamsin Partington	927	Vesper Wunderlin	284
Tanya Butler	85	Vichar Lochan	79
Tanya Hill	881	Vicki Murray	477
Tanya Johnson	17	Vicki Sinclair	784
Tarquin Calver	92	Vicky Garlick	542
Taye Carrol	169	Victoria Gaylor	369
Taylor Elliott	691	Violet James	701
Taylor Moore	745	Vishnu Nandan	833
Ted Bragg	476	Vivian Oldaker	151
Tess M Shepherd	63	Vivienne O'Boyle	621
Tessa Elliott	709	W. E. Jones	463
Thatchayani Ravanan	349	W. G. Miller	573
Thomas Belmar	873	Waltraud Pospischil	160
Thomas James Busby	320	Wanda Wright	360
Thomas O'Mara	685	Wayne B. Chorney	675
Tiarnán Murphy	280	Wayne Hewitt	12
Tiffany Williams	623	Wendy Christopher	82
Tim Gomersall	578	Wendy Fletcher	467
Tim Warren	858	Wendy Roe	336
Tom Bullimore	520	William Telford	273
Tom Gaunt	887	Wright Stone	483
Toni G.	661	Wyatt Payne	966
Toni Peers	657	Yabo Anderson	660
Tonia Nem	830	Yelena Kart	555
Tony Lawrence	735	Yvonne Clarke	721
Tony Mooney	694	Yvonne Mastaglio	885
Tony Thatcher	498	Zoe J Walker	954
Tony Tremblett	967	Zoey Rowan	791

Printed in Great Britain
by Amazon

79289116R00305